LIVING PLANET EARTH

LIVING
PLANET EARTH

Text by Petr Jakeš

Illustrations by Adolf Absolon

Designed and produced by Aventinum
English language edition first published 1994 by the
Promotional Reprint Company Ltd., Deacon House,
65 Old Church Street, London SW3 5BS

Text by Petr Jakeš
Translated by Clare Krojzlová and Slavoš Kadečka
Illustrations by Adolf Absolon

ISBN 1 85648 160 3
Printed in the Czech Republic
3/21/08/51-01

CONTENTS

INTRODUCTION

These days, it seems every time you open a newspaper, or switch on the television, there is another report on the disastrous state of the environment. The picture that emerges from scientific publications is even more alarming: the pollution of European rivers, disasters at nuclear power stations, acid rain and dying forests in Central Europe, the search for crashed satellites with radioactive energy sources on board, the extinction of large numbers of animal species (the number of biological species currently living on Earth has now dropped to its lowest level since the end of the Mesozoic age), crude oil slicks in the oceans, the drying up of the lakes of Central Asia, the pollution of Lake Baikal, one of the largest of all freshwater reserves, the deforestation of the Amazon rain forests, the loss of the land horizon, as well as holes in the ozone layer above the Arctic and the Antarctic regions. Huge amounts of fallout have been reckoned to be present over the whole of Europe, and tonnes of soil, causing devastating erosion, are carried away by large rivers such as the Yangtze every year. Pressure groups talk of environmental catastrophe, of ecological limits, of intolerable population growth on Earth; reports are written on the limited supplies and even the possible exhaustion of mineral and energy resources. These days we are speaking a new language, with terms like 'the greenhouse effect' and 'global warming' being used every day. We may even feel like running away, but this is our home and there is nowhere we can run to.

We are dependent on the Earth, an exceptional world that we have called the Blue Planet, because its surface is largely covered with water. It is exceptional if only for the reason that it is inhabited by animal and plant life. It even has its own 'intelligent creature' — Man. This precious, perhaps unique planet is our world, and to imagine that anywhere in the world would escape the effects of pollution is wishful thinking. Day by day, our home planet is growing warmer as the composition of its atmosphere changes. The Earth has only one atmosphere and one hydrosphere, and while countries can prevent people entering, there is no way anyone can keep atmospheric pollution in one area. If one country on Earth suffers from pollution, they all do. Acid rain from one country does not stop at another country's border.

There is only one Earth that we know of, and it has taken 4.6 billion years to achieve the fine and delicate balance which exists between the individual component parts of the Earth — its biosphere, crust, atmosphere, hydrosphere and core. Such a balance can be compared to a complex web, and, like every web, it has limits to its flexibility. It will be difficult, if not impossible, to repair if it ever breaks down. This kind of web, too, has places where it joins; that is, there are many complex relationships. To complicate matters even further, the web is spherical, heavy, constructed mainly of rock, with a tiny amount of living matter, and all this is flying through space at a tremendous speed.

This book is not specifically about catastrophes or ecology. It is a book about a planet, the third from the Sun. This is the home of the human race, who in their attempts to improve their home environment have succeeded in doing it great harm. It is also about how, on the other hand, Man is probably the first creature to try to explore the planet and understand it. Along the way he has made many great discoveries, perhaps the most important of which is that the Earth functions as a perfect symbiotic system, achieving, without the help of Man, perfection in recycling. Nowadays, every person should be aware that the whole future direction of the planet's evolution and ecology, and, indeed, Man, depends upon Man himself.

Grand Canyon
Permian
Carboniferous
Devonian
Cambrian
Pre-Cambrian (Proterozoic)
Pre-Cambrian (Archaean)
26 billion years

EARTH FOR MAN AND MAN FOR EARTH

1 An almost perfect testimony to the past is the deep cut made by the Colorado River of North America — the Grand Canyon. A geologist, however, reads history differently from the way he would read a printed book. Rather than at the top of the page, he begins at the bottom, i.e. at the bottom of the Canyon. Rather than concentrating on the vast, impressive rock formations of the canyon, he pays more detailed attention to the character of its rocks, their structure and arrangement. He records this somewhat technical and less spectacular picture in a section which can be seen on the left hand side of the illustration. This section reveals that the Grand Canyon begins with a series of folded and metamorphic rocks — gneisses, in which appear granite massifs marked with crosses. The folded rocks are very old (the measurement of their age points to some 2.6 billion years) and are separated distinctly from further rock strata by a clearly defined surface — perhaps representing the ancient ocean floor on which the series of sedimentary rocks originated in the Proterozoic Era (i.e. at least 600 million years ago). Their position suggests that after sedimentation considerable movements in the Earth's crust took place. The sedimentation of Palaeozoic rocks began only on the proceeding boundary. The individual boundaries as well as the missing names of some formations reveal that at that time the sedimentation was interrupted. To provide a record of that area, which would be as complete as possible, the right hand side of the picture presents the section of adjoining canyons, showing the interrupted development of this area in the Mesozoic and Tertiary periods.

The Earth, the third planet from the star known as the Sun, revolves around that star in a nearly circular orbit. Its equatorial radius is 6,378,165 km (3,986,355 miles) and it has a mass of 606.58 trillion tonnes. This pile of stone and metal with its surface layer on which, apart from rock and water, there is a further thin stratum of water and gases, is the home of the human race. A traveller in outer space would have no trouble in seeing that in the part where the Earth meets its atmosphere, there is evidence of plant and animal life. Nor would such a traveller have any difficulty in being able to see that Man, in his effort to improve his environment, has altered the surface of the Earth so much that these changes can be seen even from hundreds of miles away in space. The forests have made way for thousands of square kilometres of cleared agricultural land and motorways; airports and mining operations cut deep into the natural landscape. There are vast networks of waterways and reservoirs on one hand and rapidly

2 The picture shows the development of the Earth, according to knowledge so far. Twenty years ago, if anybody drew the picture of the 'original' Earth as an ocean of molten magma bombarded by meteors and discharging columns of hot gases here and there, such a picture would be considered pure fantasy. Even at present we realize that it is far from being a realistic picture. However, the study of material from outer space, particularly from the Moon, has proved that the early stages of the formation of such small celestial bodies took place in an atmosphere of extreme heat. The material which envelops the gravitation centre is molten and because of this and radioactive radiation, a hot crust forms on the surface of the planet. This cools surprisingly quickly.

expanding areas of desert on the other. The very composition of the atmosphere has changed and Man, through his greed and laziness, is poisoning himself. This hypothetical traveller in space, if he or she were able to interpret what could be seen from outer space in the way a human could, would probably conclude that the Earth had fallen victim to a very efficient parasite, in much the same way a gardener might see a pest on fruit or vegetables. Let us come down to earth, however, and have a look not with the eyes of a space traveller, but with the eyes of those humans who have the most down-to-earth relationship of all with the Earth, the geoscientists.

The geoscientists, and before them, geologists and palaeontologists were, and sometimes still are, regarded as eccentrics. With their little hammers they seek out the traces of extinct animal species, or follow the sequence of geological events in order to decipher the climatic conditions of the past. In this way they try to throw light on such riddles as the extinction of dinosaurs or the rise of Man. By now people have realized that a knowledge of the geology of an area can lead to the exploitation of its mineral resources. It is also known that knowledge of the ocean can lead to an understanding of the weather and effective fishing, as well as the possible exploitation of the ocean's potential energy. It is also known that information regarding atmospheric flow can assist both transport and agriculture, and that the ability to predict earthquakes could save human lives and safeguard property. The latest technology is in common use when measuring the composition of the atmosphere, water and soil. It is now routine to make use of supercomputers for studying the depth of the Earth's layers, and rockets, formerly intended for launching destructive weapons, are used for observation, surveys and research into the Earth, for the benefit of all people.

Geologists endeavour to find out about the past and present of the Earth, its solid, fluid and gaseous components, in order to be able to predict the future. They seek to understand the causes of change, so that people will either be able to eliminate them or utilize them for their benefit. The geologist looks at the Earth as a whole, and even though he encounters many obstacles on this path, he has achieved some successes on the way. He has to find ways round barriers presented by both Nature and Man. One of the greatest stumbling blocks to this process of discovery is Man's difficulty in linking his discoveries in a way which will provide an overall picture of the story of the Earth. He has yet to piece together the puzzle of the Earth, the Universe, and Nature in a way which will give him a true idea of the beginnings of the world.

Up until now, biologists have managed to record about one and a half million animal and half a million plant species. Many of these have only been present on Earth for a relatively short period of time and represent only the most recent small steps in the lengthy evolution of life on Earth. Just as every development has its milestones, so does the evolution of life and indeed the Earth itself. Each of these milestones should not be seen as the end of a piece of scientific investigation, but as a crossroad with two or three choices of direction in which to further Man's exploration. The milestones in the evolution of the Earth, which has been going on for more than four thousand million years, are almost innumerable. The most important development in the history of the planet however, and that which made the emergence of life possible, was the formation of an oxygen atmosphere at roughly halfway through the evolutionary sequence of the Earth. In comparison, the extinction of dinosaurs, the rise of mammals, or even the evolution of the human race itself are events of almost secondary importance, for without oxygen, none of that would have happened. Nonetheless, Man's present day practices and the speed with which they are affecting the Earth, its atmosphere, oceans, lakes and rivers, areas inhabited by its living creatures, far surpasses the time the Earth took to come to life. The Earth took over four thousand million years to form, and it has taken Man only two hundred years to begin to destroy it. Since the beginning of the 18th century, the Earth has lost six million square kilometres of forest, the great rivers are carrying three times

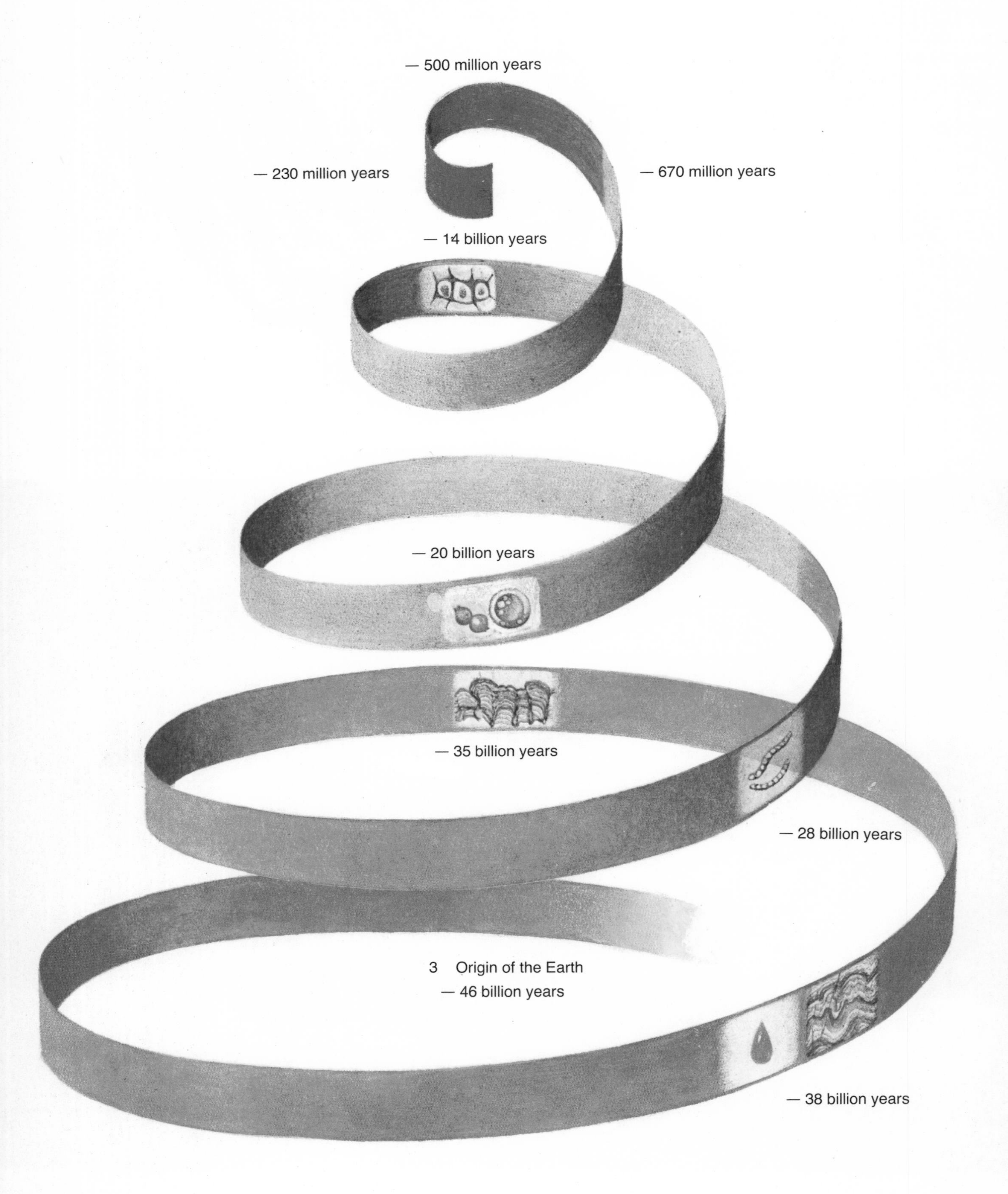

3 Origin of the Earth

◁
3 The spiral of development of the planet Earth begins with a period parallel to that which took place during the development of other planetary bodies. It is an exceedingly hot period, any evidence of which was wiped out in the planet's stormy youth. Examinable evidence does not occur until the appearance of water, i.e. when the Earth reaches an age of 800 million years. At this very depth of history palaeontologists try to find traces of life. However, at this level of geological history, the Earth does not have much to tell. Only the last 600 million years (coloured green in the picture) give a continuous record.

4 The rock in the picture comes from the Issua formation in Greenland and is 3.8 billion years old. At first sight it does not differ much from much younger rocks dating from the relatively short periods of a few dozen millions of years ago. Detailed investigation has shown, however, that the rock settled in an environment devoid of atmospheric oxygen and that the sedimentation took place in a basin filled with water. This is an astounding discovery, if we compare the period of known presence of water on the Earth with the conditions on our neighbouring planets, Venus and Mars. On these planets, where immense global changes which we might call catastrophes have taken place. It appears that the surface of Venus was overheated due to a greenhouse effect, and at some time in the long distant past, Mars lost most of its water. We can only wish that such rocks would settle in our Earth in our time, as the presence of water is the guarantee of the further development of the planet.

5 Most organisms are incapable of survival in extreme conditions. One exception is Cyanophyte, which lives not only in water with an excessive salt content, in hot springs, but is also present in the rocks of Antarctica. The colony of Cyanophyte in the picture comes from contemporary Western Australia, where these organisms live in the seemingly inhospitable, heavily salted medium of Hamelin Pool. They are arranged in formations known as stromatolites. Such formations are also found frequently in rocks dating from the early history of the Earth. The conditions, which were unfavourable for the life of the majority of organisms, were no obstacle to the vigorous development of the life of Cyanophyte.

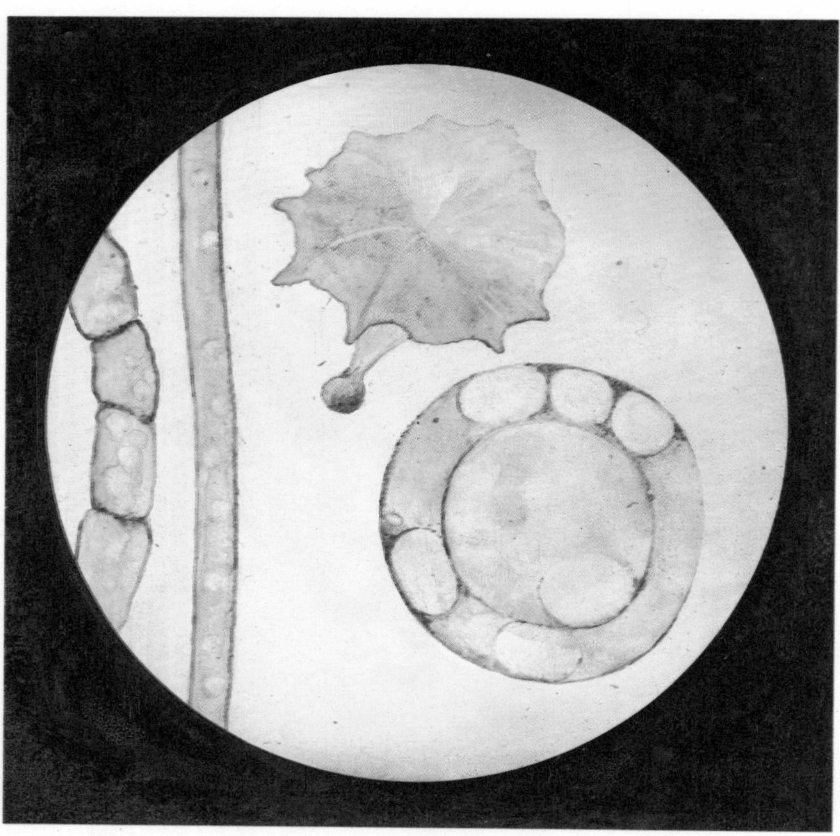

6 Among the oldest known fossils are remnants of organisms found in Precambrian quartz from north-eastern Minnesota in the United States. On the left hand side of the picture you can see fibrous structures belonging to blue-green algae, i.e. organisms capable of photosynthesis. Relations of the other two micro-organisms would be difficult to find in the contemporary world — perhaps only among soil micro-organisms.

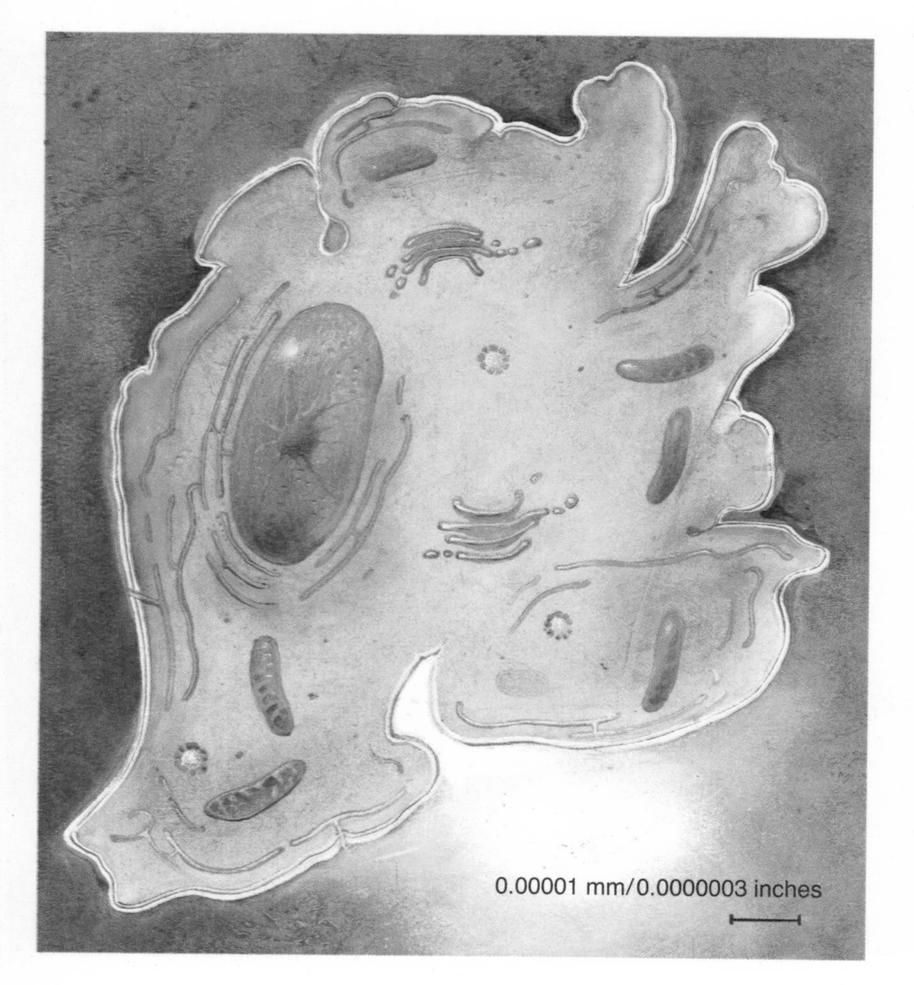

7 The standard components of a eucaryotic cell include the nucleus, separated from other parts of the cell by a heavily perforated membrane. Other parts include plastids, vacuoles, mitochondria and the Golgi apparatus. A developed eucaryotic cell is further characterized by its ability to move and change in accordance with the function performed in a living organism.

▷

8 The period called Phanerozoic or Post-Precambrian began 670 million years ago and has lasted until the present day. This is the result of the significant development of eucaryotic cells. Multicellular aquatic organisms appeared when the world consisted of one large continent. Some time later solid shelled animals came into existence. This example of the Ediacara fauna comes from South Australia and shows the representatives of the genera Cyclomedusa *and* Spriggina.

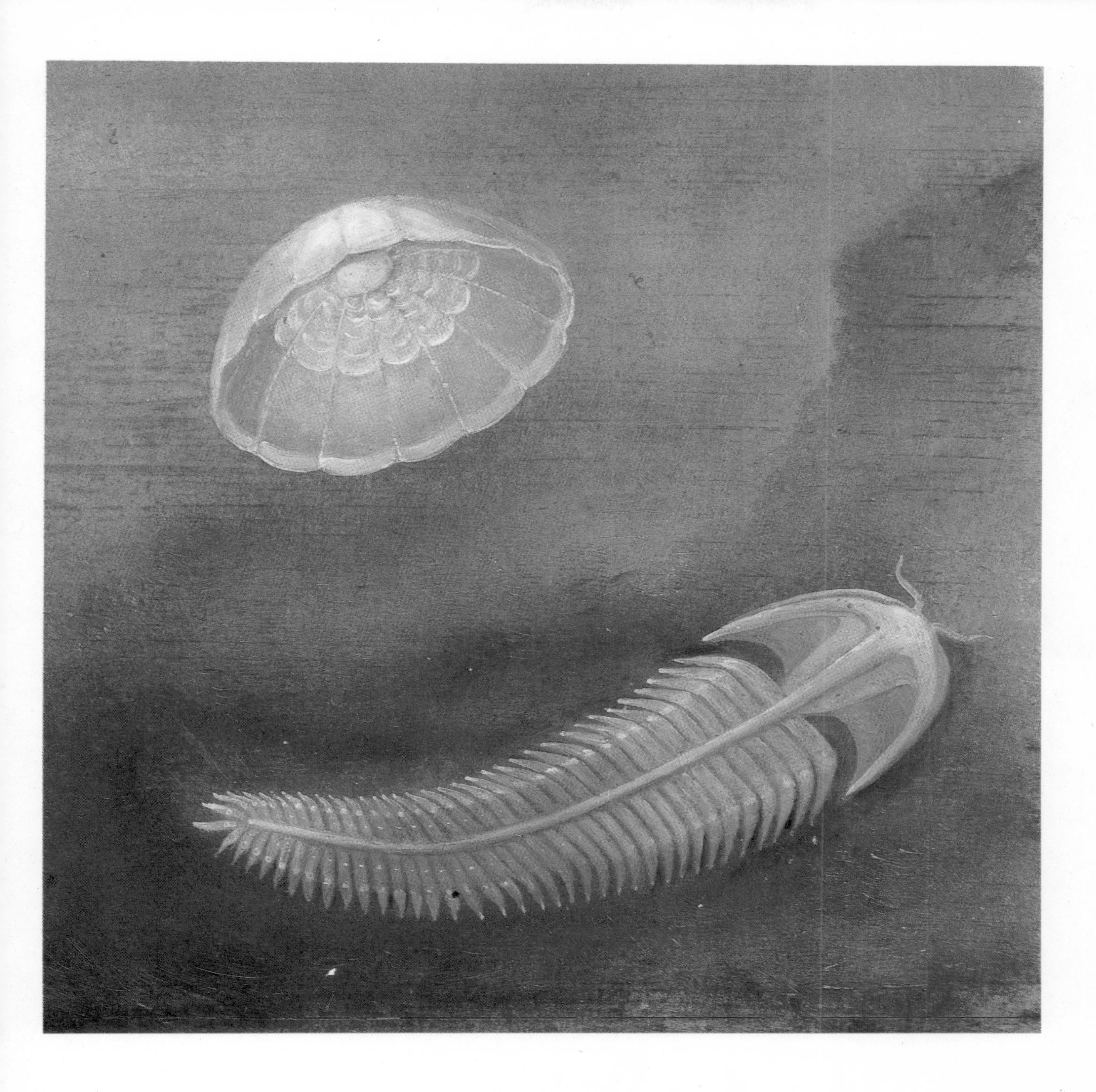

as much pollution as they were two centuries ago, and the quantities of volatile metals flowing through the rivers is ten or twenty times higher.

Most people have learned the various ages of the Earth, from the Proterozoic and the Mesozoic to the present day. It is not widely known, however, that when changes occurred on the Earth, they did not only happen in one small area, but were worldwide. Palaeontologists studying extinct plant and animal communities had already ascertained in the last century that within certain relatively brief periods of time the species composition of animals, plants or even inter-relationships between the two complete biocenoses changed, doing so all over the world. For example, 440 million years ago, at the borderline between the Ordovician and the Silurian, one particular species of trilobite began to be widespread, while other species became extinct at the same time or shortly beforehand. Between the Permian and the Triassic periods, in other words, between the Palaeozoic and the Mesozoic eras, roughly 250 million years ago, a mass extinction of most of the world's animal life occurred. The number of coral and fish species were reduced; trilobites, the first animal to have eyes and the ancestors of today's shrimps and lobsters, disappeared completely. Crinoids or sea lilies, not lilies at all, but animals which collected food from the water in which they lived, almost disappeared. To take a slightly wider view, it is apparent that events of this kind in the animal kingdom were sometimes accompanied by movements in the Earth's crust, a drop in the sea level or the flooding of dry land, and elsewhere with the emergence of massive mountain ranges such as the Himalayas or the Alps.

The discovery of radioactivity and the fact that the decay of radioactive elements can serve as a time meter for measuring the age of the Earth has altered scientists' opinion as to its age. The age, calculated by the study of biblical records at slightly more than 4,000 years, has since had a good six more zeros added to it. The current age of the Earth, determined on the basis of knowledge of the decay constants of radioactive elements, amounts to 4,600,000,000 years, or 4.6 aeons. We should note that this is also the age of the other planets in the solar system, including its mother star, the Sun.

No-one knows exactly what brought about the changes in the Earth's living world. There has been much discussion and controversy in this respect, and a conclusion has not yet been reached. Take, for example, the dispute between the catastrophists and evolutionists at the beginning of the 19th century, in particular, the French natural scientists Cuvier and Lamarck. Cuvier believed that the living world changed suddenly by means of catastrophes, and Lamarck believed in gradual evolution. Nowadays it is believed that there is an element of truth in both opinions. Research into the development of the Earth and the life on it has found much on the side of the evolutionists: on the other hand, those who spoke and wrote of catastrophes and the subsequent enormous flourishing of life have also been proved right. Whenever catastrophe has struck, the Earth has always recovered remarkably quickly; but more than this, it has become more adaptable, perhaps even 'genetically' hardier species appeared and the capacity for adaptation and change was then handed down.

In the historical sphere there were no clear victors: history acknowledged both Cuvier and Lamarck. What is gained from scientific disputes is not a victory for one group or another, but usually lies in the furtherance of knowledge itself — in scientific progress.

The picture on page 12 shows the evolutionary spiral of our Earth. Evolution is presented here in the form of a long band of film on which some frames have been exposed. It is quite possible that the most significant pictures are not on the film at all, in other words, we may only have an idea of some of the most important occurrences in the

9 The fossils found in the Ediacara site in Australia are 680 million years old. At that time an unbelievably vigorous development of life had begun, and in the relatively short time of 200 million years there appeared such perfect animals as this fish of the genus Paramblypterus *from the beginning of the Devonian period.*

▷
10 The funnel in the picture represents the growth of different species of living organisms in the history of the Earth. It is a very generalized picture which does not show how new species appeared in geological history and how this apparently continuous development was interrupted by mass extinction of some species and subsequent explosions of life: man's activities are causing a distinct reduction of animal and plant species.

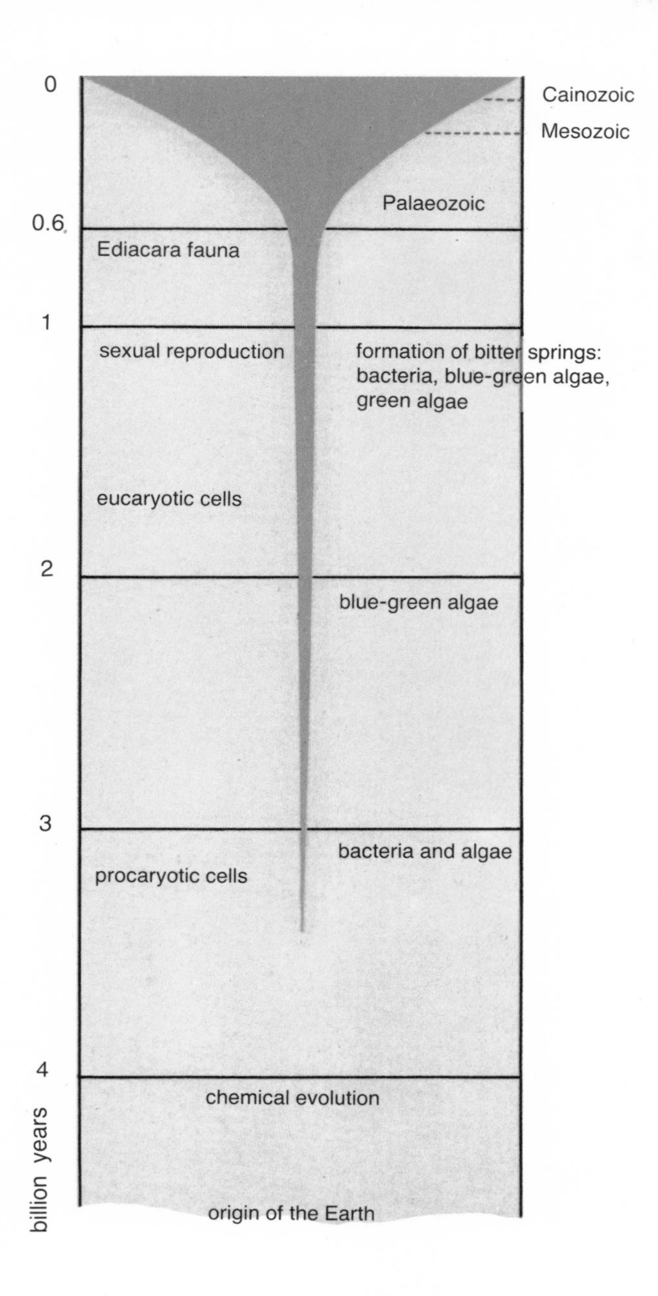

history of the Earth. At the bottom of the film is the beginning of the evolution of the Earth, the green end marked 'O' representing our own era. The longest period in the Earth's evolution, about which there is not much information, is coloured dark brown on the band of film. All early events in the Earth's history were wiped out by processes and events which occurred much later.

Scientists are still trying to fathom the Earth's very beginnings — the oldest rocks, the first signs and traces of life. In these ancient geological relics which were the first souvenirs of the formation of the Earth, there is something mystical and magical that is attractive to Man's curiosity. There is, however, virtually nothing we can find out from these earthly records. Another path had to be found, and it was. By studying meteorites, the remnants of matter left after the formation of planets, along with the surfaces of neighbouring planets and one Moon, we are able to catch a glimpse of what probably took place during the early history of the Earth.

Scientists have concluded that the initial stages, the first thousands, even million of years in the existence of the Earth, were extremely hot. The planet was formed when large and small pieces of matter, meteorites, dust, and everything within the gravitational field of the newly-forming body wrapped itself around the body's gravitational centre. This process is known as accretion. Since it was a rapid one, a considerable amount of heat was released by the formation of this mass; in other words, the kinetic energy — that which was formed by the movement of the particles — changed into thermal energy or heat. A further, apparently enormous amount of heat was produced by the decay of radioactive elements, some of which are probably unknown to us. The planet whirled in space, becoming so hot, parts of it began to melt. Its minerals and gases began to divide, becoming separate substances. The core, mantle and atmosphere were formed. The surface of the Earth was probably covered with seas of lava, which rapidly cooled. The Earth's crust, being hot and soft, flowed swiftly.

At this stage in the Earth's evolution, the Sun was also undergoing its own turbulent development, blasting large amounts of particles out into surrounding space. It is possible that this powerful solar wind blew away the Earth's original atmosphere; however, the heat emitted from the Sun at that time was not thought to be any more than 60—70 per cent of its current activity.

Only 600 million years after the Earth's formation, water appeared on its surface. There have been mineral deposits in water since that time. The emergence of water is another major milestone in the development of the Earth. It shows us that at least in some places the surface of the Earth cooled to below 100°C/212°F and that water became a regulating factor in the surface temperature. The evaporation, freezing and thawing of water are excellent temperature regulators. The amount of ice in the polar icecaps, the amount of water in the oceans or of condensation in the atmosphere constitute safety devices in the Earth's thermal system although their flexibility is not unlimited.

In this form, however, the Earth was scarcely capable of supporting life. Not even the air bore any resemblance to what we would understand by the term today, consisting of carbon dioxide, water vapour, nitrogen, carbon monoxide and hydrogen sulphide, in other words, it was full of gases which had been emitted by volcanoes. These types of gas are anything but conductive to human life. The low intensity of solar radiation was made up for by a greenhouse effect caused by the carbon dioxide, which formed a layer which prevented heat from escaping into space.

Study of the earliest forms of rock has not produced much evidence of organic life. It does reveal, however, that during the next 200 million years or so, organisms called stromatolites or 'stone blankets' appeared in the waters of the Earth. These were formations of limestone made by tiny plant cells, 'blue-green algae'. It was not for another 700 million years that fossilized worm-like remains occur in rocks. These are clearly the remains of an-

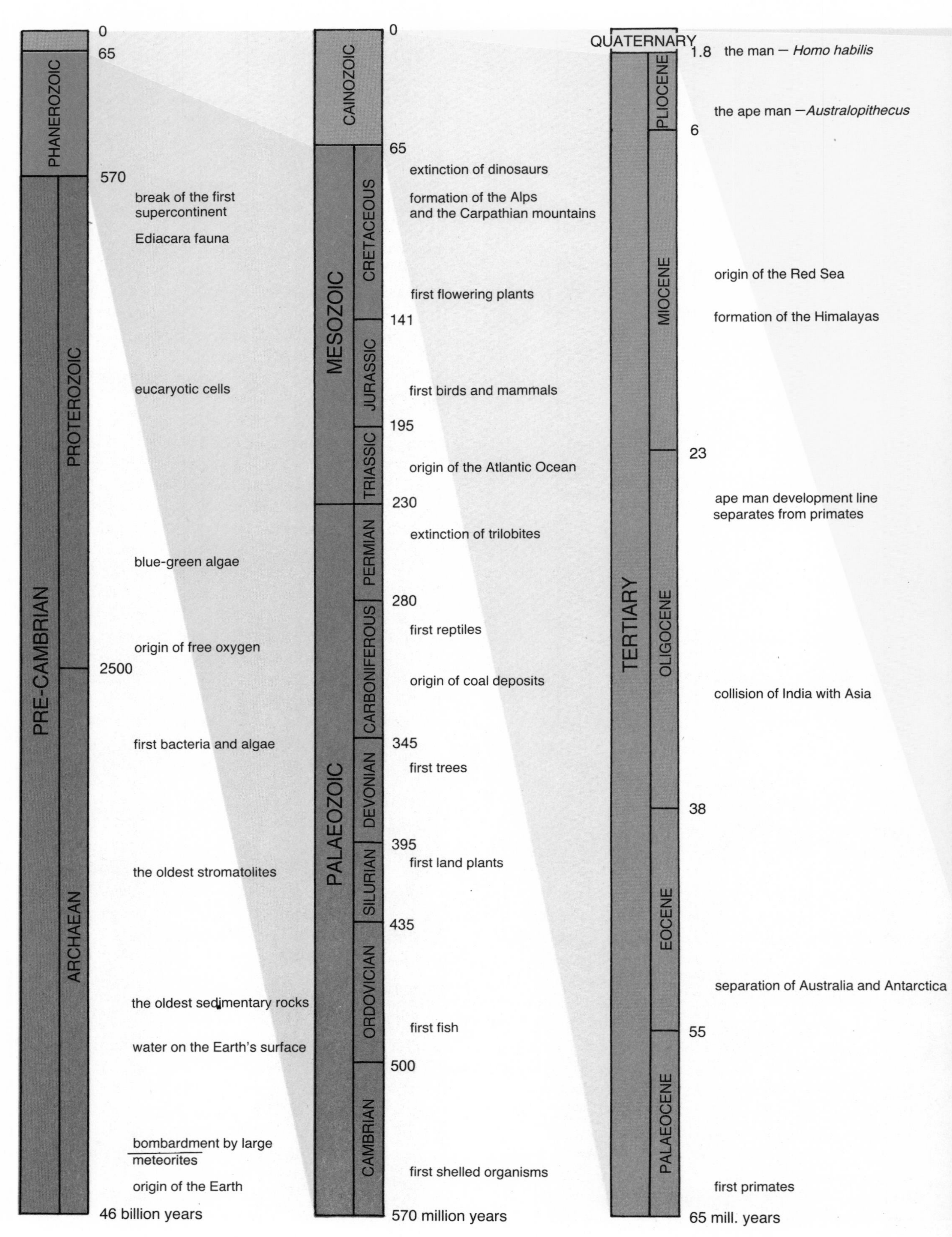
0
65
PHANEROZOIC
570
PRE-CAMBRIAN
PROTEROZOIC
2500
ARCHAEAN
46 billion years
break of the first
supercontinent
Ediacara fauna
eucaryotic cells
blue-green algae
origin of free oxygen
first bacteria and algae
the oldest stromatolites
the oldest sedimentary rocks
water on the Earth's surface
bombardment by large
meteorites
origin of the Earth
0
CAINOZOIC
65
MESOZOIC
CRETACEOUS
141
JURASSIC
195
TRIASSIC
230
PALAEOZOIC
PERMIAN
280
CARBONIFEROUS
345
DEVONIAN
395
SILURIAN
435
ORDOVICIAN
500
CAMBRIAN
570 million years
extinction of dinosaurs
formation of the Alps
and the Carpathian mountains
first flowering plants
first birds and mammals
origin of the Atlantic Ocean
extinction of trilobites
first reptiles
origin of coal deposits
first trees
first land plants
first fish
first shelled organisms
QUATERNARY
1.8
TERTIARY
PLIOCENE
6
MIOCENE
23
OLIGOCENE
38
EOCENE
55
PALAEOCENE
65 mill. years
the man – Homo habilis
the ape man –Australopithecus
origin of the Red Sea
formation of the Himalayas
ape man development line
separates from primates
collision of India with Asia
separation of Australia and Antarctica
first primates

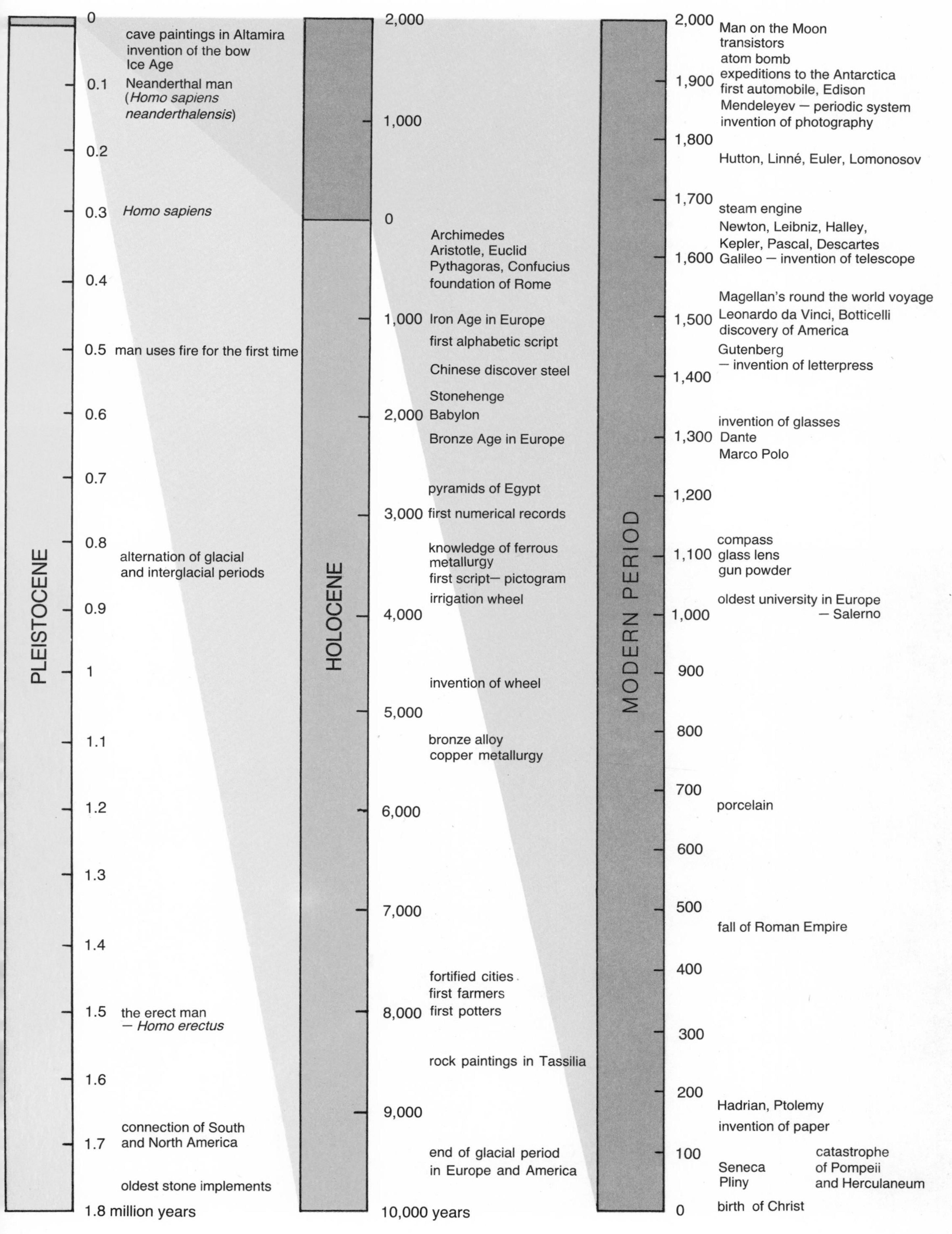

PLEISTOCENE
0
cave paintings in Altamira
invention of the bow
Ice Age
0.1
Neanderthal man
(Homo sapiens neanderthalensis)
0.2
0.3
Homo sapiens
0.4
0.5
man uses fire for the first time
0.6
0.7
0.8
alternation of glacial and interglacial periods
0.9
1
1.1
1.2
1.3
1.4
1.5
the erect man — Homo erectus
1.6
connection of South and North America
1.7
oldest stone implements
1.8 million years
HOLOCENE
2,000
1,000
0
Archimedes
Aristotle, Euclid
Pythagoras, Confucius
foundation of Rome
1,000
Iron Age in Europe
first alphabetic script
Chinese discover steel
Stonehenge
2,000
Babylon
Bronze Age in Europe
pyramids of Egypt
3,000
first numerical records
knowledge of ferrous metallurgy
first script— pictogram
irrigation wheel
4,000
invention of wheel
5,000
bronze alloy
copper metallurgy
6,000
7,000
fortified cities
first farmers
8,000
first potters
rock paintings in Tassilia
9,000
end of glacial period in Europe and America
10,000 years
MODERN PERIOD
2,000
Man on the Moon
transistors
atom bomb
expeditions to the Antarctica
1,900
first automobile, Edison
Mendeleyev — periodic system
invention of photography
1,800
Hutton, Linné, Euler, Lomonosov
1,700
steam engine
Newton, Leibniz, Halley,
Kepler, Pascal, Descartes
1,600
Galileo — invention of telescope
Magellan's round the world voyage
1,500
Leonardo da Vinci, Botticelli
discovery of America
Gutenberg — invention of letterpress
1,400
invention of glasses
1,300
Dante
Marco Polo
1,200
compass
1,100
glass lens
gun powder
oldest university in Europe — Salerno
1,000
900
800
700
porcelain
600
500
fall of Roman Empire
400
300
200
Hadrian, Ptolemy
invention of paper
100
catastrophe of Pompeii and Herculaneum
Seneca
Pliny
0
birth of Christ

other type of simple living organism. It took another 800 million years, until 2,000 million years ago (halfway along our band of film), for cell organisms to appear: these were procaryotic cells without nuclei. Another 600 million years later (at the 1.4 point on the film) eucaryotic-celled organisms appeared, having a cell nucleus which enables them to be regarded as the basis for the evolution of higher organisms.

However, almost another 1,000 million years were to pass before the appearance of the first solid-shelled animal life forms, at the beginning of the Palaeozoic era in the Cambrian period — 550 million years ago. To compare how long the evolution from the most primitive organisms to the trilobites took, it could be said that it is only a relatively short period of time from the first trilobites to Man in the overall evolution of life. During this time, life has branched out into millions of different forms, coming first from the ocean and then moving on to dry land. The whole process has taken a mere 550 million years and has seen the evolution of fish, amphibians, reptiles, birds, mammals and Man himself. Many animal species have become extinct. Our band of film has come to an end. The last 670 million years have been an era of such dramatic development that the images overlap.

The evolution of the Earth and life on it can be compared to a rocket taking off into space: a lengthy preparation and a gradual take-off, followed by acceleration to incredible cosmic speeds. The record of this turbulent history lives in the rocks on the Earth's surface. People, in general, see rocks as inanimate, in order to distinguish them from animate Nature. Rocks, minerals, geological formations and fossils are seen as cold and unchanging. They seem to lack the dynamism of movement and growth, the cyclical processes of birth and death. We likewise view the inner part of our Earth as something not alive, but as trillions of tons of lifeless matter. Only on its uppermost layer, the thin crust, where solid ground meets water and air, is there what we consider to be life.

The study of the Earth at depth may seem irrelevant, especially at this time when we are all so horrified by what is happening on its surface. The Earth's surface is not just flat, level, dry land. Ocean trenches at depths of some 11 km/7 miles, as well as the peaks of 8,000 m high mountains are all part of the surface of the Earth and linked with what we call life. Let us draw a hypothetical line 6,500 km/4,000 miles long to represent the Earth's radius, and beside it another hypothetical line 19 km/12 miles long, which represents the difference between the high-

13 The small pyramid on the left hand side represents the Khufu pyramid of ancient Egypt. The other 'hills', each many times greater in volume than such a pyramid, represent quantities of debris carried to seas and oceans by rivers every year. Much of this material is present in the rivers because of human activities: increased erosion brought about by deforestation and agriculture are the major causes.

◁
12 Man's activities which are hostile to the planet and, consequently, to Man himself can be illustrated by land 'management'. The original forests were burned to obtain agricultural soil. However, that was the moment in which the change of the landscape began. Both denuded land and land sown with cereal crops are susceptible to easy soil erosion. Water and wind erosion are, in many cases, quicker than the generation of a new soil horizon. The landscape changes not only its appeareance, but also its uses. Agricultural areas can change into steppes which have only limited uses. This process may take hundreds of years, but sometimes it takes only a decade. The Mediterranean landscape is one such example.

est peak on Earth and the deepest point below sea level — a negligible difference compared with the radius. The connection between life on Earth and rocks lying two or three hundred metres below its surface would seem to be non-existent. It would seem even more absurd to suggest that those lying at depths of up to 2,900 km/1,800 miles and that even the Earth's metal core could affect our own life on the Earth. Yet, where the Earth's core and its mantle meet is the junction of the metallic and non-metallic silicate parts of the Earth, and here there are powerful electrical currents at work like a dynamo between the core and the mantle. The flow of electricity, as elementary physics tells us, means the formation of magnetic fields. If the Earth did not have a magnetic field, considerably greater quantities of electrically charged particles from space would fall onto its surface, and it is more than likely that life on Earth would be of a totally different character, if it existed at all. A number of other suppositions could be made in connection with the relationship between the Earth's inner and outer layers. If we want to understand the Earth as a whole, and our own place in it, we will have

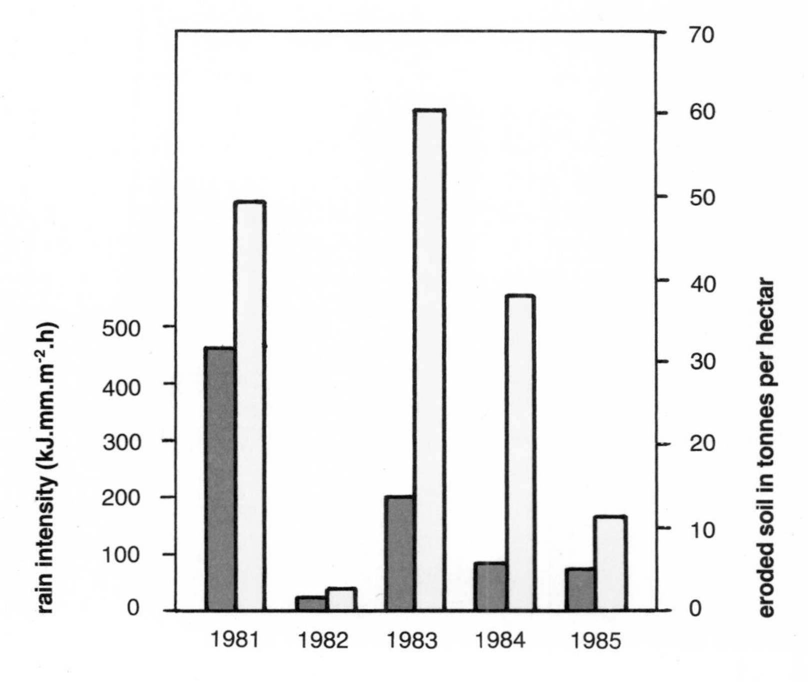

14 Rain may cause erosion particularly in treeless, agricultural areas. This diagram, from a geological measuring station near Nicosia in Cyprus, illustrates the relation between rain intensity (blue columns) and the amount of eroded soil (yellow columns). The heavier the rain, the greater will be the loss of the soil.

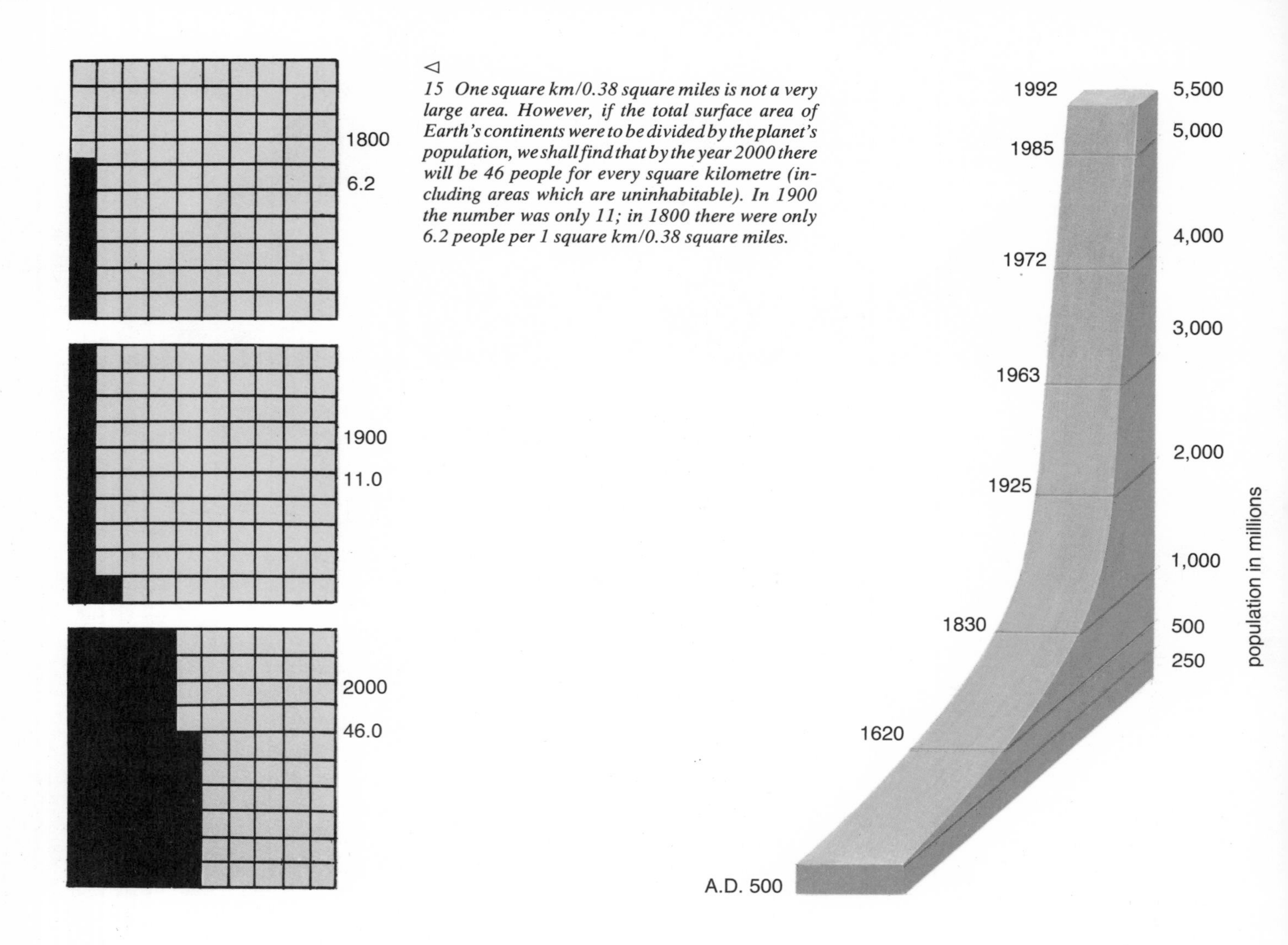

◁
15 One square km/0.38 square miles is not a very large area. However, if the total surface area of Earth's continents were to be divided by the planet's population, we shall find that by the year 2000 there will be 46 people for every square kilometre (including areas which are uninhabitable). In 1900 the number was only 11; in 1800 there were only 6.2 people per 1 square km/0.38 square miles.

to become acquainted with those parts of it which Man has traditionally associated with Hell, since it is from there that the gases arise to form our atmosphere, and there that the magnetic field of the Earth is formed.

Man does not in general see himself as having much connection with the inanimate parts of the Earth. He has his own inherited biological experience, as well as that gained throughout his own life. Our experience of Nature is shaped by the time in which we live, and each of us lives within only a tiny proportion of the overall history of the Earth. It is therefore transient and set in fleeting time-spaces. The alternating seasons of spring, summer autumn, and winter, and the weather — the biological cycles of the Earth — are what gauge our experience of living Nature. This was observed by our ancestors, who tried to create a calendar, but only one which was limited to the past and not to the future.

That which we today term 'ecological thinking' and regard as the achievement of our day, the intellectual victory of the end of the 20th century, was enshrined by our ancestors in their mythology, customs and predictions. Traditional folk tales reveal a great deal of ecological wisdom concerning water, food and the living natural world.

Our ancestors were able to fit their own version of technology into the ecological chain with practically no waste or pollution. Modern day man, however, creates so much waste that he has also created the problem of what to do with it, and as a result the precious landscape and atmosphere suffer. When people 'lived off the land' they were not conscious of 'recycling'. What they did, they did almost instinctively. They knew that they had to keep a cat so that mice would not consume their grain stores. They used bones for fertilizing the soil, mixing them with the manure of domestic animals and with ashes from wood fires. Nowadays, wherever Man deviates from an ecologically sound way of life, he creates a system for potential disaster. In the past, when man was a tribal animal, his weapons, wars and waste were small; today, he is still a tribal animal, but each tribe is a nation, and weapons, wars and waste are on such a huge scale they are almost beyond comprehension. Man has almost lost the ability to be responsible on an individual level, but of course this is the only road forward.

Man soon perceived, especially in the advanced civil-

◁
16 The population of the Earth is growing. This would be of no particular importance if the rate of population growth and the human yearning for an ever increasing standard of living were in line with the Earth's production and ecological potential. Feeding the constantly increasing population and supplying it with raw materials and energy represent some of the most serious problems of the present day.

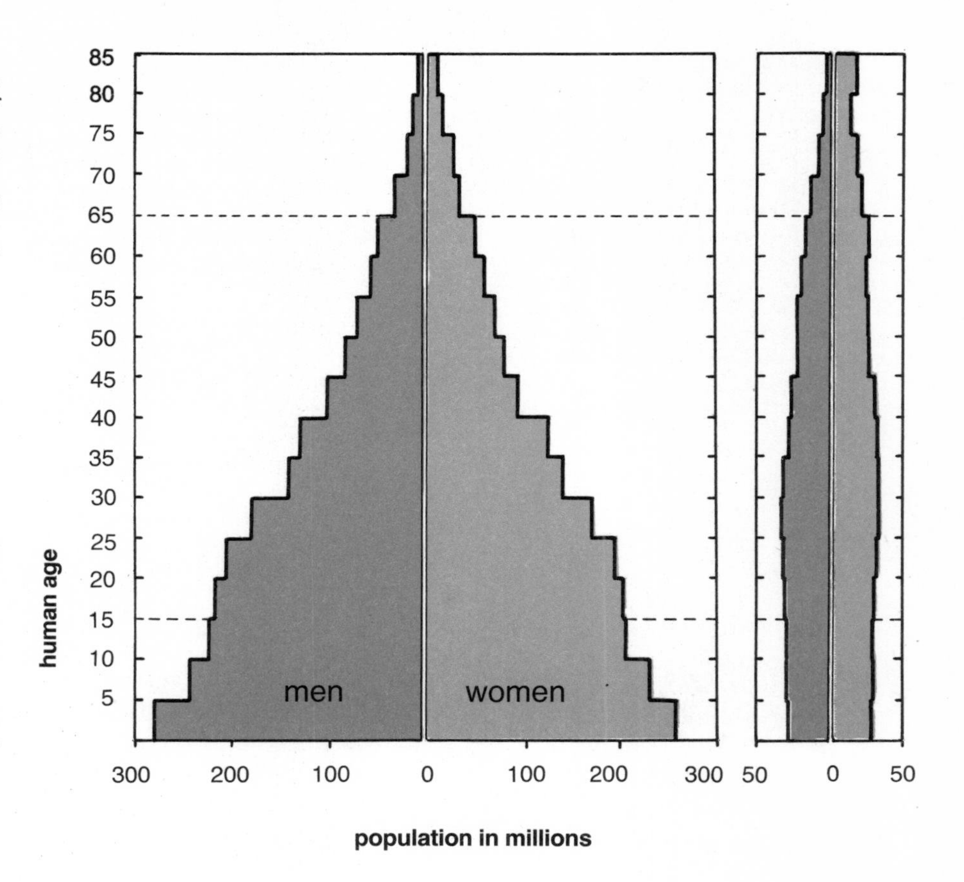

17 This diagram compares the number of people in particular age groups in developed (right) and developing (left) countries. In the developing countries more than 37 per cent of the population is at present younger than 15. This means that no decrease in the populations of developing countries can be envisaged before A.D. 2000 when today's teenagers will be parents. The labour force in these countries will increase dramatically. It is predicted that by A.D. 2050 the number of people capable of work in the developing countries will have increased threefold.

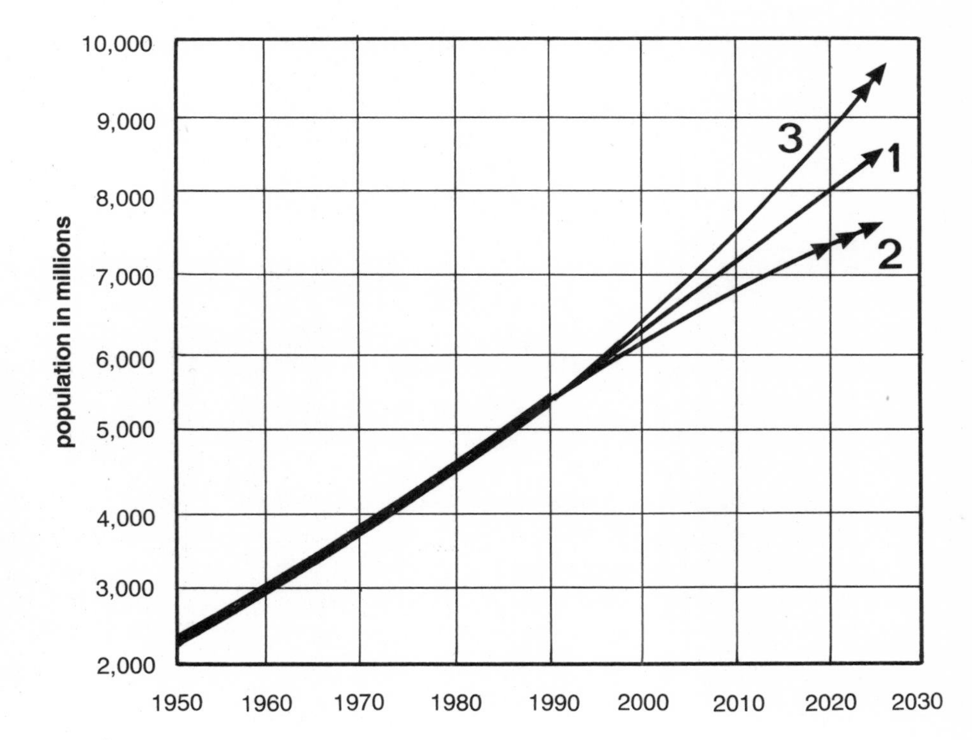

18 The Earth's ever increasing population is its most fundamental problem. Should the population increase at its present rate until the year 2000, i.e. at the rate of 1.74 per cent per year, and should this rate drop to 0.98 per cent per year after the year 2000, by A.D. 2025 the Earth will have a population of some 8.5 billion people (Curve 1). Should the population increase after A.D. 2000 at the rate of 0.59 per cent only, the number of people living on the Earth by A.D. 2025 will be 'merely' 7.6 billion (Curve 2). Curve 3 shows a higher rate of growth particularly until A.D. 2000 (1.9 per cent), which means that the Earth would be inhabited by almost 10 billion people by A.D. 2025.

19 The pace at which life is lived today is exemplified by the immediacy with which results of research are applied to our daily lives. This simple diagram shows time (by date) on the horizontal axis and time elapsed between an invention and its practical application on the vertical axis. In the middle of the 16th century it was discovered that eating citrus fruit can prevent scurvy. However, it took 264 years before this discovery had been incorporated into British Naval practice, in the form of supplying limes. The time between discovery of the principle of photography to the first photographs took only 112 years, between the discovery of the principle of radar to its application only 15 years, and in the case of liquid crystals it took only 1 year to apply the invention.

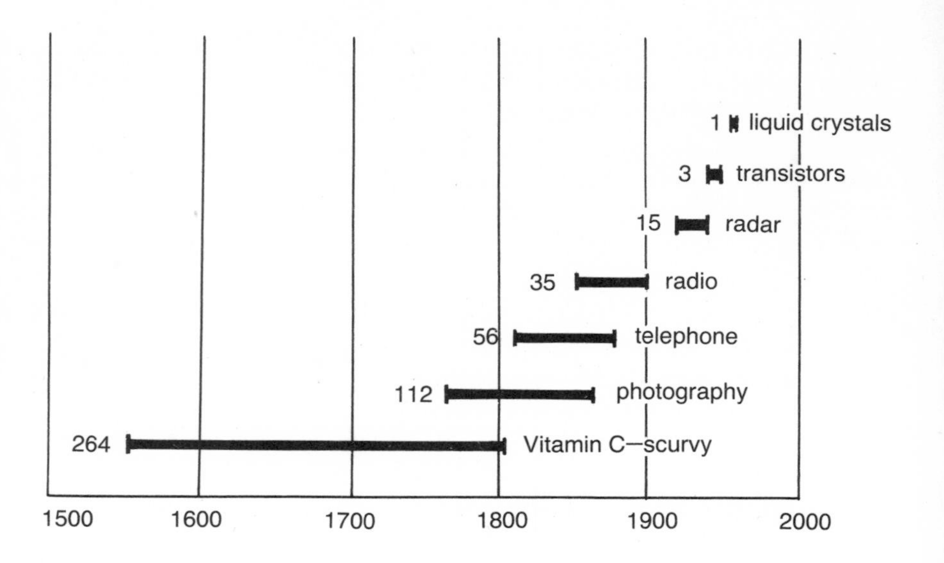

izations of the Near East and Mediterranean, that if they irrigated the land they would not be at the mercy of Nature, and also that by doing this they could make their yields several times greater. They began to draw off underground water or to divert water from great rivers, irrigating their narrow fields by way of many canals. For some years the fields showed great success, but after a time the land began to behave in a strange way. Salt deposits appeared, crop yields dropped and a salty wasteland appeared where there had once been fertile ground. Only as far back as the beginning of this century in North America, underground water in permeable levels dropped by several metres as a result of drawing off. In addition to rising salt levels in soil, the land dried out, causing deformation of the Earth's surface. The land subsided. Where sheep had grazed on grass and other vegetation, and where woodland had been felled, massive erosion occurred. This was especially the case throughout the vast Mediterranean region. So much soil was eroded that agriculture is now unthinkable in such land conditions, and it is highly unlikely that a new land horizon will form within the next ten generations.

The common denominator in these catastrophes is a failure to understand not the animal world, but the very substance of the Earth itself. The rocks and soil which

20 Energy is, to a considerable extent, a limiting factor in the development of human society. Energy consumption is increasing at an even faster rate than the world population. This means that every person uses a greater amount of energy every year. It is also apparent that the way energy is consumed is changing. The diagram shows the way people coped with their energy requirements in the past, and also looks into the future. The annual energy requirements are considered as 100 per cent, broken up in accordance with each different method of energy generation. It is clear from the diagram that the future relies on the increased production of nuclear energy and that the amount of energy produced by burning wood has been reduced to a minimum.

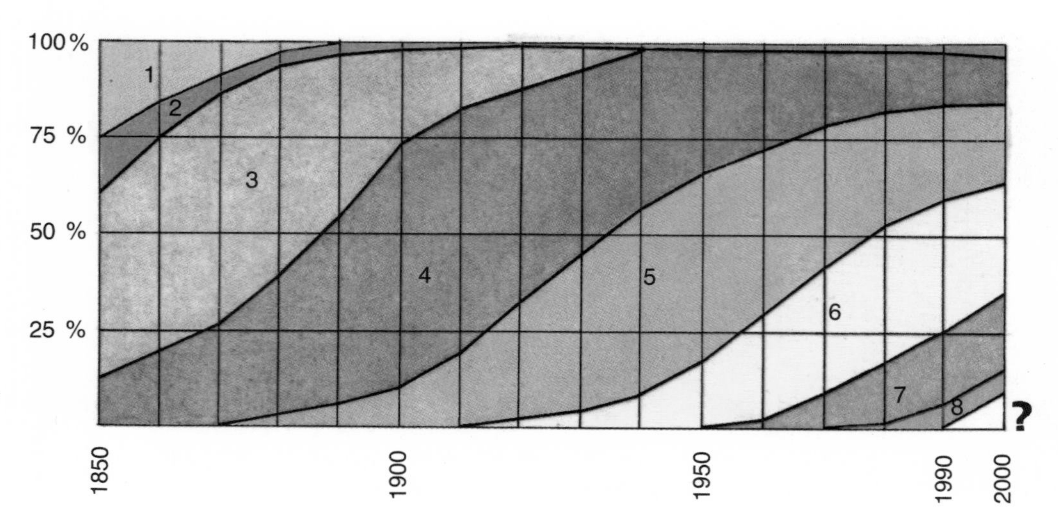

1 — muscles
2 — wind and water
3 — wood
4 — coal
5 — oil
6 — natural gas
7 — nuclear fission
8 — sun, tidal forces, heat from the Earth

form the fabric of our planet are not dead. The falling levels of underground water, and the vast areas of soil erosion could not be forecast within one generation, for they were the results of many years of what are now known to be unwise agricultural practices. People had no knowledge of what these new innovations in farming would do to their land, for the very reason that they were new — they had never been tested before.

However, these are not the worst cases. The land horizon which takes perhaps a million years to form, can be exhausted within a single generation due to intensive exploitation and incorrect use. It can, in theory, be restored if one is prepared to wait several thousand years. Under favourable conditions such as sufficient moisture and vegetation cover, it will regenerate itself through the activity of water and organisms, and Man can assist this process. Exhausted sources of underground water can also be restored over a period of hundreds or thousands of years (provided, of course, no climatic shifts have occurred as a result of these changes). All this should therefore be regarded as a restorable balance and as renewable resources, just as we regard organic matter to be a renewable resource.

However, mankind needs and is dependent upon non-renewable resources for his activities, and to stop this need is impossible. Where a coal seam has been mined, fresh coal will not 'grow'; the places from where crude oil has been drawn off will not fill up again; and although mined ore will be turned into metal, a great scar will appear in the Earth where it has been taken. But there is more: what happens to the coal we burn? We cannot be satisfied with the answer that it produces a bit of ash and an enormous amount of oxides. The same applies to the question of what happens to the metal left lying on scrap-heaps after use. What will happen to the water-bearing strata if we draw water off faster than rain can replace it, or if we go on expelling into the ocean the same quantities of waste that we have been doing in the 1980s and '90s? What in fact will happen if the rivers flow with a greater silt content than they have previously? The answer is simple. By exploiting non-renewable resources and extracting them from the environment, as well as by the excessive exploitation of resources which are renewable in the long term, mankind is walking into a dead end, since this material will not return to the Earth. People have not yet developed the habit of recycling all the materials they obtain from the Earth. Moreover, a mass of waste is accumulating at the end of this blind alley, not only of ash, rusty metal and sewage, but also of invisible substances such as gases which we know can bring about dramatic changes in the atmosphere. (This is called the greenhouse effect.)

We have grown accustomed to looking back on our social and political history and the history of the world and learning lessons from it. We see moments in history which are exceptional in a way — perhaps peaceful or violent.

Through our knowledge of history, we try to pre-empt unpleasant events. Not everything can always be solved by negotiation, but the desire to understand one another without the use of force, the desire to comprehend conflict and its causes, can often lead to creative solutions, acts of generosity and to harmony among people.

21 Central Europe is an area of dense population and intensive land use.
Agriculture takes up 55 per cent of the land surface,
30 per cent is covered with forests,
6 per cent is built-up,
5 per cent is put to use by communications,
2 per cent is covered by water, and the rest is used for sundry purposes such as playgrounds, storage or waste land.

There is another conflict involved here, however: that between Man and Nature. Not only does Man not seem to know how to take care of the beasts of the Earth, but his greed and selfishness blind him to the fact that the fabric of the Earth needs care and attention also. People tend to avoid looking at what is happening to the Earth as a long-term process, and only see it through the eyes of short-term existence. Man seems to think that anything that goes wrong with the Earth can be put right within a few years – yet how can this be so, when it took billions of years to tune the balance of Nature? Even the ground we walk on is essential to our life functions. Let us look back, for example, on remote history. The amount of carbon dioxide in the atmosphere in the geological history of the Earth was compensated for not only by the amount of green vegetation, but also by the emergence of carbonate rock formations. The surplus of solar energy on the Earth manifested itself in a global surge of vegetative growth. When the plants died and were broken down, over more millions of years the plant material was again stored by the Earth, that time in the form of coal. All processes of this kind form part of the natural dynamic balance of our planet.

Geologists are able to calculate the amount of rock formation produced by volcanic eruptions many millions of years ago. They can determine from the study of rock deposits how much of what kind of material was carried by rivers in the past and how material is carried today. They have worked out, for example, that in the last 650 million years 25 million tons of iron and 375 thousand tons of copper have reached the oceans via rivers. If we compare amounts of these minerals reaching our oceans in the past with the quantities which flood into the Earth's waters today, it seems almost beyond our comprehension. Every day huge amounts of minerals are poured out into rivers and oceans. Why? The desire of Man to make money. Our living, breathing, delicately balanced planet, with all its glorious natural wonders, is being sent into a state of shock – purely because of greed. We cannot see it happening, but beneath our feet, who knows what reaction the Earth is having – and whatever it is, it will happen worldwide.

The balance that has taken the Earth thousands of millions of years to achieve, with all its finely tuned interrelating ecosystems, has been severely disturbed. The Earth has learned to manage with shortages as well as with excesses of heat, with the amount of organic, fragmentary material as well as with the amount of weathered rock. It has been through catastrophes and contended with cosmic bodies. Even the composition of its atmosphere has changed. Breaking up and colliding, forming and being flooded, its floating plates have crashed into one another, causing earthquakes and volcanic eruptions, but the Earth has gone on in its own way, because these are all natural occurrences and the Earth can cope. Then came Man: building dams, roads, cultivating vast areas of land, and through mining and other kinds of excavation, moving enormous quantities of material around. Elements which were formerly scattered all over the terrestrial crust in minute quantities, in the forms of mineral ores are now being deposited into the Earth's waterways in a pure form which so far Nature has not had to deal with. All this shifting around of the Earth's resources is so that Man himself can live more comfortably. Most people in the advanced industrial world are aware of the imminent crisis, but let us be honest: few of us are prepared to give up the comfort of a heated or air conditioned home, convenient transport or a full plate of meat. Nevertheless, we who live in the advanced industrial world account for barely 25 per cent of the entire global population, and yet we use up 60 per cent of its energy resources, the greater part of its raw materials

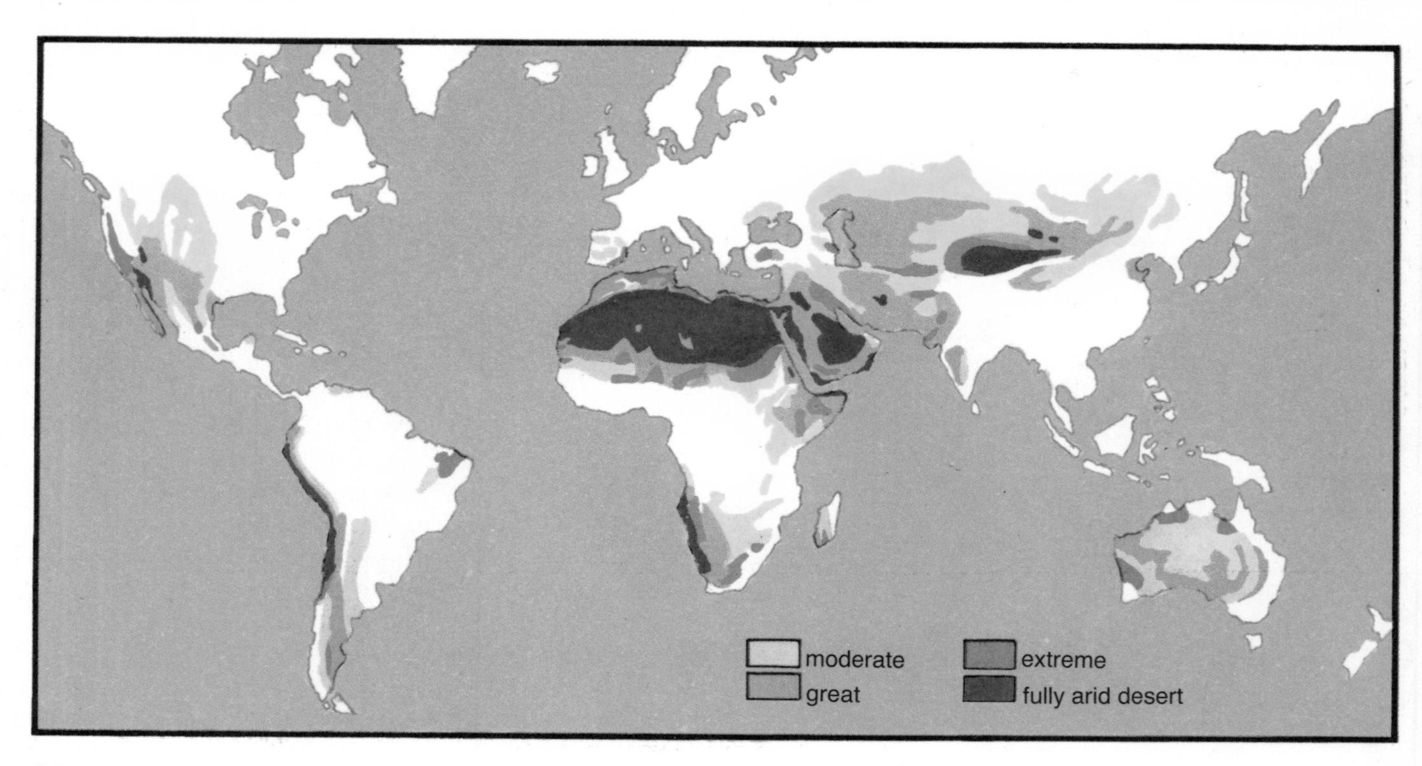

23 In the Kufra basin in Libya 'green-suns' are built up, artificial oases of corn fields. In the centre of such an oasis is a borehole which reaches water-bearing strata. Water is drawn by pumps and used to irrigate an area of some 0.7 sq km/0.28 sq miles. This is a common way to use land resources; however, intensive irrigation causes degeneration of the soil and an increase in its salt content.

◁
22 The danger of land becoming desert: moderate (light yellow), great (orange), extreme (red). Dark brown denotes the areas which are already desert.

and huge amounts of food. The amount of waste is equal to the amount used — it is vast.

The number of the Earth's inhabitants is increasing, but so are their demands. In the Neolithic Age, the Earth was inhabited by between 5 and 10 million people, whose numbers increased quite slowly. Based on growth rates of 2,000 years ago, it would then have taken 1,600 years for the world's population to double. Our growth rate has increased so much since that it took a mere 37 years, between the years 1952 and 1989, to increase from 2.5 billion to 5 billion. Even according to sober estimates by United Nations experts there will be 8.5 billion people living on Earth by the year 2025. This growth rate of 3 billion, however, will occur not in the advanced industrial countries, but in the developing countries. These estimates are, moreover, based on a reasonable assumption — on limited population growth, not on its present levels.

In order to meet at least his minimum needs, Man has to exploit the resources and mineral raw materials of the planet. He wants sufficient food and consumer goods, therefore using the Earth so that he can provide heat, build dams and have enough gravel or cement for their construction. He, therefore, moves around a greater amount of material annually than Nature herself does in the course of her own processes. These massive amounts, however, are not moved by Man himself: the majority of these shifts are brought about by 'induced' movements. To give an example, we deforest the landscape in order to obtain sufficient arable land, without realizing that we are setting a geological merry-go-round in motion. As erosion of the land horizon increases, the amount of fertile land decreases. To maintain agricultural production levels, however, we compensate for these and other losses which also

24 The struggle of man against the desert is an ancient one. The protecting walls which surround a well and small oasis in the Algerian part of the Sahara must be continuously heightened and improved, otherwise they would be 'flooded' with sand.

▷

25 Water-the source of life. This applies both to dry and humid areas. Economical use of water and its sound management was achieved when cultivating rice by the people of Asia. They succeeded in using a method called 'step farming' (terracing) on steeply sloping areas of land. In this way they practically eliminated erosion.

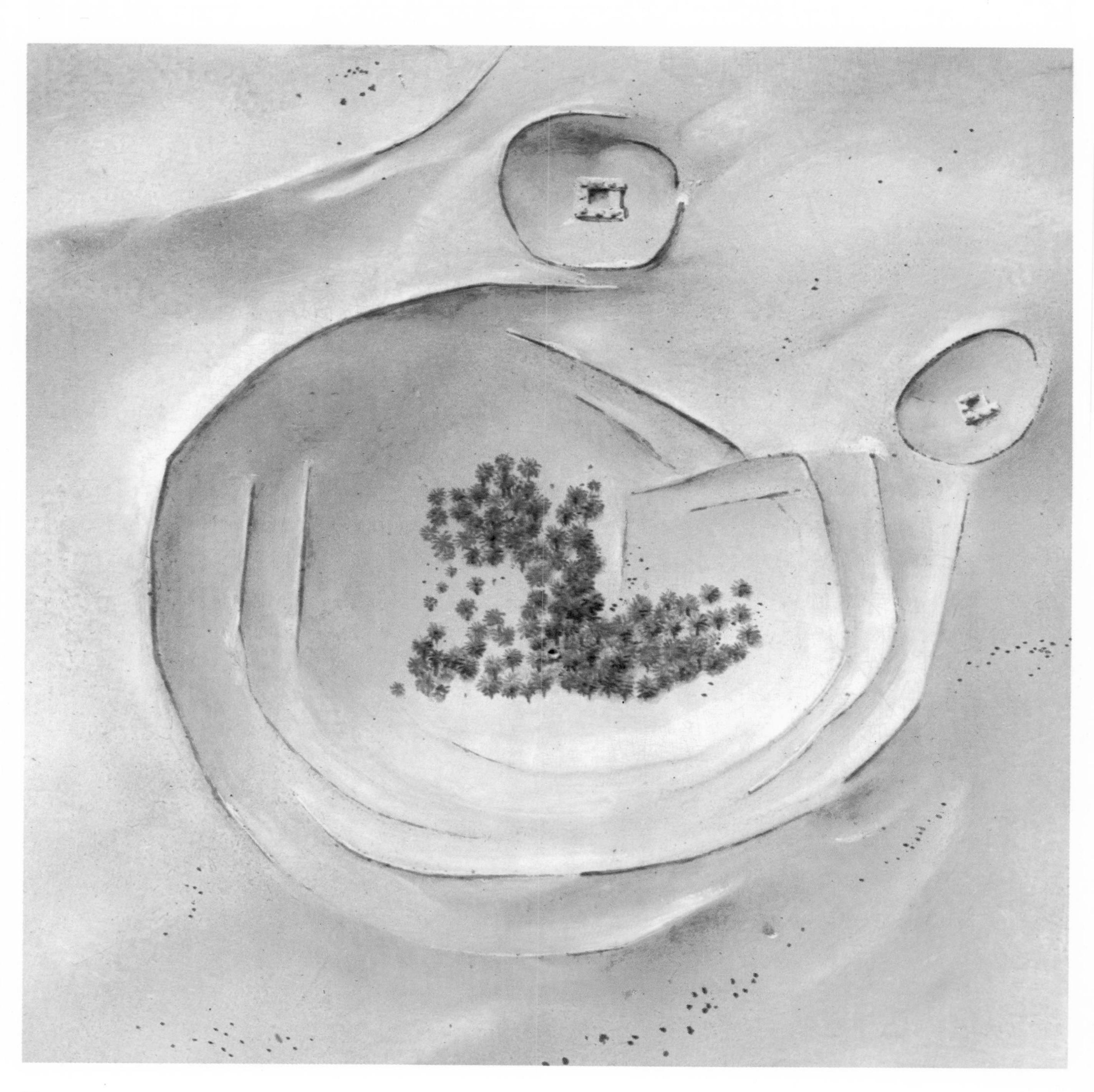

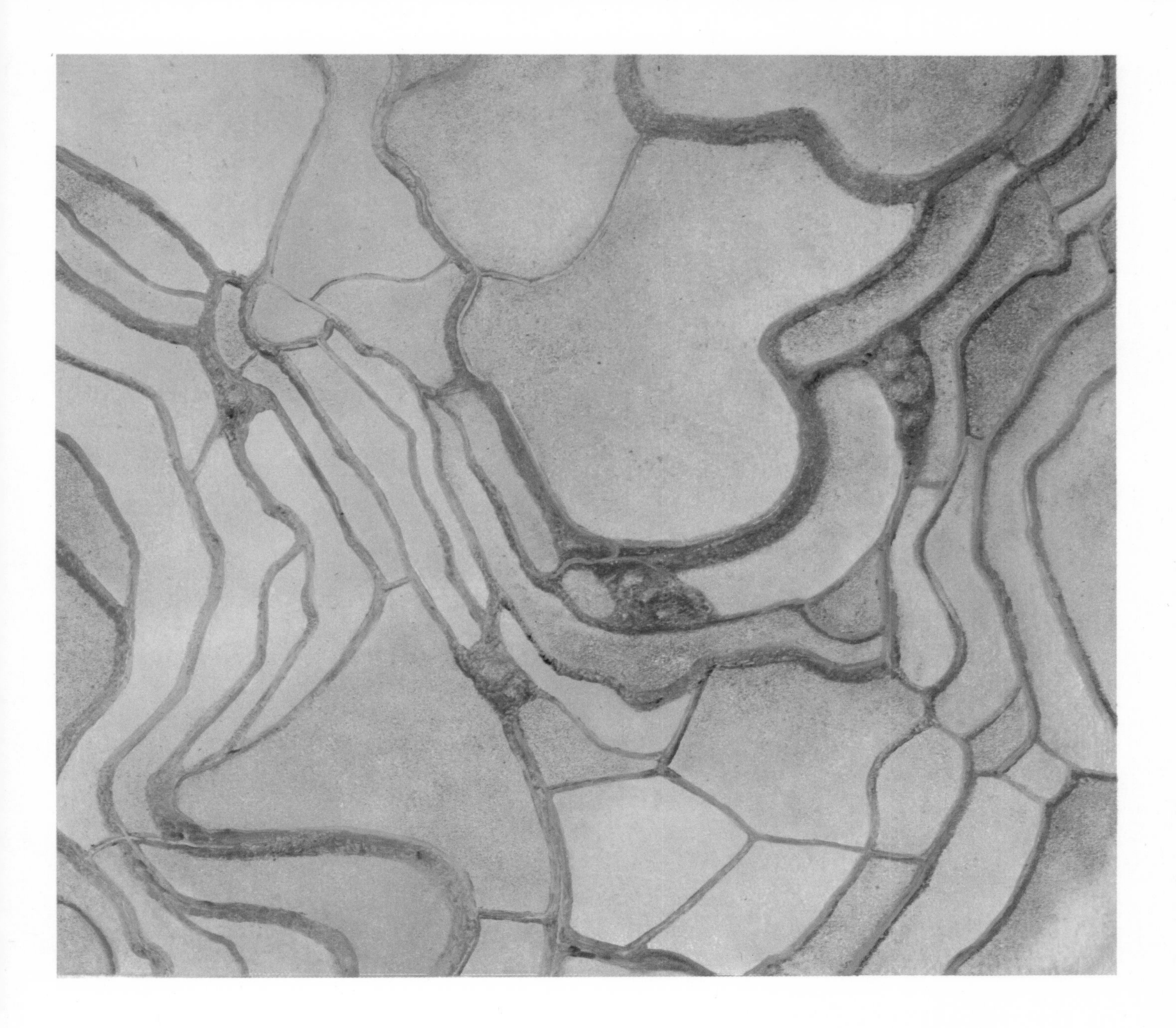

occur as a consequence of using heavy machinery by adding industrial fertilizers. These alter a chemical balance which has been established over thousands of years. Some components are stripped from the soil, others remain combined, while others occur in excess. We have only a vague notion of the effects of these changes.

Geologists have been studying the history of the Earth for a long time, and if required to predict the future they have examples from the past at their disposal. Let us look, for instance, at the picture showing temperature changes on Earth during the last 160 thousand years, together with the curve showing changes in the carbon dioxide levels in the atmosphere during the same period. All this is geological data about the past. Is it necessary to look for a link with the present? Such a link is obvious: the planet's temperature is rising and Man is contributing to this process.

So far the Earth has managed to recover by itself from shocks caused either by the surrounding universe or from within itself. However, balance is often restored at a high price. Whole populations of animals and plants become extinct, others adapt and new ones appear. How high a price is Man prepared to pay, and is the Earth capable of coping with the results of his activities?

In order to resolve this conflict with Nature, we shall have to reach an agreement with her. Before we can do that, however, we shall have to get to know ourselves better and try to understand the Earth and treat it with consideration. To expect Nature stretched to its limits to manage this alone is more than unreasonable.

Man is so far the only living creature able to learn intentionally about his planet, this carefully constructed house of cards. We must study the cards one by one to see how they fit together to form the whole, otherwise we may find ourselves pulling out a supporting card, and then it may be too late.

IRELAND
(EIRE)
Northern Ireland
Londonderry
Belfast
Sligo
Carrick on Shannon
Dundalk
Clifden
Galway (Gaillimh)
Kinnegad
Shannon
Tralee
Limerick (Luimneach)
Killarney
Carlisle
Newcastle
Preston
York
Bolton
Manchester
Sheffield
Nottingham
Leicester
Birmingham
Cambrian Mountains
Northampton
Cambridge
Norwich
Ipswich
Swansea
Cardiff
Oxford
Bristol
London
Exeter
Bournemouth
Brighton
Rotterdam
Breda
Antwerpen (Anvers)
Gent
BELGIE
Bruxelles
Brussel
BELGIQUE
Lille
Arras
Charleroi
Amiens
Saint Quentin
Rouen
Picardie
Caen
Normandie
Brest
Saint Brieuc
Quimper
Bretagne
Rennes
Alençon
Chartres
Versailles
Paris
Reims
Châlons-sur-Marne
Luxembourg
Nancy
Saint Dizier
Troyes
Le Mans
Orléans
Saint Nazaire
Angers
Tours
Nantes
Anjou
Vierzon
Bourges
Langres
Besançon
Poitou
Poitiers
Châteauroux
F R A N C E
La Rochelle
Montluçon
Saintes
Angoulême
Limoges
Vichy
Mâcon
Lyon
Brive la-Gaillarde
Bordeaux
Grenoble
Guyenne
Montauban
Toulouse
Tarbes
Carcassonne
Narbonne
Nîmes
Avignon
Arles
Toulon
Nice
El Ferrol
La Coruña
Lugo
Vigo
Braga
Porto
Viseu
Coimbra
Valladolid
Palencia
Burgos
Logroño
Huesca
Zaragoza
Salamanca
Segovia

THE FACE OF THE PLANET

When, at the dawn of aviation history, the famous French writer and pilot Antoine de Saint-Exupéry wrote of his impressions looking at the face of the planet, he was amazed at how distorted our view of the Earth is. People are accustomed to walking along roads leading from one dwelling to another, one water source to another, from the village to the field or into the town. They are familiar only with these sights, shaped by civilization. The vistas seen by the first pilots were a reminder that the greater part of our Earth is covered with deserts or vast areas of primeval forests. However, even this view has changed in the sixty years that have elapsed since Exupéry observed it. The expanse of desert, especially in Africa, has increased, while an area of tropical rain forest equivalent to the size of Europe has been lost over the continents of Asia, Africa and South America.

26 A tourist's perception of the landscape differs markedly from that of a geologist. Where the tourist sees only the surface of the sea, the geologist wonders what lies beneath: whether, for example, it may conceal an oil pool. He recognizes high mountain ranges (shown in brown on geographic maps) as areas of continent collisions, which occurred in the case of the Alps and the Pyrenees in the Mesozoic Era, and in the case of the Kjölen Mountains in Norway in the Palaeozoic Era. He enriches his personal image of continental seas with the idea of sedimentary rocks and pollutants lying on the sea floor. Although he knows the extent of the seas, he considers the areas represented on maps in light blue as parts of continents because of their geological structure.

Although Exupéry flew across the ocean between Africa and South America, he was evidently not particularly captivated by the ocean realms. In the intervening fifty years, however, we land-dwellers have gained from the expanse of ocean much the same impressions as those gained by astronauts travelling into space. Their view is the whole view, the view of cause and effect with which we should also learn to look upon the planet that is our home.

Let us first take a look at the outer surface of the planet. The surface of a body can suggest a great deal about what is concealed in its innermost parts. Just as with a healthy or sick person, an experienced doctor can detect outward signs of a patient's state of health long before proceeding with X-rays, blood tests, and so on.

Most of us get to know the planet in a somewhat roundabout way, by sitting over a map and in our minds easily crossing thousands of kilometres of desert and effortlessly climbing mountains many metres high. This perspective can be given by television, films or books, and this is enough for some of us. For others, however, the travel bug will always be there, and it gets worse the older they get.

Let us open an atlas at the pages which show the whole Earth in two hemispheres. This should be marked in brown for the mountains, green for the lowlands and blue for the oceans. We shall begin with the oceans, for they, more than anything, still hold many secrets, not only

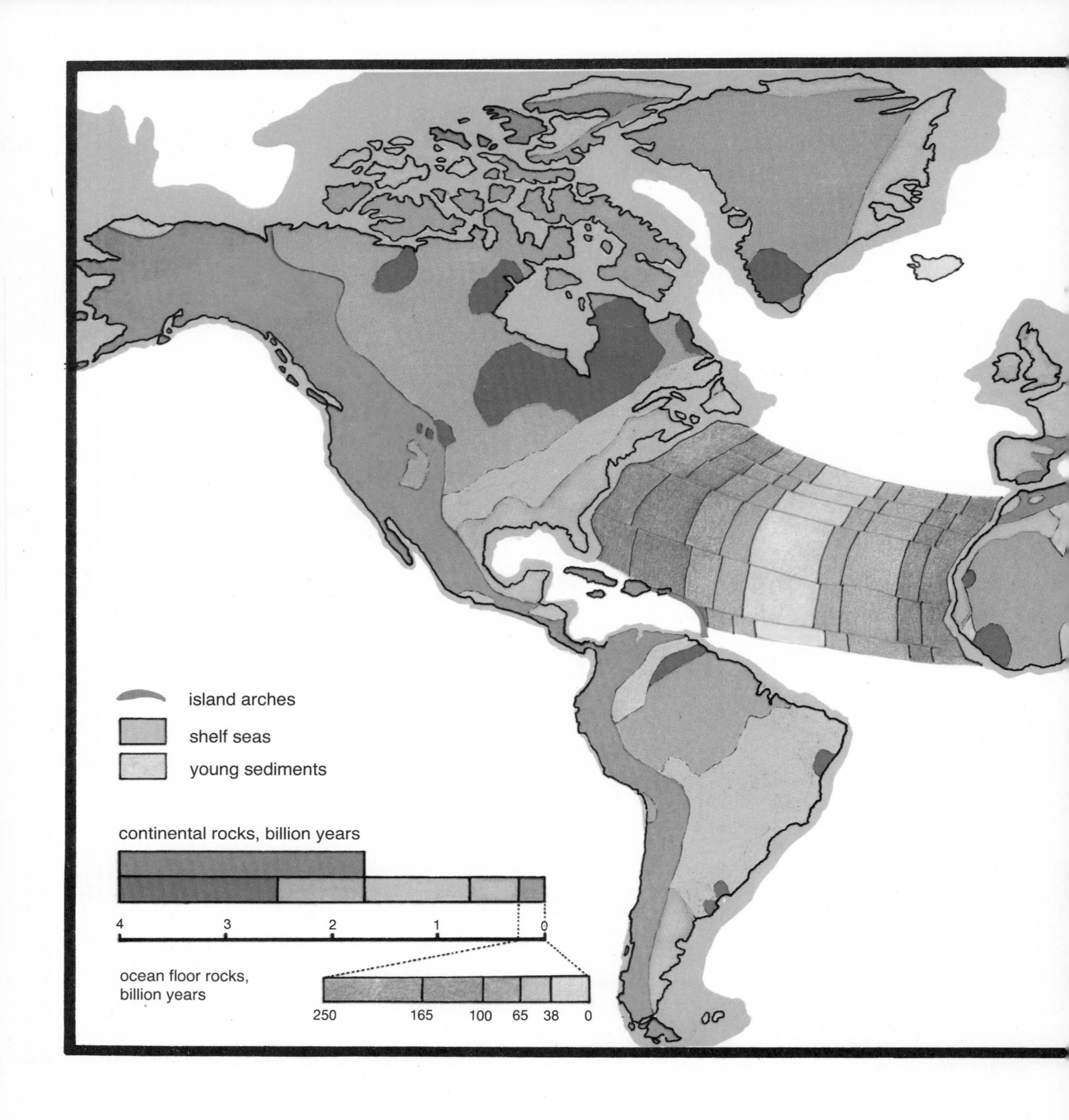

27 The oldest parts of the Earth are 'Archaean'; they include all rocks older than 1.7 billion years, or 1 aeon, and are represented by violet to pink. They include the Canadian, South African, Baltic and Siberian shields (the solid and very aged parts of the Earth), also called continental nuclei. Somewhat younger are the areas presented in grey in which rocks of the Proterozoic aeon occur. Still younger are the Palaeozoic terrains, shown dark green. The young orogenic zones (rusty brown) are of Mesozoic age. If we look at the area which is part of the Atlantic ocean, the yellow tones represent the youngest rocks of the ocean floor; the violet tones represent the Mesozoic (Cretaceous and Jurassic) rocks of the ocean floor. The island archipelagoes (red) are geologically very young formations, their evolution being measured in millions and tens of millions of years. However, as the island archipelagoes are places of collision between lithospheric plates, older rocks, which are in fact parts of continents, may be found. For instance, in Japan and New Guinea geological formations older than 300 million years have been discovered. The light blue colour along the continental edges does not denote age, but suggests the presence of the continental crust, where the geographic map shows the seas. The areas of recent sedimentation are shown in light green.

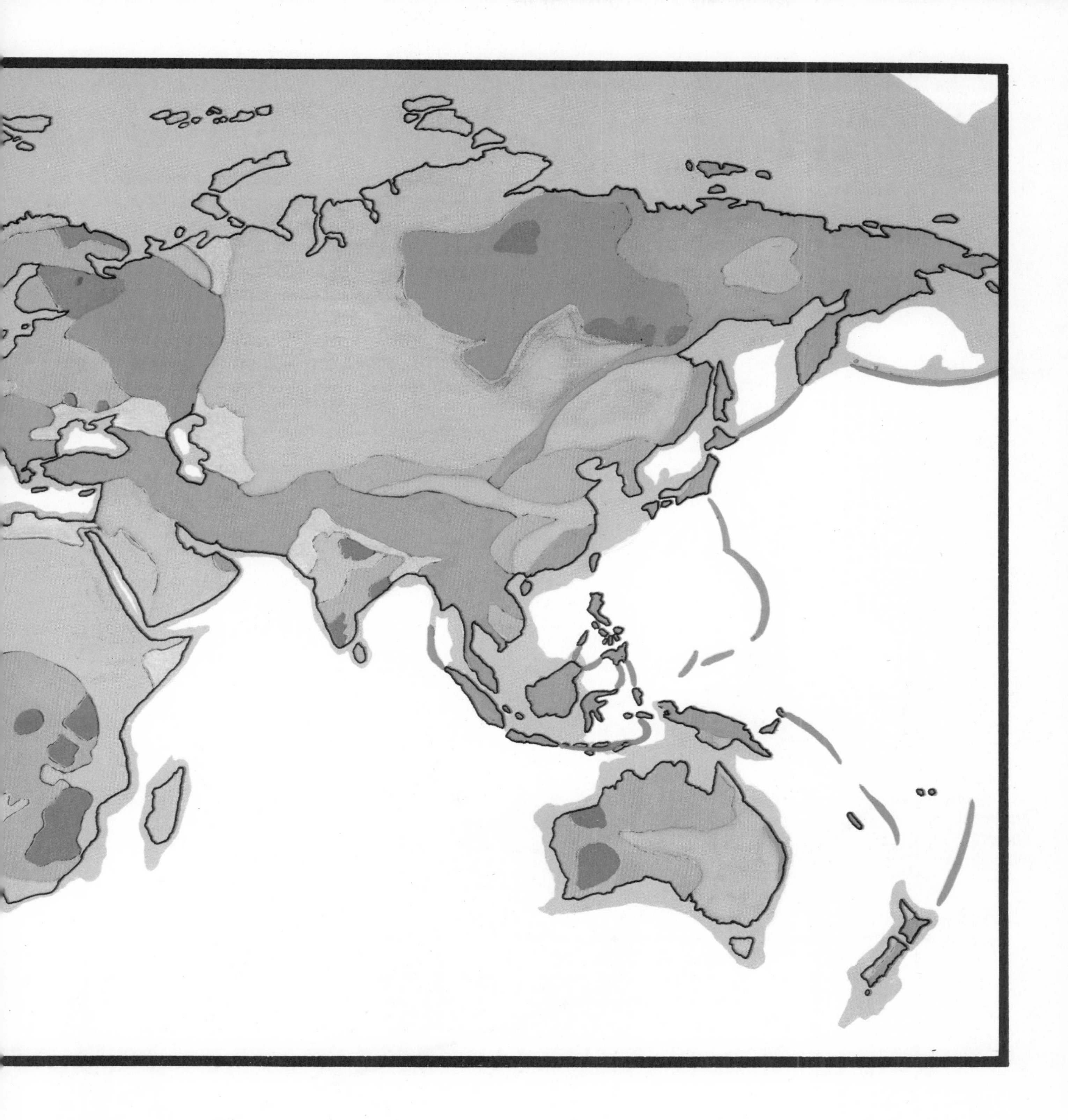

within their animal kingdom but also in the geology of the ocean bed, an area which has brought much new and, in some cases, revolutionary knowledge in recent years.

The amount of information about the oceans, especially concerning the formation of the bed, has increased greatly in the last thirty years. Knowledge of the continents, their formation, altitude and topography, on the other hand, were more or less complete over a century ago. A geographical atlas shows all too plainly the predominance of oceans over land masses, giving information about their average depth, the quantity of water in the oceans, the asymmetrical distribution of the continents, and whether a hemisphere is rich or poor in water. Research into ocean and sea beds, however, originally oriented towards military rather than geological aims, has led to discoveries which have compelled us to change our conception of the Earth and its life processes. It was also through observation of the surface of the ocean bed, the

28 The vertical zoning of the Earth's surface is the result of a number of geological and climatic factors — internal and external forces colliding on the surface of the Earth. The hypsographic curve characterizes the break-up of the Earth's surface into individual elevations and depths below sea level. It suggests that the prevailing majority of dry land has a lowland elevation (up to 200 m/656 ft above sea level) and that the deep sea floor occupies some 56 per cent of the Earth's surface. On the other hand deep sea trenches and extremely high mountain ranges comprise only a very small part of the planet's surface.

subsequent measuring of the surface of the ocean bed, the subsequent measuring of heat levels in rock formations, of heat flows, terrestrial gravity and magnetic properties, that we altered our notions about how the Earth functions inside.

A map showing the various depths of the ocean bed can prove most informative. The greater part of the ocean bed is made up of abyssal plains, inert, formless, vast undersea expanses of rock deposits. It might be assumed that these huge quantities of rock have accumulated on the abyssal plains over millions of years, but in fact this is not so. The ocean bed is not rich in deposits. This is not because it is a long way from the continents and therefore there is nowhere to bring the material from. The cause is elsewhere. Beneath the thin layer of deposits there are usually igneous rocks, or basalt lava. However it is not only the small quantity of deposits on the ocean bed that is surprising,

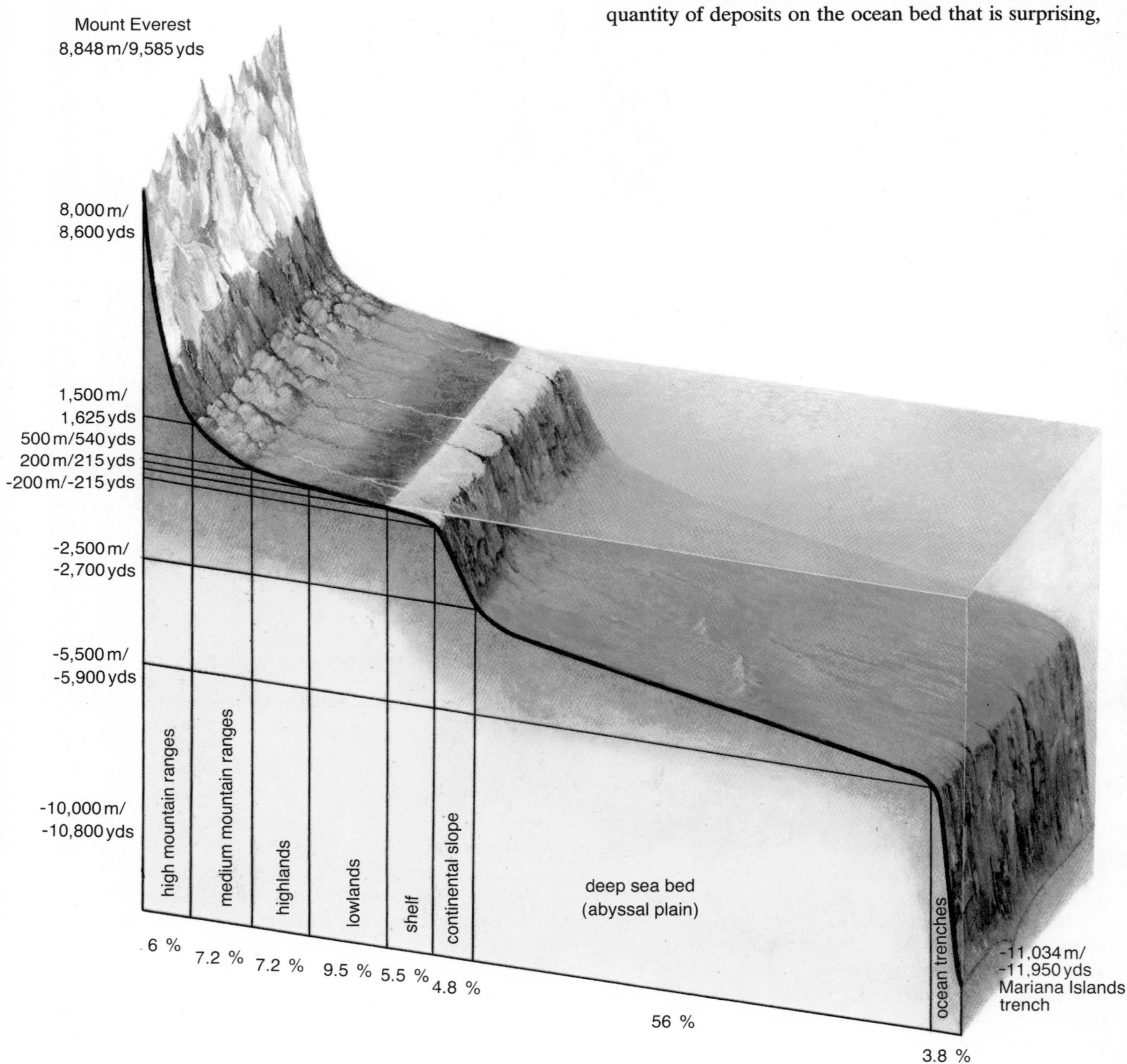

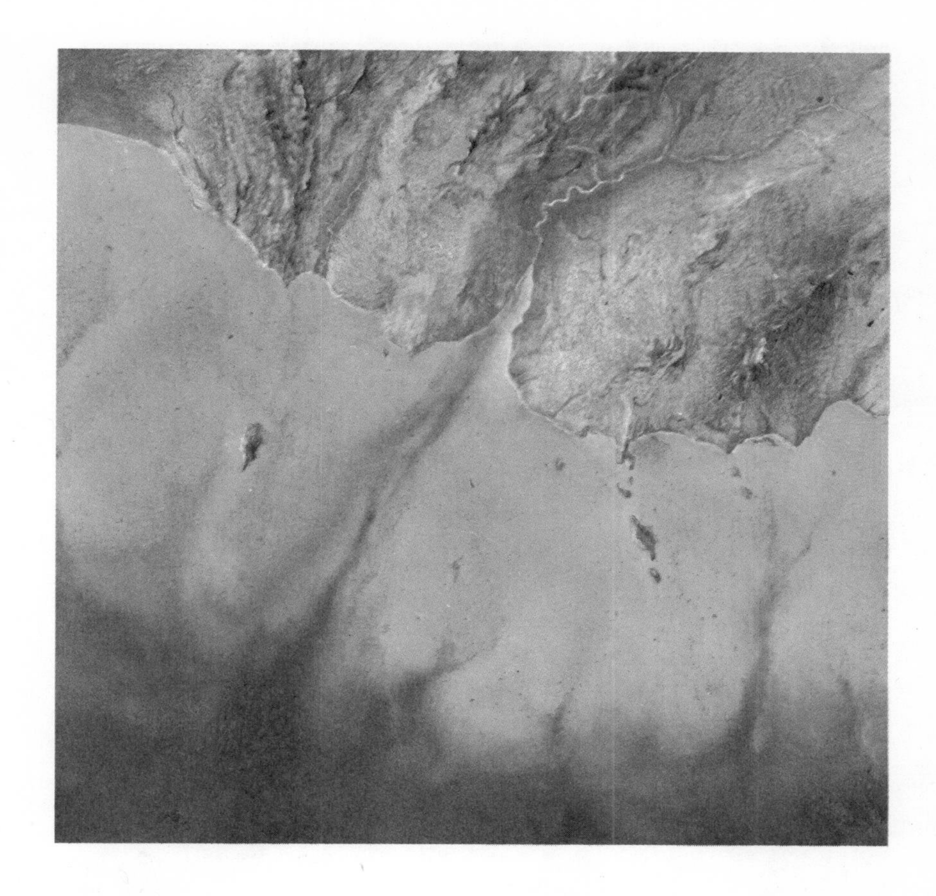

29 The geological difference between a continent and an ocean floor lies in the structure and composition of the crust. The continental crust is 35 km/22 miles thick on average and usually has a granite or grandiorite composition, while the ocean floor crust is only some 15 km/9.3 miles thick and is basaltic in composition. The continental crust, however, occurs in most sea boundaries. Its transition from continent to sea floor (dark blue) is masked by a shallow continental shelf (light blue). It is usually an area of sea with a continental crust of no great depth (up to some 200 m/656 ft), furrowed with a network of underwater canyons some of which link up with continental rivers. The picture shows the difference between the sea shelf and the ocean, and the position of the canyons, furrowing the continental slope.

but also their age — all rock deposits on the ocean bed are very young. Bearing in mind that the Earth is 4.6 billion years old, it would seem mysterious that all rock formations found on the ocean bed are less than 150 or 200 million years old. This is not because oceanologists have probed only the uppermost layer of rock. On the contrary: they have made abundant boreholes in the bed, but the picture that emerges is always the same. It is moreover apparent that the rocks on the ocean bed are oldest in proximity to land masses, whereas the rocks occurring in the inner parts of oceans are geologically very young.

More or less in the middle of every ocean are formations known as mid-ocean ridges. These were still unknown in the last century. Their structure is symmetrical and clearly visible from data gathered from the study of the oceans. Although the ridges are mostly concealed beneath the surface, in isolated instances they may appear above it, as in the case of Iceland, which forms part of the Central Atlantic ridge.

Measurement of heat flows reveals a 'heat surplus' which, together with the presence of fresh lava and intensive volcanic activity in the central rift of the ocean ridge, indicates the discharge of red-hot matter. This is caused by the force of gravity. The magnetic properties of these eruptive rocks, which similarly correspond to the time of their eruption, are also characteristic of the mid-ocean ridge. We would be unable to find one of similar dimensions on land.

One of the basic formations of the mid-ocean ridge is its central rift, where volcanic activity is concentrated. Shallow earthquake activity, which focuses at depths of around 20—40 km/12.5—25 miles or less, is another of the main features of the rift, which is bordered by high mountains. If we were to draw a map showing the ages of rock formations on the ocean bed, we would see that the oldest formations of the ocean are those closest to the continents, whereas the newest are those close to or directly on the mid-ocean ridges.

The converse of the mid-ocean ridges, which rise up from the ocean plateau, are the deep sea trenches, which, so to speak, plough their way through them. These are most numerous in the Pacific Ocean, around which they form a ring, and are easily discernible on geographical maps. There are similar trenches in the Atlantic and Indian Oceans which, like the abyssal plains, are also surprising for their small amounts of deposits. These are the largest depressions on Earth, which would lead one to assume them to be rich in mineral deposits. They moreover occur in places where material would accumulate easily: there are many volcanoes in the vicinity, and the differences in altitude between their peaks and the trench beds are substantial. All of these factors tend to lead to rapid accu-

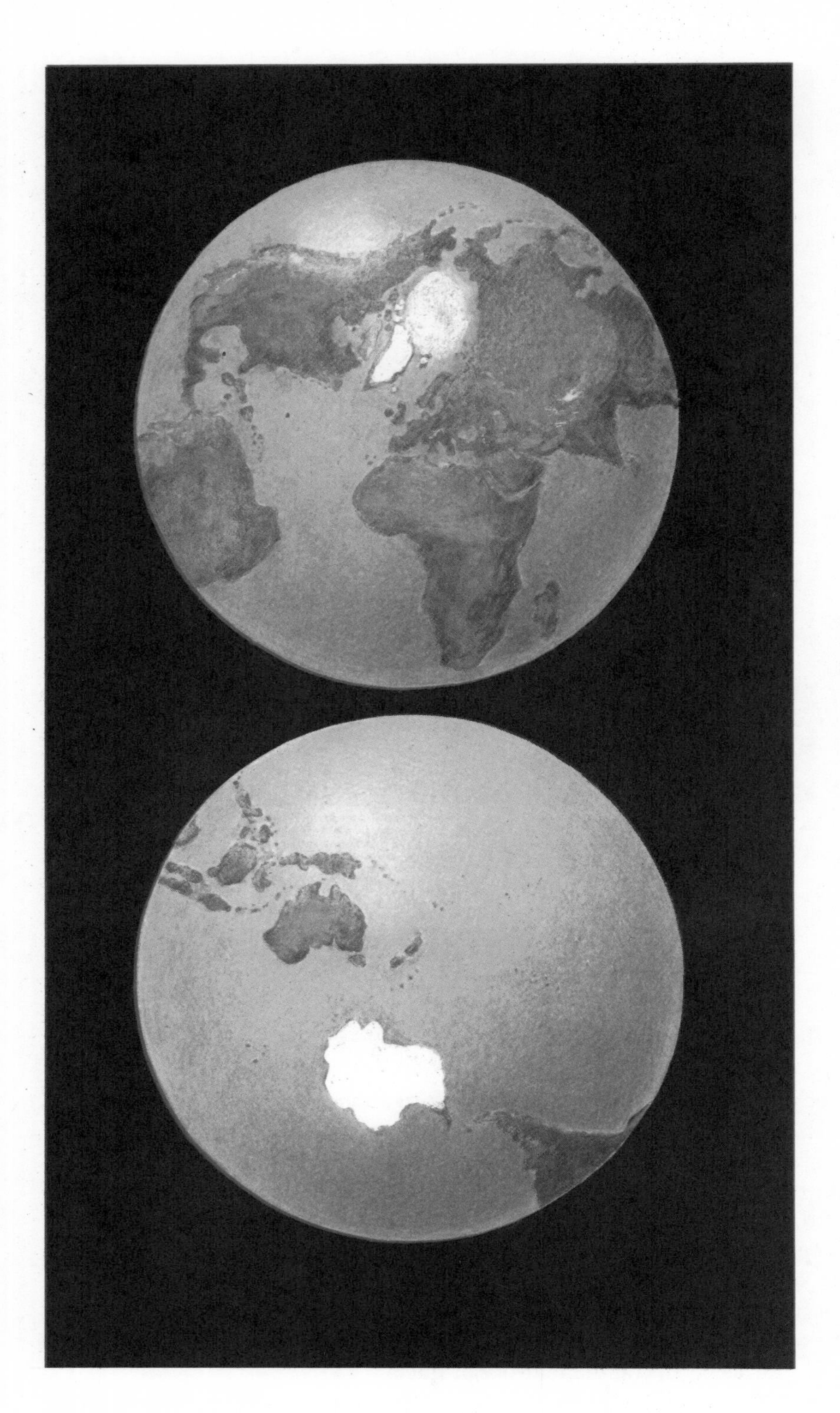

30 View of the Earth divided into two hemispheres: the 'dry' hemisphere containing most continents, and the southern or the 'wet' hemisphere covered mostly by oceans.

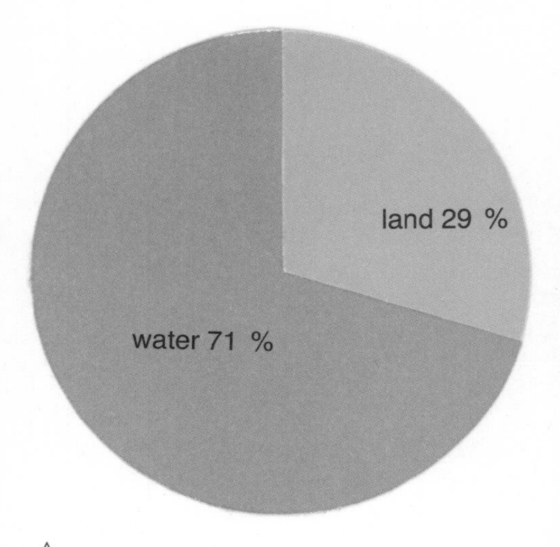

△
31 Ratio of areas of dry land to water surfaces on the Earth.

mulation of deposits, and yet the trenches are almost empty. The only possible explanation for this is that the deposits are accumulating somewhere else.

Rock formations in deep sea trenches are cool, and measurement of heat flow indicates that no heat escapes from the Earth at these points. Other characteristics of deep sea trenches are equally unusual: measurement of terrestrial gravity indicates a loss of material. If we measure the gravity of the mid-ocean ridge, it suggests a surplus of matter. The lowest points of the deep sea trenches are not seismically inactive either, with shallow earthquakes occurring here, increasing in depth the closer they get to the continents. Scientists have deduced from these observations that the ocean bed, together with its deposits, is sinking beneath pieces of continental crust in these places.

An accompanying factor to deep sea trenches is often volcanic activity on adjacent land masses or islands: there is a solid chain of volcanoes around the deep sea trenches, both in Indonesia and Japan. They occur at very regular intervals in the form of a 'volcanic front', a chain of the most active of all volcanoes, at a distance of 100 km/65 miles from the axis of the deep sea trench. The most famous of these volcanoes are Fujiyama and Sakurajima in Japan, Bezymyannaya in Kamchatka, those in the South Sandwich Islands, in South America and in the Aleutian Islands. The trenches, with their massive depressions and the volcanoes at the edge of the land masses, both with distinctive, positive morphological features, are somehow connected. Because both are at the point where transition is being made from the ocean to the continent, it is difficult to decide whether volcanic islands such as the Aleutians or Kuriles are part of the ocean structure, or whether they are part of the land mass.

However, the volcanic islands which border the deep sea trenches, the island arcs (also in the illustration), are not the only islands which occur in oceanic regions. Let us take, for example, the Hawaiian Islands, the Galapagos Islands or the islands of French Polynesia. These also consist of volcanic deposits, volcanic activity having brought them into existence, but they are in no way connected either with the deep sea trenches or with the edges of oceans or continents. They are even situated beyond the chain of mid-ocean ridges. Study of the measurement of heat flow, formation and the long-term geological activity of these volcanic centres has led to the conclusion that these places of volcanic activity originate deep in the terrestrial crust. Wherever time has gnawed away such an ocean volcano, a coral reef occurs, as long as the island is in a region where the water is sufficiently warm.

The rock formations of these volcanoes also differ from those of the island arc in terms of composition. It has not yet been possible to ascertain any kind of regular pattern in volcanic activity of this type. These volcanoes occur where substantial amounts of heat energy are emitted from the inside of the Earth in the form of lava. These places are known as 'hot spots' in the specialist geological literature, bringing colour to the rather monotonous formation of the abyssal plains.

Where the ocean meets the land mass and an ocean bed becomes a continent, a land slope is formed and then, closer to the land mass, a shelf. The shallow parts of the ocean or sea are marked in light blue on a geographical map, but if the border between a land mass and an ocean were drawn by a geologist, he would draw in these sea shallows as part of the land mass. They are a continuation of land mass structures, the geological units of the continent, and the rock formations here are indistinguishable from those occurring on the continents themselves. It should be pointed out that there is a geological distinction between an ocean and a sea. The geologist uses the term ocean to denote that part which has an oceanic crust. We shall see later that this is thinner than the continental crust and has a basalt composition, whereas the crusts of shallow seas have a continental, granite composition. On geographical maps we can find areas described as seas which are nevertheless geologically closer to oceans in character, their crusts displaying all the features of an oceanic crust, and where eruptive basalt rocks and small amounts of deposits occur. The Red Sea, the narrow strip of water between the African and Asian land masses, may be called a sea, but on its bed there are rock formations which are virtually indistinguishable from those of the Pacific Ocean, for example. The Mediterranean is another instance, although the geological structure of its bed is highly complex.

Every major geological formation on the ocean bottom, be it the mid-ocean ridge, continental slope or eroded submarine volcano, has its own distinctive features, characterized by its gravity, magnetic, and thermal fields. The mid-ocean ridge, for example, has a high flow, and submarine volcanic geysers are quite comparable in activity with those of continental volcanoes.

The continental slope on which rock deposits accumulate is, on the other hand, a place of great diversity in form. Submarine canyons occur here, accumulating a great mass of continental material brought here from the land by rivers. The material not only builds up in the canyons, but

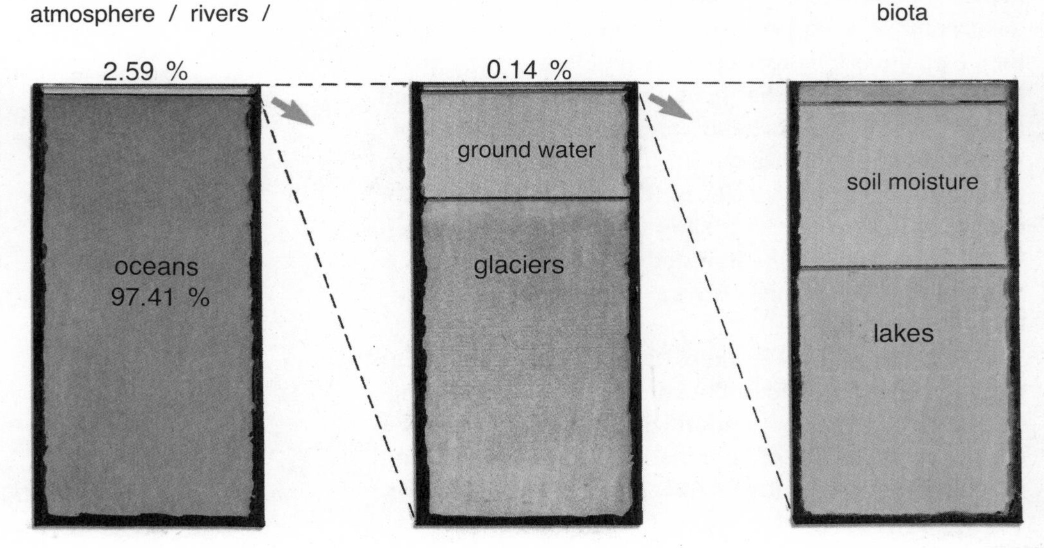

32 The prevalence of salt water areas over fresh water areas on global scale is obvious. It can also be seen when looking at the distribution of seas, dry land and freshwater lakes. However, the fact that most fresh water occurs in the form of ice is not so obvious. River water contributes little to the global water balance.

tends to slide downwards, behaving exactly like waterlogged sand. Elsewhere there are massive mud flows, which can be powerful enough to cause earthquakes. Each such region has its own biological characteristics, its own vegetation and animal communities. Near underwater geysers situated by the mid-ocean ridges live animals which do not need oxygen to live as much as they need sulphur. Twenty years ago we would have dismissed the existence of such organisms as impossible. In the same way, the deep ocean trenches have their specific fauna, which have only become known since the invention of diving equipment capable of enabling man to reach ocean depths. All environments, even those which seem at first glance unable to support any kind of life, turn out to have their own finely balanced ecosystems. Despite the general belief that our planet has been thoroughly explored and mapped and that all its details are known, specialist journals continue to publish fresh evidence of discoveries of previously unknown species in the deep sea trenches of the ocean. This only goes to show us that the Earth, which we all seem to think is exhausted as far as exploration is concerned, is still in many ways a 'terra incognita' (an unknown country).

Unlike the ocean bed, whose history has only comparatively recently begun to be documented, there is considerably more known about the land masses of the Earth. The present arrangement of land masses into high mountain, volcano chain, or flat lowland regions is relatively recent.

33 Significant information about the structure of the continental and ocean floor crusts is obtained by seismic measurements. One particular observation is the location by the staff of the Lamont-Doherty Geological Observatory of a magma hearth below the mid-ocean ridge, between the ocean floor crust and the upper mantle, in the East Pacific Rise. The position of the magma hearth, which is in a relatively shallow position below the ocean floor (approximately 2 km/ 1.25 miles), was easily detected from the recorded profile. The fuzzy limits of the magma reservoir and the thinning of the crust on the site of the mid-ocean ridge are unique in the history of such observations.

▷

34 Scientists have been able to obtain more accurate ideas about the morphology and structure of mid-ocean ridges only in the last twenty years. The picture shows a simplified section of a mid-ocean ridge (note the different scale in comparison with the preceding picture). This is a diagram of the Arab-Indian Ridge in the Indian Ocean.

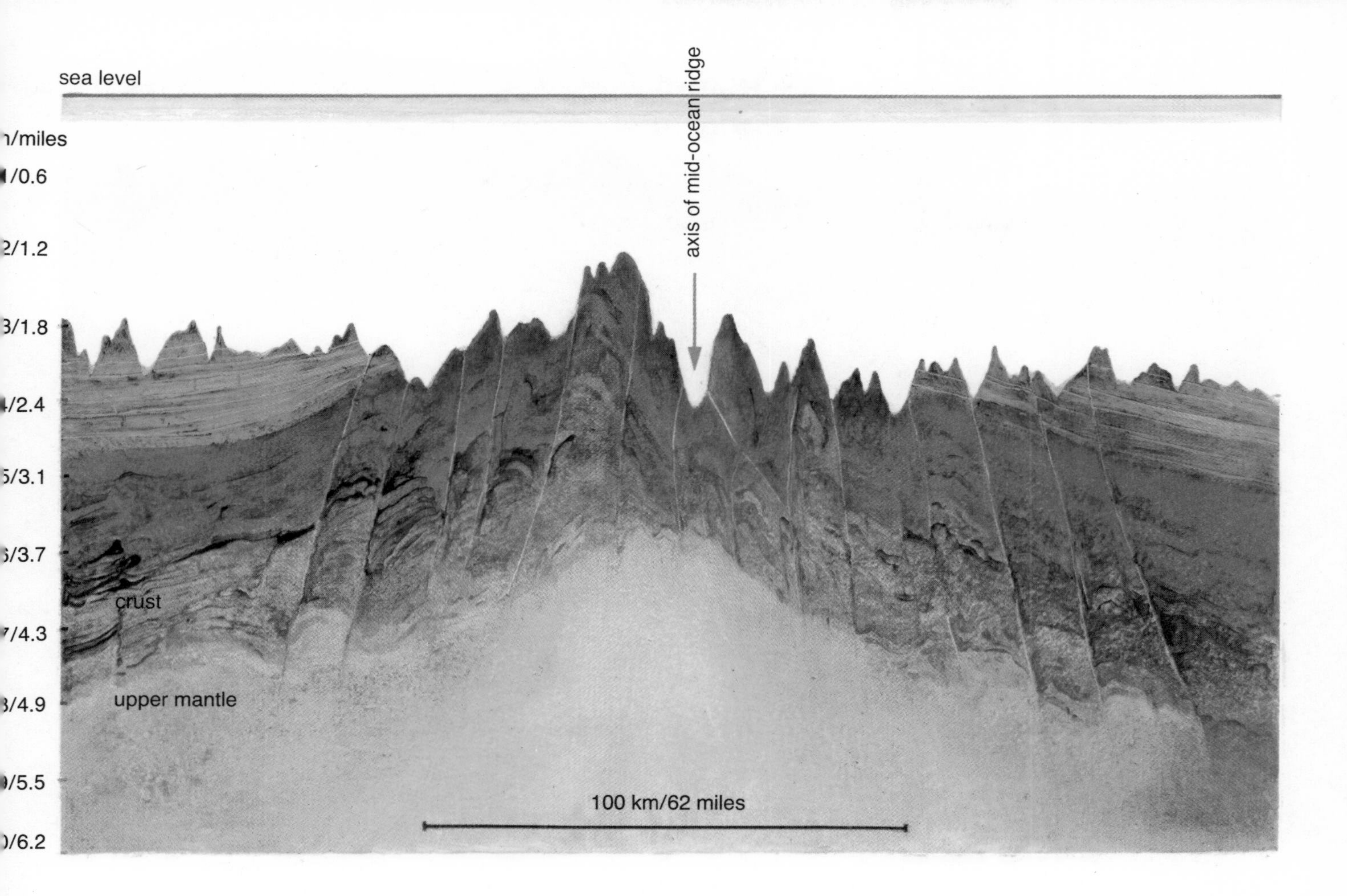

Some tens of thousands of years ago the whole of Northern Europe was covered by a glacier, and the seas were also differently arranged. Where the Alps rise today, twenty or thirty million years ago there were ocean basins; three hundred million years ago, in what is today known as Central Europe, rose belts of moutain ranges, possibly similar to the Himalayas of today. On the other hand there are, on the continents, many areas which have been land masses for thousands of millions of years, having been only occasionally flooded by the peripheral shelf seas. These regions are known as shields, for example the Ukraine, Canadian or Brazilian shields, parts of Siberia, and regions of Greenland or South Africa. The shields constitute those parts of the Earth where mountain ranges, oceanic and continental masses rose thousands of millions of years ago, undergoing a turbulent history in the process.

Both the attention of a space traveller and the armchair traveller leafing through his atlas would be caught by something other than the political boundaries of the continents – that is, the high mountain ranges. These extend across the Eurasian continent from the Pyrenees via the Alps, the Carpathians, the Balkan Peninsula, Anatolia, the Caucasus and Tien Shan across Karakorum to the Himalayas. Another such belt of high mountains stretches from the Antarctic across the whole of South, Central and North America. All these are young mountain ranges which came into existence as a result of collision between two continental plates. These regions are geologically active and are marked correspondingly on geological maps.

A map of the world on which are marked the ages of various formations compared with a map of the world on which the focuses of earthquakes and of volcanic activity have been drawn in can, even to the untrained eye, reveal surprising correlations. All currently geologically active, young terrains, that is, those which demonstrate internal geological activity by way of earthquakes or volcanoes, are highly distinctive in form, both on land and in the oceans. They form a vast belt of mountain ranges, volcanic islands, deep sea trenches and mid-ocean ridges. There is also a higher level of heat outflow in these places. It is understandable, therefore, that such evidence would lead to the supposition that in these areas the Earth's crust is in communication with the lower, deeper parts. These places are known as plate junctions (we shall be seeing in the chapter on The Stable and Restless Planet why these are called plates), and in the high mountain areas mentioned above these plates collide.

A current map of colliding plates reveals high mountains which were formed as a result of folding. The Alps, Himalayas and Canadian Rocky Mountains began to form only a few million years ago, and are continuing to fold. This does not mean that all the rock formations in them are young; they also contain older rocks which have been dawn into new active geological processes, regenerated rocks, and rocks which were once part of other geo-

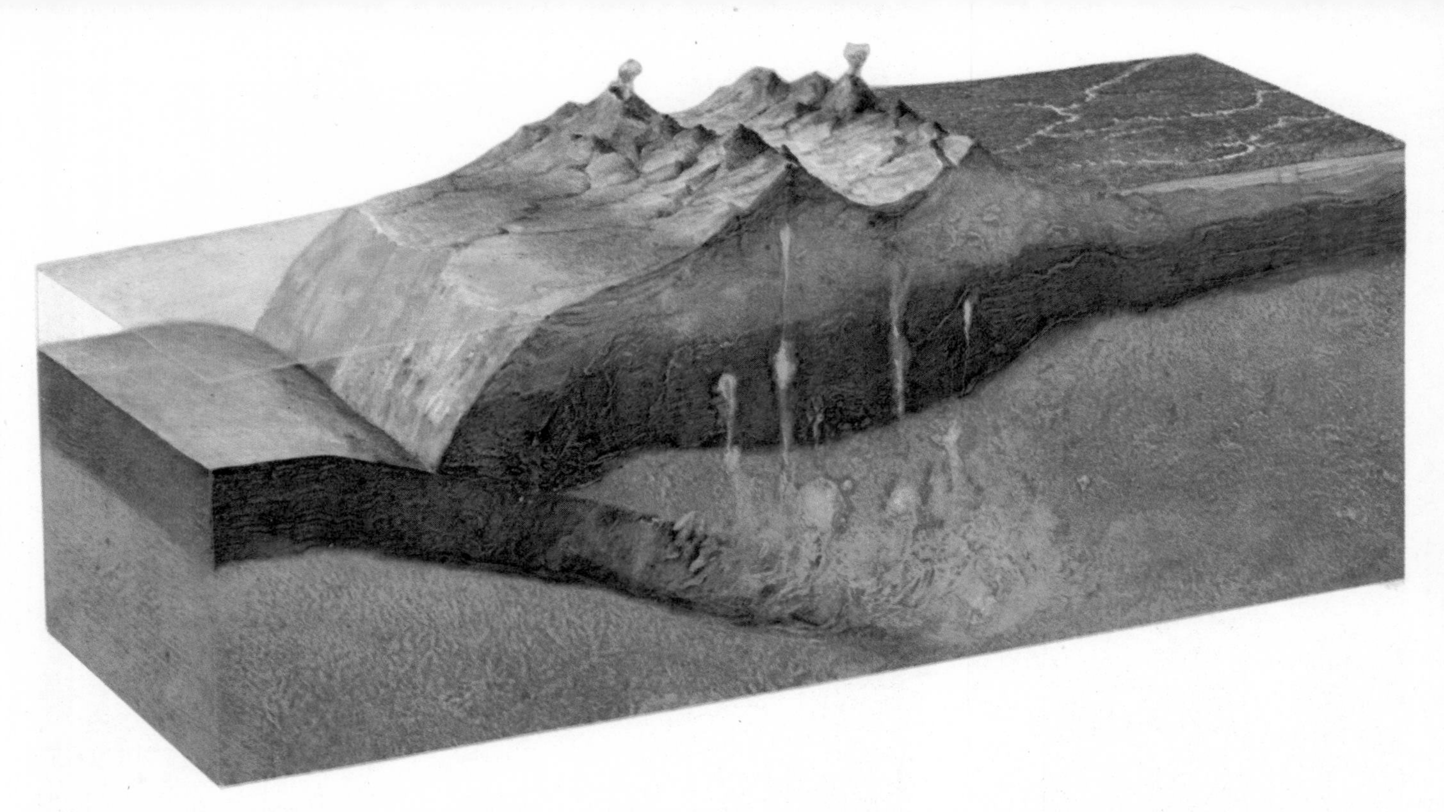

35, 36 The relation between the processes taking place in the depth and on the surface of the Earth are best observed in the geologically active parts of the planet. Such places include the western margin of South America (Fig. 35) and certain island archipelagoes, such as the Aleutians, the Kuriles or the Tonga-Kermadec Islands north of New Zealand (Fig. 36). One characteristic feature of such an area is an ocean trench. This is a deep 'scar' reaching a depth of as much as 10 km/6.2 miles, and suggests a place where the ocean plate submerges. On the edges of continents or island archipelagoes masses of settled rocks may come together, forming so-called 'non-volcanic' archipelagoes. These can either protrude above sea level or be concealed below it. The rocks carried from the continent or the archipelago form part of a fore-arc; however, its principal part is made up of the rocks which have been 'scraped off' the sinking ocean floor plate. The continent proper or the archipelago consists of volcanic rocks, and the places where these appear are called 'volcanic fronts'. The position of the volcanic front alters with the angle of subduction of the ocean-floor plate. In an area close to a continent, where the angle of subduction is usually smaller, the volcanic front is situated at a greater distance from the ocean trench (Fig. 35). Where the plate is subducted at a steeper angle (how steep the angle is can be ascertained from earthquake foci) the volcanic front is situated nearer the ocean trench (Fig. 36). Two characteristic features of the continental margin are the presence of a high plateau and great quantities of igneous rocks which have solidified beneath the surface. Also the overall crust thickness in the continental margin is greater than in the centre of the continent. The geologically active regions, i.e. the continental margins and the island archipelagoes, have a varied morphology not only as a result of volcanic activity, but also because of great vertical differences. The difference between the trench floor and the volcanic peaks is more than 10 km/6.2 miles. For this reason also, erosion is more extreme.

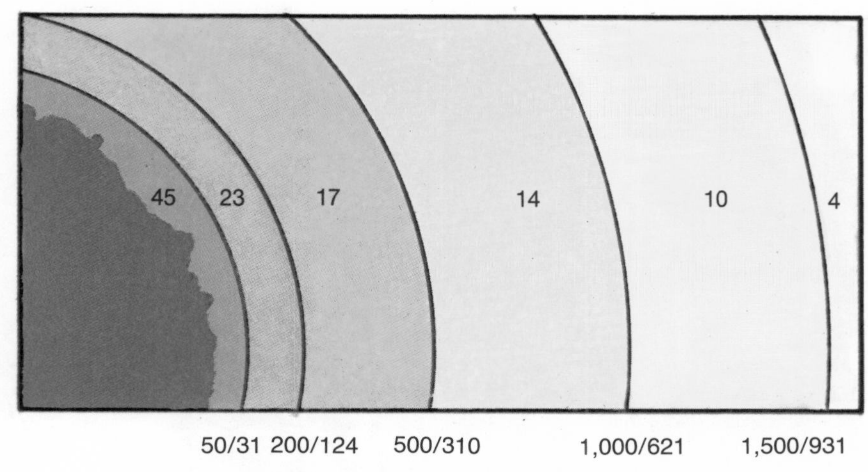

37 Sea coasts produce most of the biomass as this is where food is most easily obtainable. Therefore human population density on the Earth is also highest in coastal regions and falls markedly further inland. The figures give mean population densities per 1 sq km /0.38 sq miles.

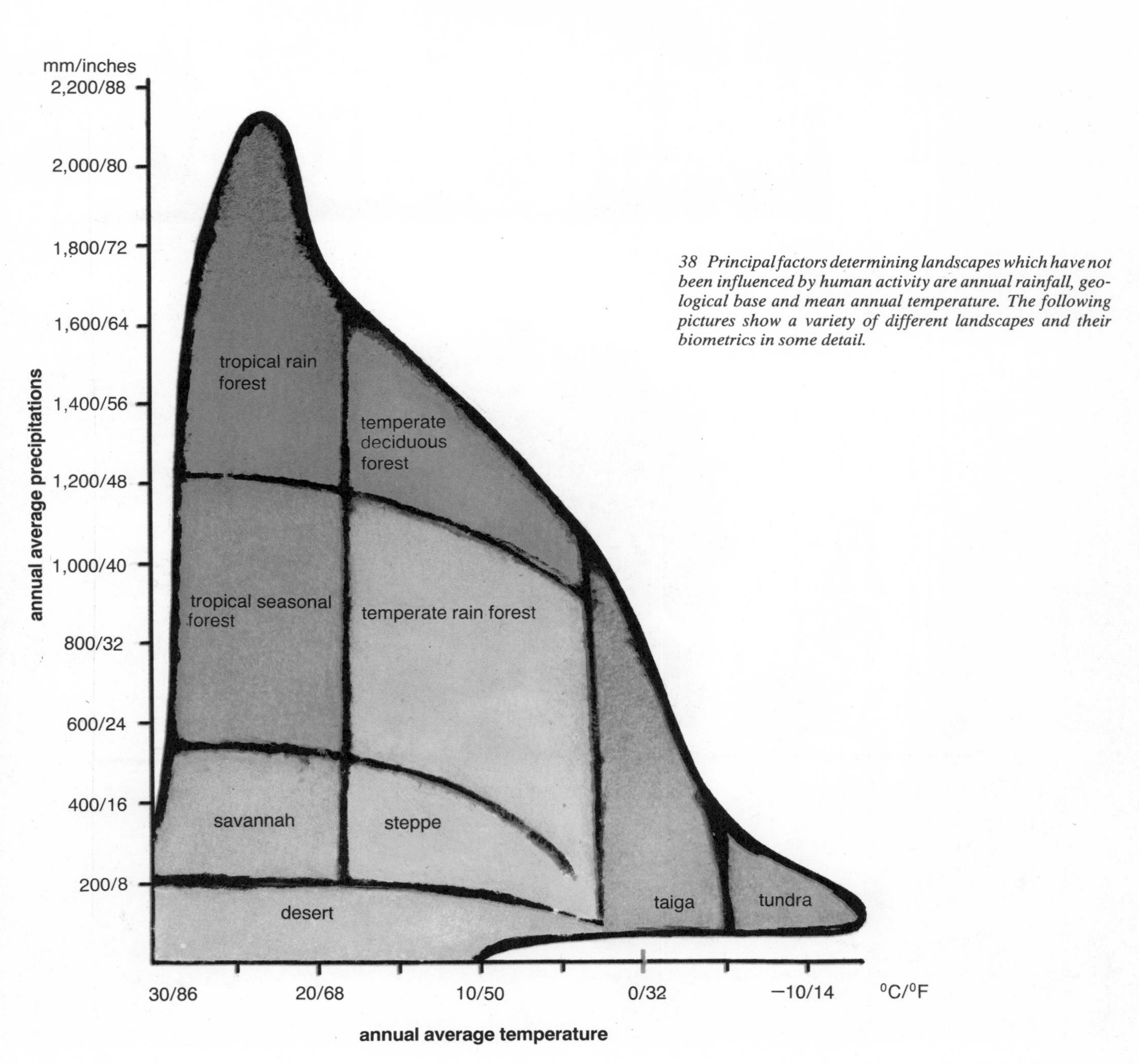

38 Principal factors determining landscapes which have not been influenced by human activity are annual rainfall, geological base and mean annual temperature. The following pictures show a variety of different landscapes and their biometrics in some detail.

39 In the regions with prevailing low temperatures and climates which are not favourable for deciduous trees, coniferous forests occur. The example in the picture is a mountain forest of Central Europe. Similar forests, however, cover major parts of Northern Europe and North America. The soil of these forests is usually of podsol character and low in nutrients. For this reason the biomass production is also low.

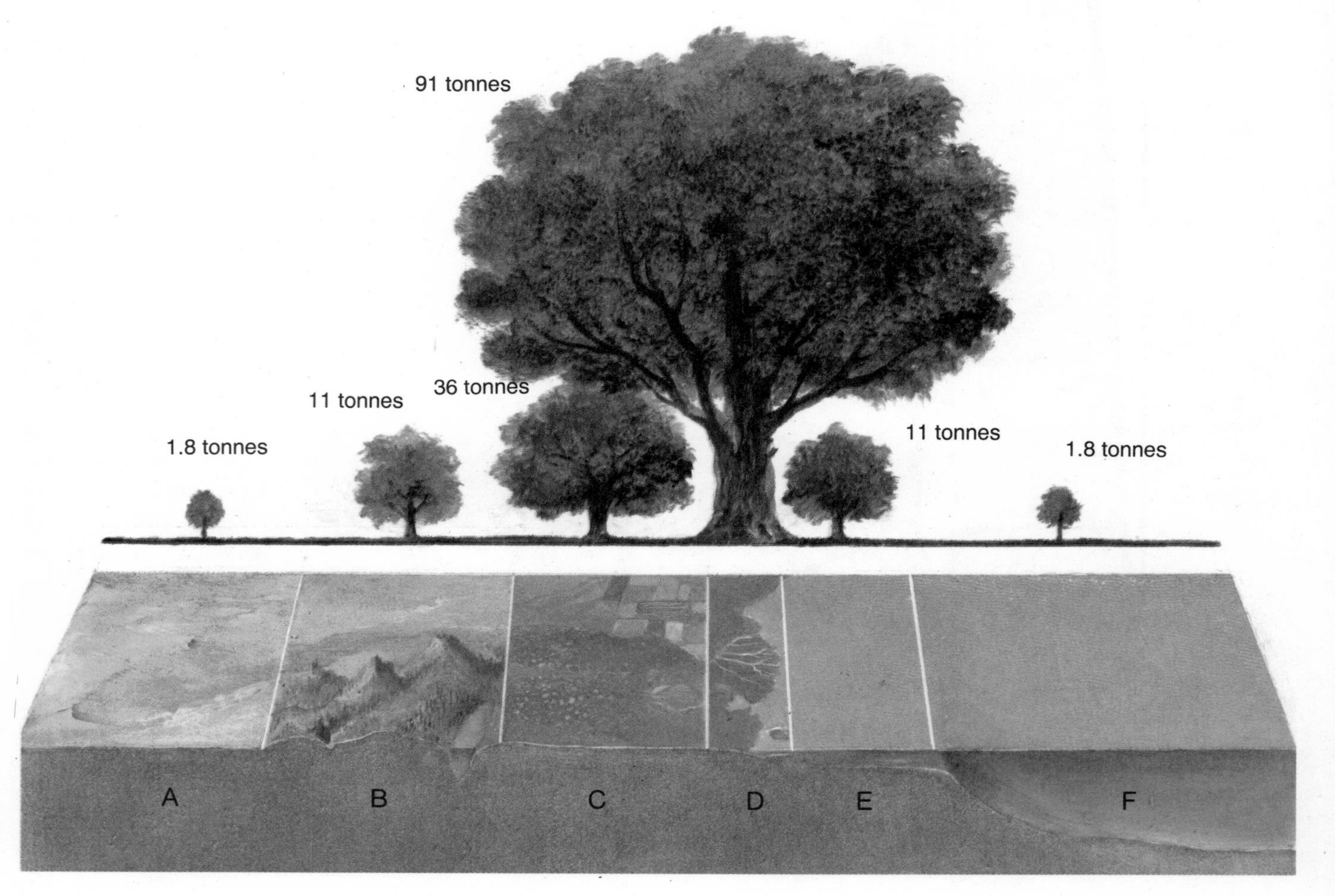

41 The conditions in which tropical rain forest ecosystems occur are those of high balanced mean temperatures and extremely high rainfall. Present are characteristic vegetation floors which, however, differ from area to area. In this picture from Trinidad, the top vegetation floor is interconnected, while the lower floors are sparser. The lowest plant floor is often absent in tropical rain forests, as the higher floors do not allow enough light to pass through.

logical formations. A look at the character of rocks and the way they became deformed in currently actively forming mountain belts reveals that they are nothing exceptional, and that similar formations have arisen many times in the geological history of the planet. Europe consists of mountain belts which began to form both at the end as well as at the beginning of the Palaeozoic era. The younger one, formed at the end of the Palaeozoic era, is known as the Hercynian orogenic (mountain-forming) belt, and runs across France, Germany and the Czech and Slovak Republics. A collision range from the beginning of the Palaeozoic era, the Caledonian orogenic belt, on the other hand, forms part of Great Britain and Norway. The Appalachian range in North America is of similar age. Detailed geological research has shown that the above mentioned areas of Europe were once joined to geological formations on what is now the east coast of the United States.

Geological history has witnessed many such mountain belts, even in regions which we today regard as geologically inactive and where there is no longer any folding or deformation, that is, the shields. Here, old, usually pre-Cambrian rocks are to be found on the surface; where the

◁

40 This schematic section of dry land and sea illustrates the plant production of various ecosystems, measured by the weight of dry matter in the biomass produced. The following key gives the meaning of the letters appearing in the picture. A = semi-deserts, B = savannahs, steppes, boreal forests, C = commercial forest, agricultural land, fertile pastureland, D = regions of fluvial plains and forests, sea and land margins, intensively cultivated agricultural regions, E = sea shelf, F = open seas and oceans.

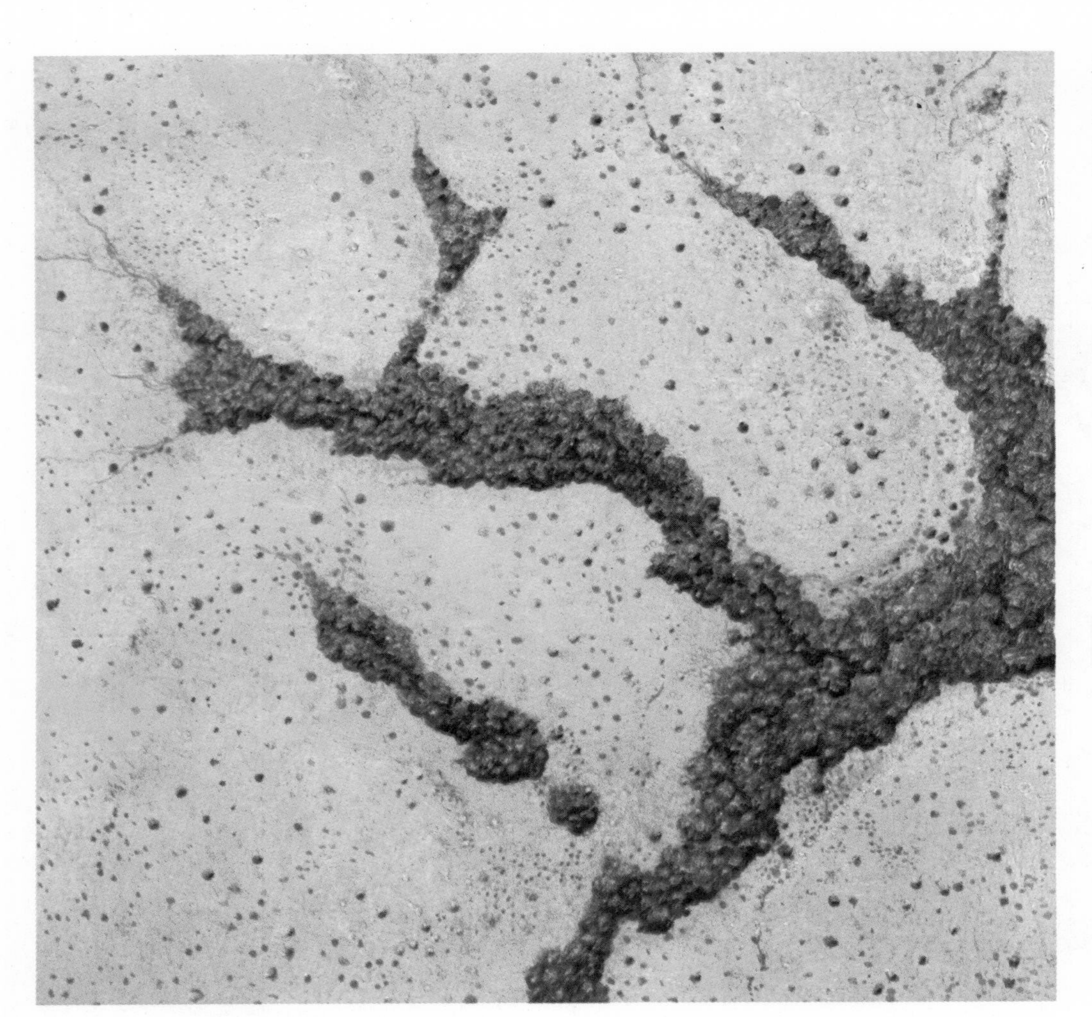

42 Savannahs are caused in tropical zones by alternating of dry and rainy periods. They are highly sensitive to the amount of annual rainfall; in dry periods they become areas of semi-desert. This serial photograph shows tree vegetation along streams, that are drying up where the ground water table is relatively high.

shields are covered with young, unfolded rock formations, they are called platforms.

In this way, the continents bear traces of their age and of the turbulent or smooth development of major global geological formations, which are evident from the shape of the landscape. Young mountain belts have a turbulent, disorganized internal structure which later manifests itself in haphazard formations. The surface of the Earth reflects its internal state, whether tense or calm, compressed or expanded. Older mountain belts have been smoothed by the passage of time, the traces of their tempestuous development worn away and less visible, even though they can be examined and deciphered using geological methods. The case is the same with shield regions, where the effects of climate and atmosphere make their marks like lines in a human face, and whose overall character displays a certain stability which comes with greater age.

This chapter has merely glanced at the face of our planet as if looking at it from a great distance without noticing the finer details of the landscape. Since it has been a look at the whole Earth, it has been necessary to treat all regions equally. Even though this view has been an overall one, it is possible to discern signs of the activities of Man: deforested areas and new water reservoirs replenishing

44 Base rocks are reflected in the character of the landscape, particularly in localities where dry weather conditions and poor vegetation cover occur. Consequently these are areas of considerable erosion. This is illustrated by the granite terrains of the Indian shield of the Aravalli Mountains.

▷

43 High mountain ranges form narrow zones which cut across whole continents. They originate in places where continental plates meet and geological history shows that their formation is a relatively speedy geological process. They crumble and disappear just as quickly. Areas such as these, which are high above sea level, have their own particular forms of vegetation and frequently contain glacial formations.

themselves rapidly. If one looks beneath the 'skin' of the landscape, however, this brings surprises. The deposit content and composition of rivers are changing. Forty years ago schoolchildren were taught that the deltas of great rivers such as the Nile were flooded with fertile mud, which formed the basis for agriculture. European rivers such as the Rhine or the Elbe have enormous quantities of such mud, which has accumulated during recent decades. The problem is that it is unusable for agricultural purposes, as it contains very high concentrations of toxic metals such as mercury, zinc and cadmium. Sedimentation of this kind, in quantities which are many times higher than naturally occurring geological deposits, inevitably takes its toll on the face of the Earth.

However, with careful observation it is not difficult to link the surface of the continent and its underlying geological structure. Let us take a fairly obvious example. In areas where calcites predominate, the landscape is dramatic and full of canyons and almost inaccessible valleys, rock shelves and abysses. A granite landscape has a different appearance, being lightly rolling and fissured, which means it will also have a regular river network. Every place on the planet has its own particular geological formations which stem from its individual characteristics and which, together with climatic factors, determine its surface structure, type of soil and consequently, its plant and animal communities. Even without detailed examination of the planetary body it can be said that its face can give us a reasonably good idea of its internal state.

A fundamental difference can be discerned on the face of the planet between ocean and land mass regions, and from this comes the difference in their geological behaviour. Ocean rock formations are young and non-deformed, forming and disappearing from the surface of the planet rapidly, which means that not many traces of the past are to be found on the ocean bed. On the other hand the land masses constitute a record of virtually the entire history of the Earth. They contain older rock formations continually forming mountain belts, which are in turn eroded by winds. The products of this erosion are carried into sedimentary basins, then proceeding to the deeper parts of the Earth, where they are regenerated, remelted and eventually resurface as fresh construction material for land masses. This method of constant reprocessing and

45 The transition between savannahs and tropical semi-shedding forests are tropical bushy forests, also called woody savannahs.

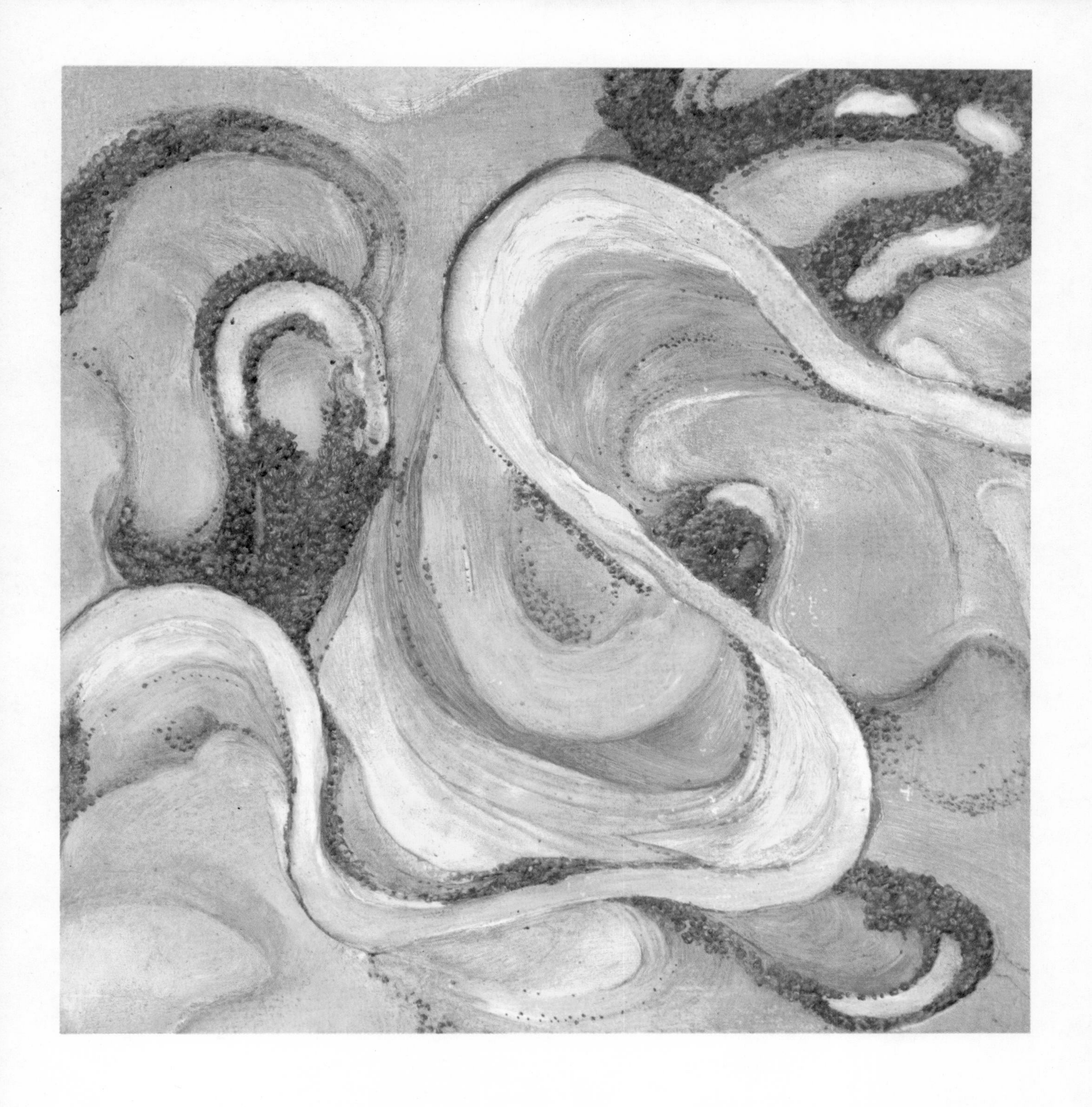

46 This meandering river bed, with its horse-shoe lakes and traces of sediment, is characteristic of lower river courses of the temperate zone. The rapidly changing morphology and vegetation cover are often the result of human activity.

recycling of already existing continental material has evolved over millions of years. Now, Man is upsetting even this ancient system, and influencing natural geological processes in small sedimentary basins and rivers, and by bringing about a one-way flow of polluted matter into the oceans. The short term effects of these activities can already be seen in the extinction of many marine species; the long term effects will not be apparent for many years. However, unless steps are taken to slow down, and eventually reverse, this process, it cannot be denied that a global change of unknown proportions will occur.

THE ANATOMY OF THE PLANET

47 We still do not understand the origins of our solar system. The study of its beginning and of more distant stars is bringing with it much specialized knowledge. Astronomers record changes in far distant outer space and interpret signals of distant lights, electromagnetic waves and temperature, which are all that remain of long ago events in outer space. Using this evidence, scientists are able to construct a picture of the beginnings of the Universe. Scientists studying carbon based meteorites are able to collect evidence of the formation of solid matter–a kind of foundation material used in the construction of planets. They have ascertained that this material also contains particles older than our solar system. Therefore, it would appear that our solar system is partially constructed from material which existed before the formation of our Sun. It is also possible that they were used in even older planetary systems. Scientists studying samples of soil and rocks from the Moon, along with pictures of the surface of other planets obtained by space probes, are attempting to ascertain the conditions under which the planets developed. Although it is possible to reconstruct and describe in some detail some stages in planetary development, the time element, the speed with which they were formed and how their layered structure occurred are still a matter of hypothesis. Our perception of the universe is changing. Despite this, however, most scientists favour the 'Big Bang' theory, which begins with a huge explosion in which the Universe was formed. On these two pages the artist depicts various stages in the formation of the Universe.

When geologists with drilling equipment arrive in a cultivated landscape, people begin to wonder what lies concealed beneath the thin surface layer of soil. People see the soil as something familiar but uninteresting and of not much consequence. Yet the soil of the Earth is a rare substance in our solar system. It is the only surface covering formed from organic compounds, which in turn are fertile enough to enable food to grow in order to support its human, animal and vegetable populations. The other planets in our solar system do have a form of covering on their surfaces which could loosely be termed soil, but which is better called 'regolite', a mixture of rock fragments which landed as fall-out from cosmic bodies or were brought by the wind. Many people are surprised to learn that at depths accessible to drilling equipment there is nothing other than solid rock. The only difference between this rock and the surface matter is that the surface matter has been broken down and mixed with organic

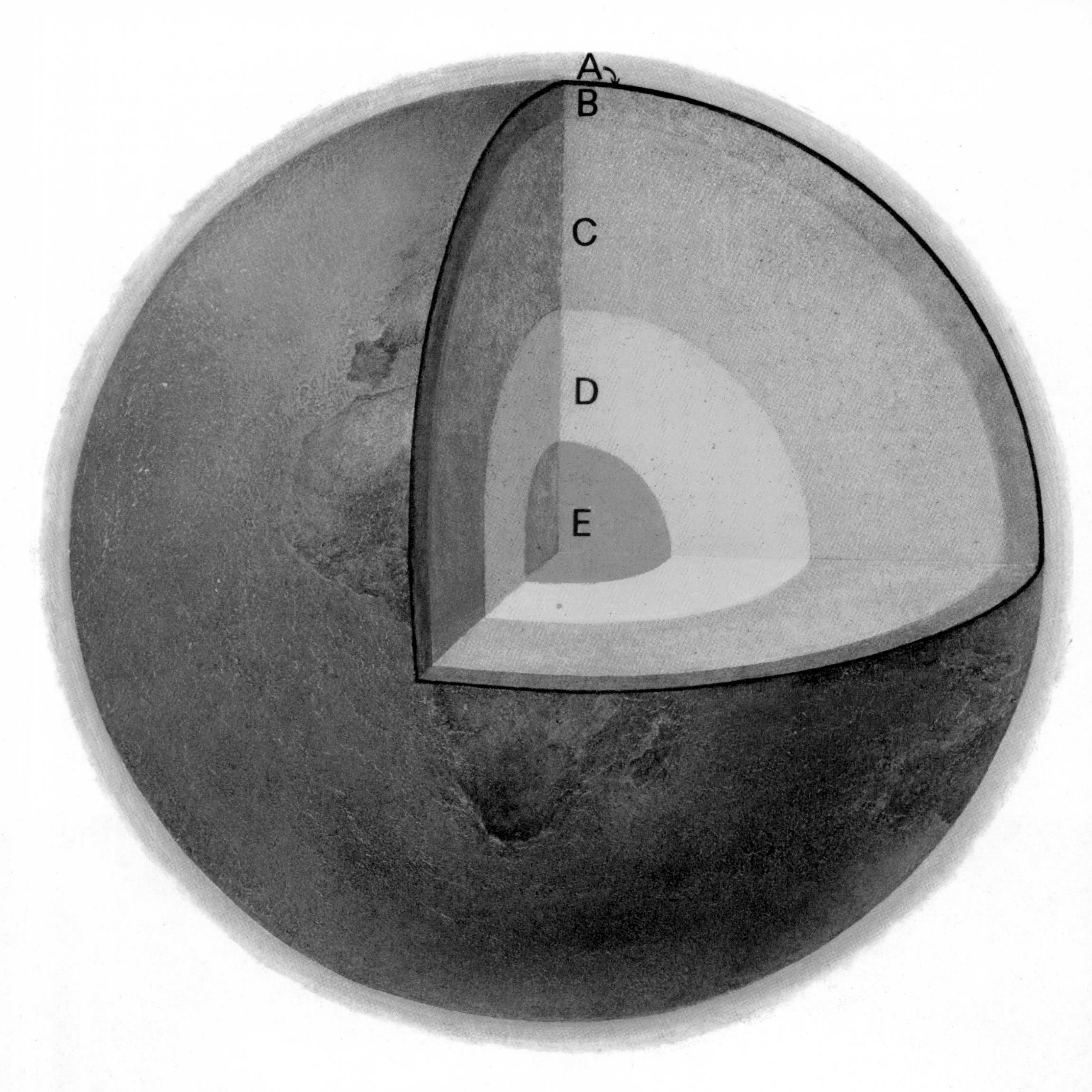

48 The Earth is roughly divided into the following layers:

A — crust (continental and ocean floor crust)
B — upper mantle
C — lower mantle
D — outer core
E — inner core (nucleus)

▷
49 The existence of magnetism was known to the ancient Greeks. However knowledge of the existence of the Earth's magnetic field is more recent. The idea of 'permanent' bipolar magnetism has been accepted since the 16th century. However, this hypothesis cannot explain many geological observations, primarily changes in its position and intensity throughout the Earth's geological history. Today's explanation of the origin of the Earth's magnetic field is barely 50 years old. The Earth has a partly liquid metal core in which flow takes place, due to temperature differences. The Earth itself creates a magnetic field by its movement. Because these phenomena are similar to those taking place between the rotor and stator of a dynamo, this is called the dynamo effect. Both ideas are illustrated here, the permanent dipole (a) and the dynamo model (b) with flow in the core.

matter from plants and animals, and minerals brought by water and wind. It will also be discovered that useful constituents do not increase with depth in the terrestrial interior, that ores are not richer or more abundant, and that not all underground water is drinkable.

In order to understand everything that takes place inside this ever-changing terrestrial body, we need to know what it is made of, and also to be aware that the material forming the terrestrial crust and occurring on the surface has already been processed many times. This material is specific to it, but not at all typical for the body of the Earth as a whole. If the interior of the Earth were constructed of the kind of rock material occurring on its surface, it would be entirely different and have different physical properties. If the whole Earth contained the same amounts of heat-producing radioactive elements as the surface rocks, it would be much hotter. Geophysicists have suggested that, if this were the case, the terrestrial mass, the velocity at which seismic waves are propagated, would be different. The superficial geological products which form the bedrock of the landscape, for example granites, gneisses, calcites, diorites, conglomerates, argillaceous rocks and loesses, are only found to a depth of 30 km/19 miles. The first question, therefore, is what material was in fact available for the construction of the Earth. The answer to this takes us back to primeval times, when the history of the Earth began.

The moment at which the Earth began to exist as a solid cosmic body differs considerably from that of the universe as a whole. Although the precise age of the universe is unknown, it is certainly more than 15 billion years old. The Earth and the other bodies in the solar system are only 4.6 billion years old. We also know that the Earth differs substantially in its composition from the rest of the universe. This has been demonstrated by astronomers, who study the stars using spectral methods, and by geochemists, who study the composition of our planet. The most significant difference lies in the fact that the Earth does not have such great amounts of volatile elements as the surrounding universe, having only minute quantities of the latter's most abundant elements, hydrogen and helium. Similarly the amounts of oxygen and carbon on the Earth are not comparable with those elsewhere in the universe. However, the Earth does have an abundance of elements which are not particularly volatile, but which tend to condense and form solid substances, such as silicon, iron, magnesium, calcium and titanium. The ratios in which these elements occur, for example silicon to magnesium, or calcium to aluminium, are easily discernible as being the same as on other large and small planetary bodies, and in the stars. The ratios of elements on Earth are similar to those of non-volatile elements in the Sun. This is worth noting, and derives from the fact that the Earth consists of materials which do not particularly differ, aside from the content of volatile elements, from other parts of the solar system. In view of the similarity in these ratios of non-volatile elements, geochemists assume that the planets of the solar system, including the Earth and the Sun itself, originated from the same single source.

Some detective work is necessary to find this common primeval source, the material from which the Earth was formed. Many of its characteristics have already been discovered. Cosmochemists have found, in stony meteors, material used in the formation of planets of the solar system. This provides the most significant proof of the system's origins. Since world museum collections, particularly those specimens obtained in the Antarctic in recent decades, are made up of many thousands of meteorites, it is possible to give a brief overview of them.

Meteorites can be classified, according to content, into metal, stone and mixed. Scientists classify them more simply still into modified, or differentiated, and non-modified, non-differentiated. Differentiated meteorites comprise all metal ones (iron), all those containing large amounts of metal and silicates (mezosiderites), and all those resembling basalts (achondrites), whether they originate from unknown small planetary bodies, or from the Moon or Mars. This still leaves a large number of meteorites in the non-differentiated class, such as chondrites, the most common type and the least attractive from the

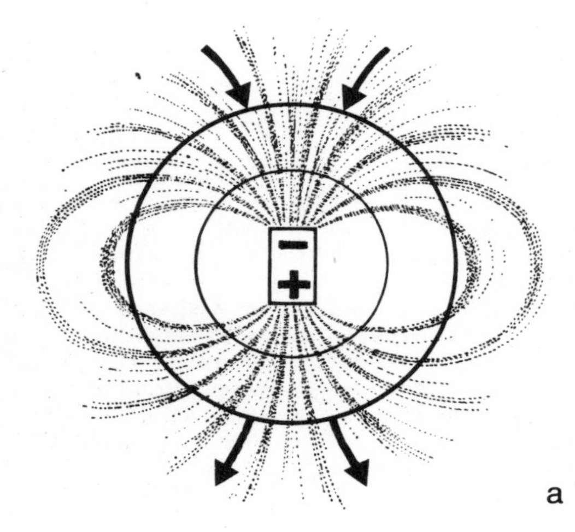

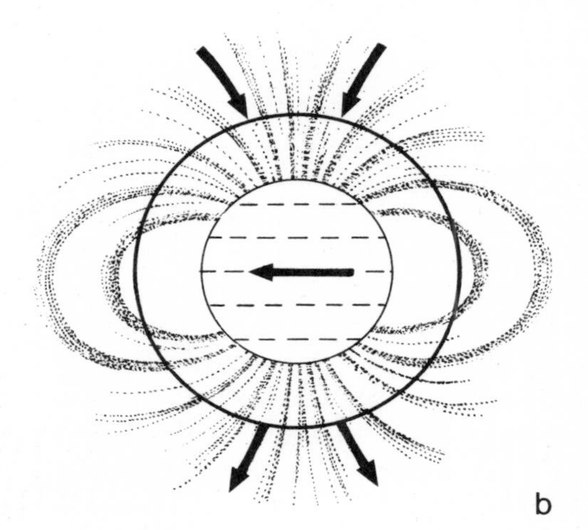

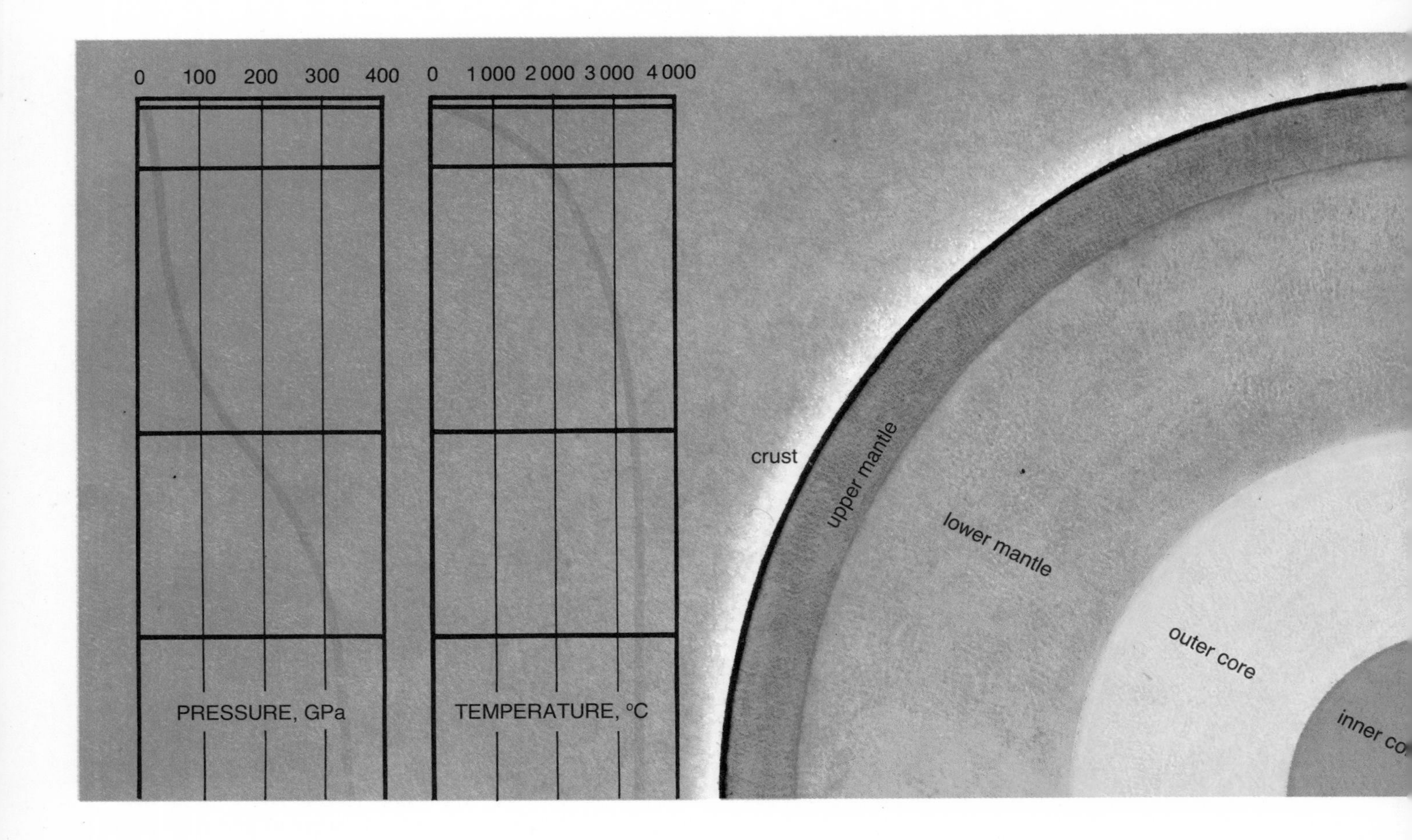

layman's viewpoint. Among these non-differentiated ones, however, we may still distinguish those which were once subjected to high temperatures and those which have not been modified in any way by heat or compression, or chemically. There are not many meteorites of the latter type, but they are in any case remarkable for the amout of information they can provide. They contain, for example, most chemical elements in the same ratios as are to be found in the non-volatile sectors of the solar system, a certain amount of water, as well as carbon and organic compounds of carbon (even amino acids), and metal fragments. In other words, they represent a mixture of materials from which it would be possible to form a planet with a crust, a mantle, a metal core, and an organic surface shell. It has been proved that these non-differentiated meteorites were part of larger planets, and these particular ones contain key information which has not been destroyed either by melting or great heat. Cosmochemists and petrologists have even found in them some particles which do not originate from our solar system at all, but are believed to be from some earlier stage in the evolution of the universe, being in fact recycled particles.

The composition and structure of meteorites also show how these small pieces of matter became molten matter, forming larger and larger pieces until they became the small planetary bodies or 'planetesimals' from which the

50 The Earth divided into layers, showing the changes in its principal physical parameters according to depth, i.e. increases in pressure, temperature and specific weight, and the increase of the velocity of propagation of seismic waves.

▷
51 The quantities of chemical elements present in the solar atmosphere (photosphere) and meteorites are almost identical, however differences exist in their gas contents. (If the numbers of elements were absolutely identical, the points representing the contents of individual elements would be situated on the straight line shown in the picture.) The similarity between the chemical element content of the Sun and meteorites leads us to believe they both originated from the same source. By the same token, because the composition of meteorites and the Earth is to a great extent identical, it is assumed that the Earth and the other planets of our solar system have one common ancestor.

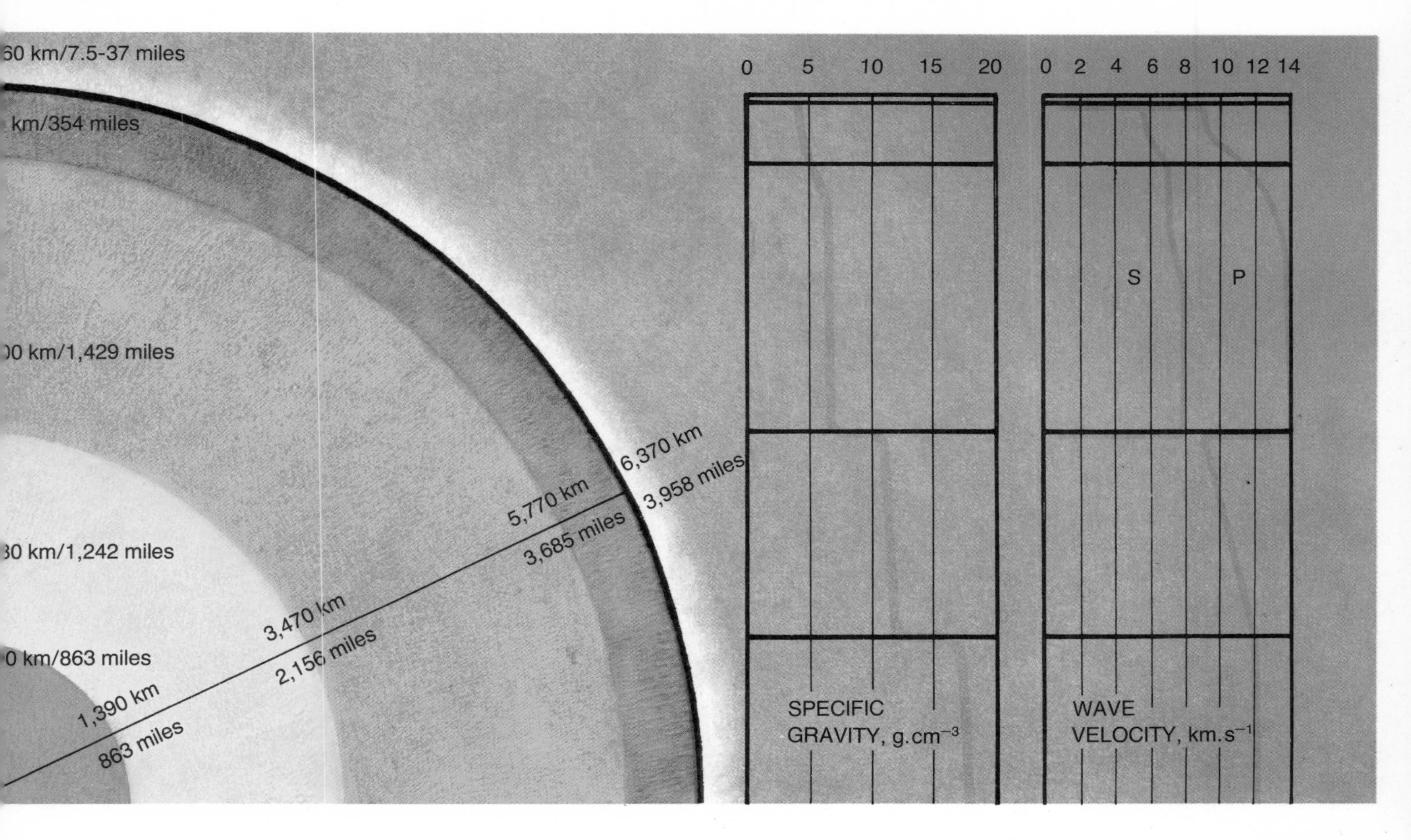

60 km/7.5-37 miles
km/354 miles
00 km/1,429 miles
30 km/1,242 miles
0 km/863 miles
6,370 km
3,958 miles
5,770 km
3,685 miles
3,470 km
2,156 miles
1,390 km
863 miles
0 5 10 15 20
0 2 4 6 8 10 12 14
S
P
SPECIFIC GRAVITY, g.cm⁻³
WAVE VELOCITY, km.s⁻¹

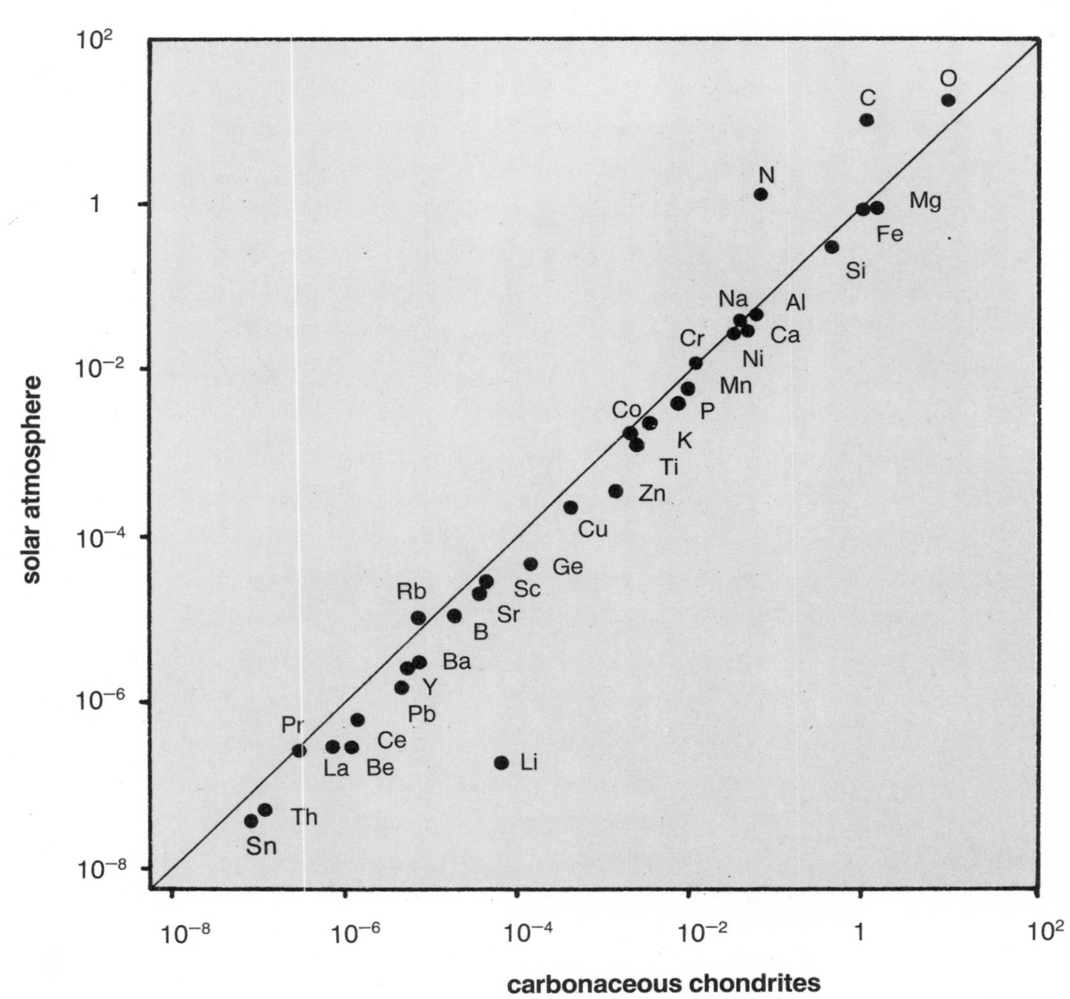

solar atmosphere
carbonaceous chondrites
10²
1
10⁻²
10⁻⁴
10⁻⁶
10⁻⁸
O
C
N
Mg
Fe
Si
Na
Al
Ca
Cr
Ni
Mn
Co
P
K
Ti
Zn
Cu
Ge
Sc
Rb
Sr
B
Ba
Y
Pb
Pr
Ce
La
Be
Li
Th
Sn

Earth was formed 4.6 billion years ago. Meteorites contain not only pieces from previous solar systems, but even components which condensed directly from gases in the original solar nebulae. It is thus highly likely that one single grain of matter on the surface of the Earth, a single atom of even a commonplace element such as silicon has a complex history behind it.

Since we have a rough idea of the composition of the materials that led to the formation of the Earth, it is possible to put together a likely scenario of how this came about. It will undoubtedly contain the following steps: agglomeration, accretion and intensive heating, involving melting down and the separation of silicates from metal. Metal, that is iron, on account of its specific mass, sinks to the centre of the planet, forming the primeval core of the Earth in the course of early separation of its various layers.

Geophysicists study the physical properties of the Earth's land masses. Briefly, all theories about the deep interior state of the Earth are based on its mass, volume, and specific density. Rocks with a relatively low specific density can be found on the surface of the Earth. Granites, for example, which are the most abundant type, have a specific density of 2.64 g cm^{-3}. We know from physical measurement that the Earth as a whole has a substantially higher specific density – at 5. 517 g cm^{-3} roughly twice as high as granites. This means that rocks which are found on the Earth's surface cannot exist at great depths, since the Earth would then be much lighter. There must be 'heavy material' in the terrestrial interior.

52 Most illustrations show the Earth as a perfect sphere, but it is, in fact, a slightly 'squashed' ball. The degree of flattening is so tiny that it is almost impossible for an artist to depict. Measurements taken by satellite cannot be shown accurately. To illustrate the imperfect nature of the Earth's shape, the artist has greatly exaggerated the differences of scale. The bulges represent excess mass, the depressions its shortage.

53 Seismologists, using advanced technology, can detect not only the velocity of the propagation of seismic waves, but also their different character: among elastic waves they are able to differentiate longitudinal waves (P-waves) and transverse waves (S-waves). The picture shows the appearance a wire fence would acquire after the passage of one or the other type of seismic waves. In the case of P-waves the wires of some parts have come closer to one another, those of other parts have moved away from one another. In other words, compression and extension have taken place. In the case of S-waves, the wave propagates in a way that is similar to waves on the surface of water.

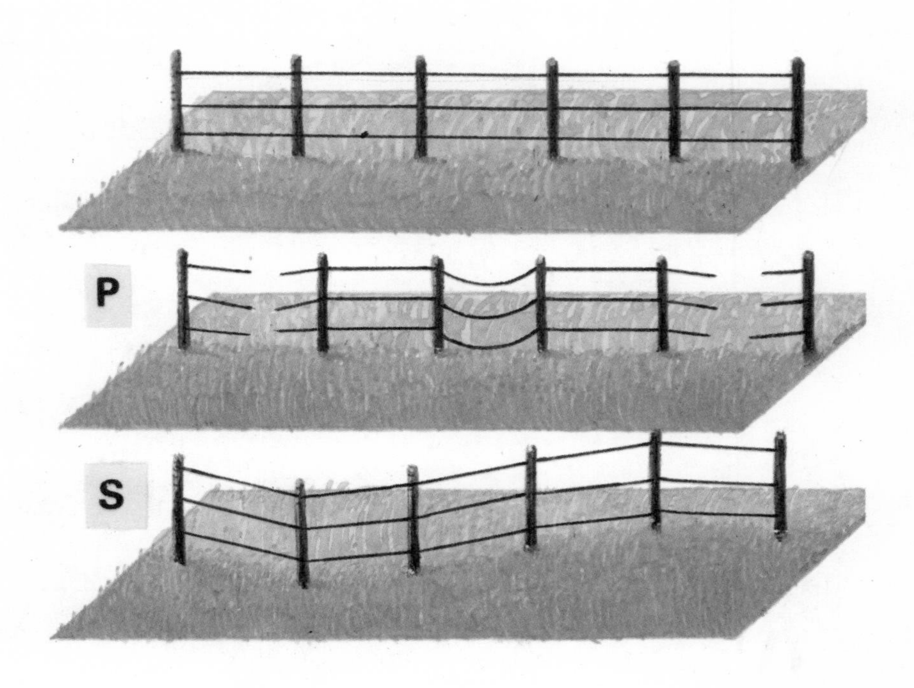

54 The different behaviour of longitudinal and transverse waves (P-waves and S-waves) prove the existence and dimensions of the liquid core of the Earth. Physicists know that transverse waves (S-waves) do not propagate in liquids. Longitudinal waves (P-waves), however, do propagate in them. Since there are, in some parts of the Earth, seismic shadows which cannot be explained by wave reflection or refraction, the simplest explanation is the presence of molten matter. The picture simulates this situation. A strong hypothetical earthquake originating at the North Pole is recorded only in the northern hemisphere as S-waves, while P-waves are recorded in both hemispheres, with the exception of the shadow caused by refraction.

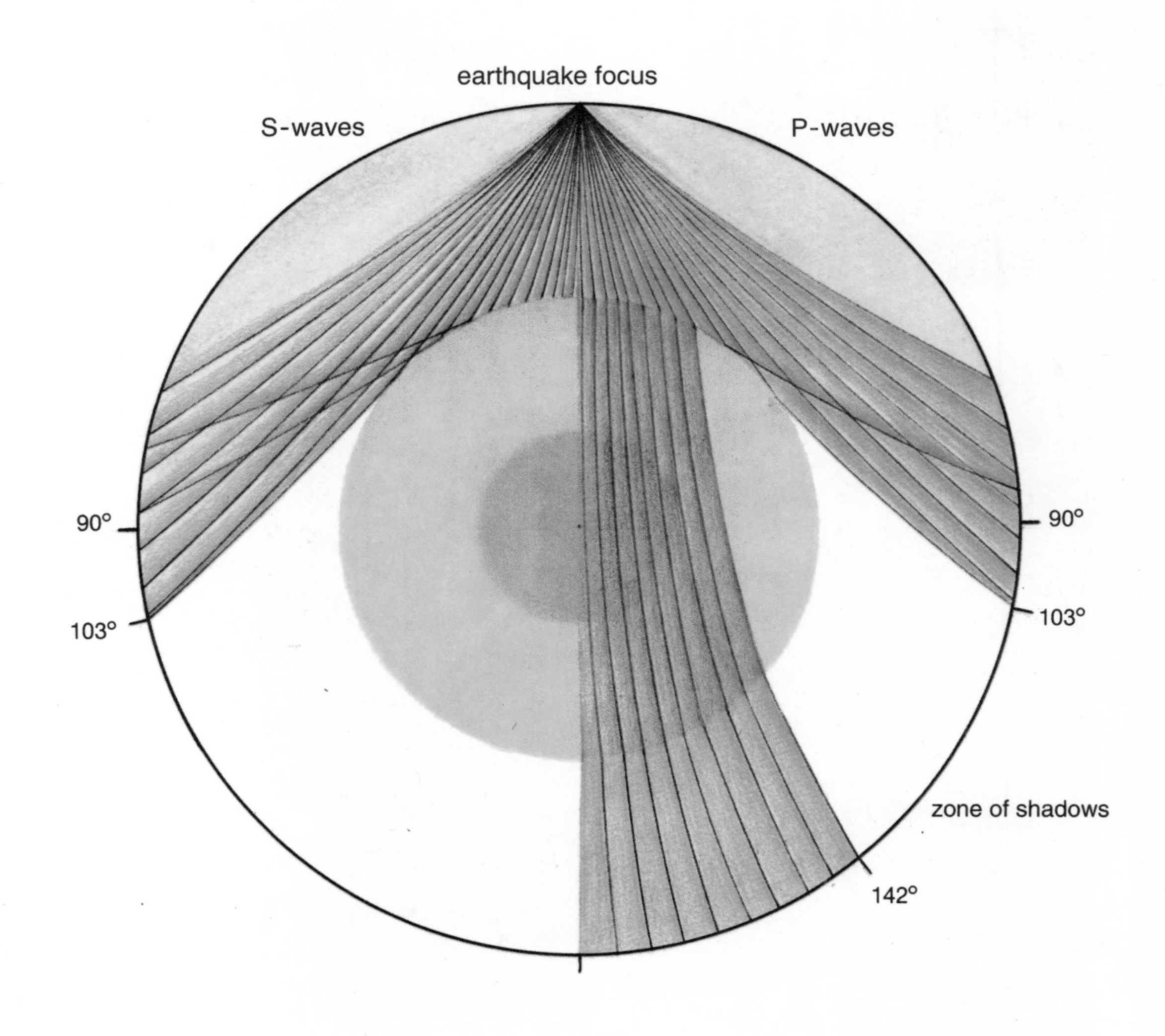

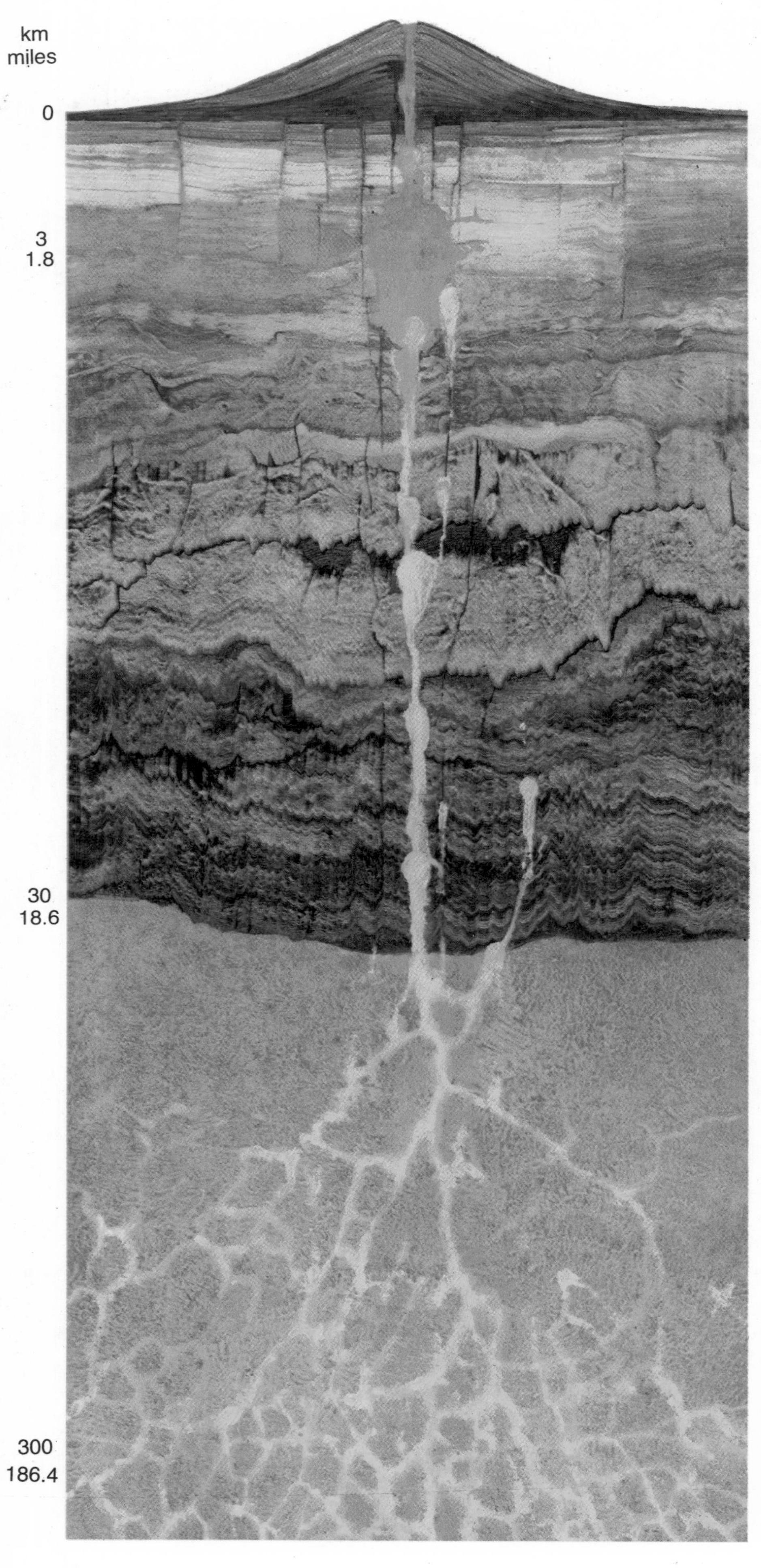

55 The picture shows the depth at which magma occurs beneath the surface of the Earth. Basaltic magma occurs during partial melting of the mantle. In some cases only 1 per cent, in others as much as 25 per cent of a particular area of mantle is molten. As the magma has a lower specific density than the surrounding solid, unmolten rocks, it rises and collects in pockets and large reservoirs. If it stays in these reservoirs for very long, it reacts with the surrounding rocks. If, for instance, its temperature decreases or if it loses volatile substances, minerals, such as olivine, begin to crystallize. The structure of magma changes frequently as it passes through the crust. Parts of the crust melt more easily than the mantle and the magma becomes impure. Under favourable conditions, i.e. when the density of the magma is lower than the density of the surrounding rocks and the Earth crust is permeated with cracks, magma appears on the surface. If it solidifies on the surface, it is an 'extrusive' rock; if it solidifies below the surface, it is an 'intrusive' rock.

Other important information about the internal state of the planet is provided by ordinary observation of volcanic activity. It shows that there is a substantial outflow of heat from the terrestrial interior and that a certain proportion of rocks, either below the surface or at a slightly deeper level, must be in a molten state. On the other hand, earthquakes occurring on the surface and which originate from depths of many kilometres indicate that the majority of these deeper parts of the Earth are solid, since they shake and the shock waves spread out as if passing through a solid body. This means that they spread both longitudinally and latitudinally; if the level immediately below the surface contained completely molten rocks, the latitudinal shock waves would not be able to pass through it. Seismologists have observed an odd phenomenon during major earthquakes: although the shock waves pass through the whole planet, something known as a 'shock wave shadow' always appears on the opposite side of the Earth. Latitudinal waves could not reach that, even during the most massive earthquake. This led seismologists to consider the possibility that the outer core of the Earth might be in a molten state. The velocity at which shock waves spread also changes according to the depth at which they occur, increasing unevenly, in abrupt surges towards the centre. This seems to indicate that there is a distinct boundary surrounding each layer of the Earth.

More knowledge about the physical state of the planet can be gained by studying the electrical currents responsible for the Earth's magnetic field which is a dipole character. The magnetic field changes in the course of time, not only over days and months, but, it must be assumed, throughout the entire history of the Earth. Even the north and south magnetic poles change. It would follow from this, therefore, that the source of the magnetic field lies within the Earth itself and, it may be presumed, is linked with its activity. From this, there may be gathered a range of other information about the Earth's physical properties such as electrical conductivity, the separation of the origins of terrestrial gravity, or the reasons for the shape of the planet, which is not a perfect sphere. All this knowledge, when put together, helps to create a picture of the inside of the Blue Planet.

If it were possible to cut a segment from the Earth, exposing its interior, it would be seen that the centre, or core, of the planet consists of extremely hot matter. Although not much is known about the Earth's core, the way in which seismic waves behave when they pass through the Earth during earthquakes would indicate that the innermost core is solid. The inner core has an extremely high

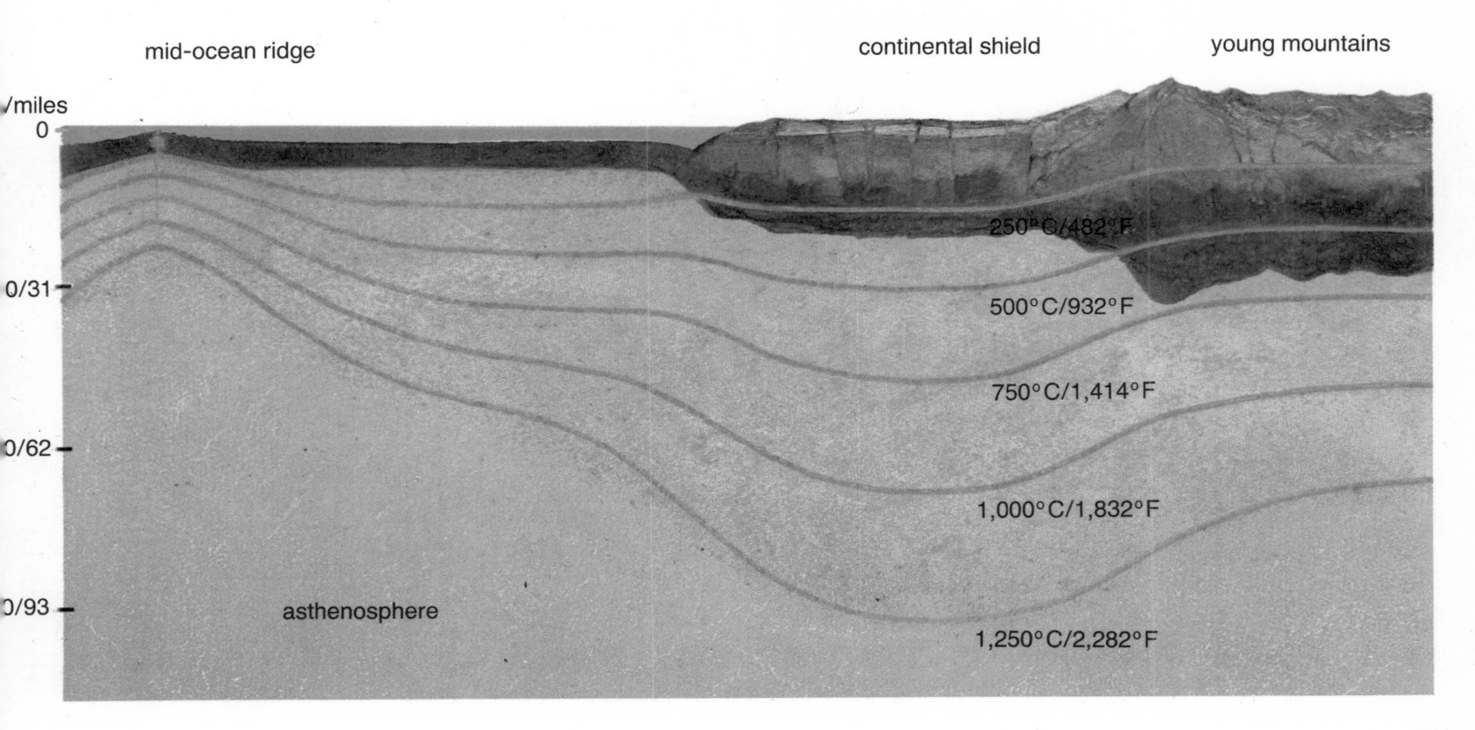

56 The difference between the lithosphere and the asthenosphere is defined by the different physical properties of each. The lithosphere is more solid, while the asthenosphere is softer and more plastic. However, that part of the lithosphere which forms part of the upper mantle does not differ substantially in chemical composition from the asthenosphere. In fact the different physical properties of each are determined by temperature. The asthenosphere is hotter and, consequently, softer and more plastic, the lithosphere is colder and, therefore, more brittle. The picture shows the temperature distribution in the upper mantle below the principal geotectonic units, i.e. mid-ocean ridge, ocean floor, shield and high mountain plateau. The greater thickness of the lithosphere below the continents is obvious. In mid-ocean ridge areas the thickness of the lithosphere is minimal.

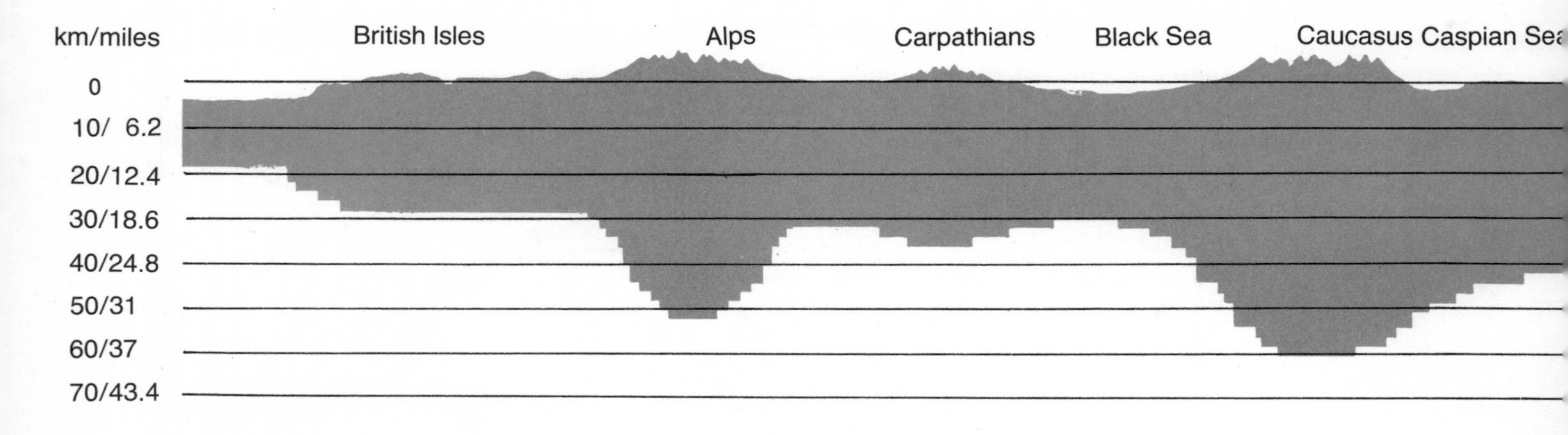

57 The profile of the Eurasian landmass from Western Europe to the Japanese islands shows the power of the continental crust below the high mountain range, below the area of the continental peak/ plate and the area of young seas.

temperature, and while it is impossible to measure it, it is reasonable to assume that it would be several thousand degrees. The high specific density of the core – its great weight – results from its composition. Assuming that it has a similar composition to a meteorite, it is reasonable to suppose that it is made up of an alloy of iron and nickel plus a few other elements which lighten it somewhat. Physical measurement has shown that the terrestrial core does not have a weight and mass consistent with this quantity of a mixture of iron and nickel only. It is thought that it may also contain metallic hydrogen or silicon.

The solid inner core is wrapped in an outer core of roughly the same composition, also of a high temperature and probably in a molten state. A considerable amount of convection occurs in the outer core, as in any liquid. This convection and the different convection velocities of the core and the surrounding siliceous wrapping of the lower mantle are important for the Earth. These movements produce an effect similar to that of a dynamo, creating an electrical field which in turn produces terrestrial magnetism.

Above the core, from depths of roughly 2,900 km/ 1,800 miles, 'rocks' similar to those which are found on the surface begin to occur. This part of the Earth is known as the 'mantle'. It contains much heavier and denser rocks than those which can be found on the Earth's surface. These rocks possess a different composition from surface rocks, having been formed under massive pressures (around 1 million atmospheres) and at a temperature of over 3,000°C. They are still in solid, crystalline form, but are largely molten at the edge, therefore being softened and ductile. The ductile part of the mantle is known as the 'asthenosphere', on account of these properties. Convection of matter also occurs in this part of the Earth, throughout most of the mantle, although only reaching low velocities comparable with the flow of ice – a matter of centimetres or metres per year.

Geologists and geophysicists make a distinction be-

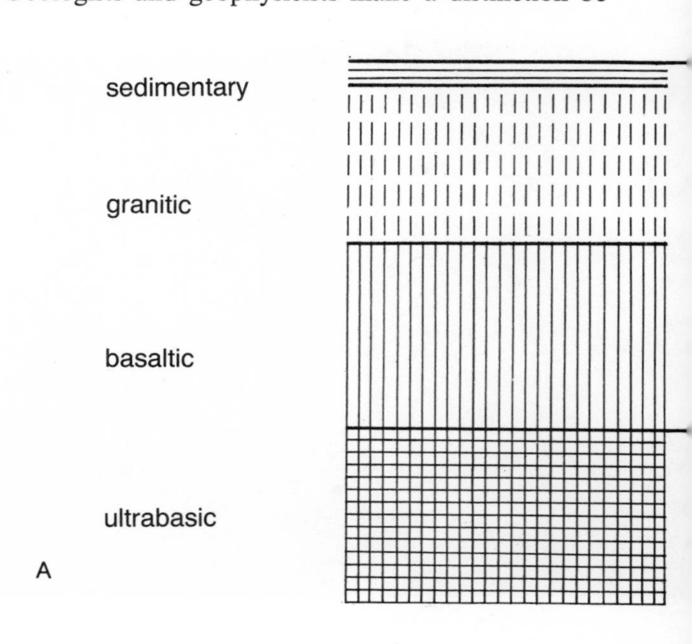

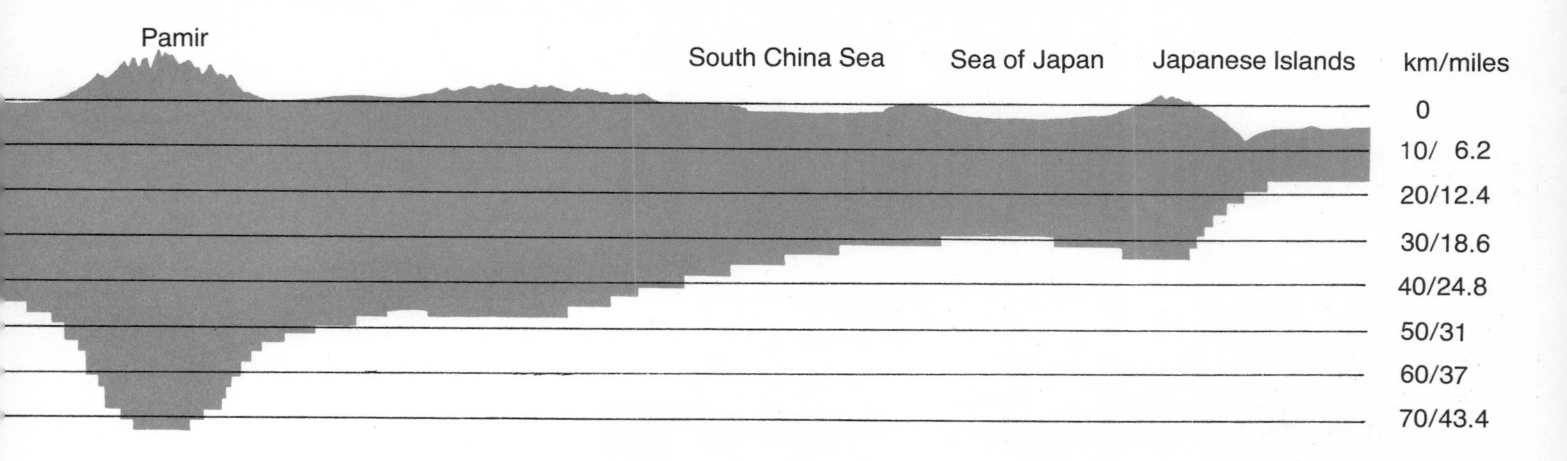

tween the upper and lower parts of the terrestrial mantle. The uppermost part has a chemical composition similar to the rest, but because of different thermal and pressure conditions is in a solid, non-ductile state. It is firmly connected with the uppermost, thin crust. Together, the crust and upper mantle of the Earth are known as the 'lithosphere' (*lithos* meaning stone). The stone is solid but can be broken, whereas the consistency of the ductile asthenosphere is comparable with butter or toothpaste.

Geochemists and petrologists have recently provided a considerable amount of evidence of both the chemical composition and the mineralogical and petrological states of the Earth's mantle. One fact that emerges is that the mantle must be composed of rocks which are able to produce basalt in their partially molten state. Further evidence stems from direct observation of mantle rocks, especially kimberlites which become enclosed in volcanic rocks during sudden magmatic emissions. Mantle sequences on the continents are also observed. During major tectonic processes, part of the mantle can sometimes intrude into the Earth's outer surface. Petrologists then have an opportunity to observe mantle rocks inside the crust. Geophysical observations made at this point are able to establish quite precisely the physical properties of the mantle rocks. All this data is compiled to form a model of the upper and lower mantles.

Boring into the Earth holds a certain magic for the geologist, as it reveals secrets which are almost mystical in their nature. Nevertheless, the careful observer is often able to see something without studying the geologist's borehole. Cross-sections of the uppermost part of the Earth's crust are easily visible in deeply-gouged valleys, canyons or on slopes of high mountains. In these places, the jaws of time have gnawed away the landscape to a depth of 5—10 km/3.25 — 6.25 miles. These places are not exceptional; they occur in every part of the world. Geologists studying the Earth's crust like to return to such places, if not to see the actual geological processes

58 Changing ideas about the nature of geological processes which affect the Earth as a whole, particularly in respect of significance of the alteration of the land horizon, has also resulted in a reassessment of ideas about the structure and composition of the uppermost part of the Earth's crust. A number of observations have stemmed from the use of modern seismic methods. One of these is the chaotic structure of the upper parts of the Earth's crust, which is shown in part B of our picture. Part A shows a schematic drawing of the Earth's crust. The upper crust is covered with sedimentary rocks, below which there is a stratum of granite rocks. Beneath that there is a basaltic layer and at the bottom is an ultrabasaltic upper mantle.

B

A

59—67 (pp. 60-65) Very thin but very important is the soil layer or pedosphere. It is that part of the Earth on which human and other dry land life depend so much; it is the substrate on which their food grows and the beginning of the food chain. The formation of soil is an extremely slow, varied and complicated process. The degeneration of the land horizon in a region may be caused by a single generation of irresponsible agricultural practices. The opposite process, i.e. the generation of a new soil horizon, however, takes centuries. The principal factors determining the character of the soil are the rocks which occur below the soil, the climatic conditions of the given region and the ground water table.

The first series of three pictures shows the soils originating in similar climatic conditions, but on the top of different geological beds: (A) — ranker of quartzite (thin soil layer on top of a resistant skeleton), (B) — brown soil on sandstone, (C) — podsol on gneiss.

The next series of three soil horizons has a common denominator in the fact that their beds occur in loess soil, i.e. a soil containing fine rock particles and which came into existence by an aeolian process or wind blowing, in postglacial and glacial periods. (D) — brown soil on loess, (E) — black soil (chernozem) on loess with carbonate concretions in the lower part of the soil horizon (kavyl, esparto, steppe), and (F) — pseudo-gley on loess loam. (Gley is a blue-grey soil which occurs in areas with a high ground water table.)

The last series contains an example of gley soil originating on the alluvial deposits on a flood plain (G), and two examples of soils which originated in limestone beds: (H) — terra rosa (soil formed by the accumulation of iron oxide and clayey remnants during the weathering of limestone), and (I) — rendzina (humuscarbonate soil).

at work, at least to see their results. However, let us not run too far ahead. First let us take a look at the composition and appearance of the rocks that form the crust.

There is a division, or discontinuity, demarcated by physical and chemical differences, between the mantle and the crust. There are differences in the specific density of rocks, the velocity at which seismic waves propagate and in the chemical and therefore also mineral composition of rocks. This division is known as the 'Mohorovičić discontinuity'. Generally speaking the mantle rocks, that is those below this division, have higher magnesium, iron, nickel and chrome contents, while in the crust, silicon, aluminium, potassium, sodium, calcium and trace elements such as rubidium, barium and strontium are more abundant.

It has already been said that the oceanic crust differs from that of the land masses. It is younger and consists of a relatively simple layer of various deposits with underlying eruptive igneous rocks and basalts, and beneath them residual rocks and remnants of the upper mantle. The continental crust is substantially more complex, containing all those rocks occurring on the Earth's surface: granites, gneisses, granodiorites, amphibolites, slates, sandstones, conglomerates and mica schists. Until recently, scientists assumed that the crust also had a dual-layered structure, its upper part having a chemical composition similar to granites and containing all the above mentioned rock types, the lower part of the crust being typified by a basalt composition and therefore consisting of basalt equivalents, i.e. amphibolites and gabbros. A division was discerned between the upper and lower part of the crust, known as Conrad's discontinuity. However, detailed study, part of which included a very deep borehole on the Kola Peninsula, where the Conrad boundary should have been found at a depth of 7 km/4.5 miles, has shown that this division is not a global phenomenon. It is often entirely absent or, as in many places in the world, weak or imperceptible, the rocks of the crust being so jumbled together that they are known, somewhat ironically, as 'chaotically arranged'.

In the 1960s and 1970s geological and geophysical research focused largely on oceanic regions giving rise to

B

C

D

today's modern notions of the physical structure and metabolism of the Earth. Studies conducted in the 1980s concentrated more on the structure and composition of the continents.

Major technological discoveries brought about by the search for fossil fuel resources are nowadays applied in research into the structure of the Earth's crust. Earthquakes are simulated using explosives, and measuring equipment is placed in the surrounding area. Very sophisticated computers are then able to produce three-dimensional images of the resulting measurements and the velocity at which seismic waves spread. This is similar to tomography, a technique used by doctors in the diagnosis of human disease. The study of the terrestrial crust using seismic methods provides as it were an idealized picture of the underlying parts of the crust, for instance to depths of 30—50 km/ 20—30 miles. Based on such study, in some of the more advanced nations scientists drill boreholes into the crust. These are referred to by geologists as very deep and ultra-deep boreholes. Even so, the deepest of these, and those which are not yet completed, penetrate not much further than 10—20 km/6—12 miles, being intended to discover the strucure and composition of the crust and penetrate into its lower part. There is one such borehole on the Kola Peninsula which has reached a depth of 13 km/8.25 miles, and another is planned. Some of these boreholes are located in places where, in addition to discoveries about the lower structure of the crust, mineral ores are also anticipated. Elsewhere, deep boreholes are located in terrain which looks promising for crude oil deposits. In the United States as well, where scientists pioneered research into the terrestrial crust, deep boreholes are being drilled in places which are interesting from the point of view of vulcanology and sources of heat from the interior, as well as in crude oil-bearing terrain. In Germany, on the other hand, preparations are under way for what will probably be the deepest borehole in the world — intended to determine the links between the geological units in Central Europe, and where a 'laboratory at the bottom of a borehole' should come about to make it possible to study the fluids and gases at these depths, where heat levels exceed 300°C/636°F, and where normal drilling equipment becomes useless. Compared with Man's progress in space exploration, reaching a depth of only 16km/10 miles of the Earth's 6,370 km/3,980 mile radius, does not seem very impressive. The process is, however, obviously not as straightforward as sending a team of astronauts hurtling into space at great speed.

In the past, scientists who studied the Earth tended to separate their chosen subject and study it in isolation. Only after they had described and classifed their findings did they begin to realize that they were linked to many other subjects which were also being studied in isolation. For example, the upper parts of the Earth are classified, on the basis of 'mechanical' properties, into the lithosphere, which is solid and rigid, and the asthenosphere, which has ductile properties. Both the continental and oceanic crusts, and the upper, solid part of the mantle form part of the lithosphere.

Within the continental crust we must further distinguish, on the basis of structure and composition, between the pedosphere (the land horizon region), and the cryosphere (the icy region). The atmosphere (the Earth's gaseous layer), the hydrosphere (the aqueous layer) and, finally, the biosphere may also be regarded as part of the continental crust. It is very easy to describe each of these outer layers separately, but much more of a problem to attempt to describe the relationships between all of them. The interaction between the individual regions of the solid Earth and its volatile, gaseous layer are so complex that it is impossible to describe their functions separately. For example soil, the pedosphere arises out of weathering processes acting on parent rock (part of the lithosphere), being affected by water (the hydrosphere) or its frozen parts (the cryosphere), the air (atmosphere) and by living organisms (the biosphere).

It is relatively difficult to picture the mutual exchange of materials and energy among the Earth's solid layers. In describing those 'spheres within spheres' where this exchange is discernible, it is easier to content ourselves with an overall view of the picture. Even so, it will show how

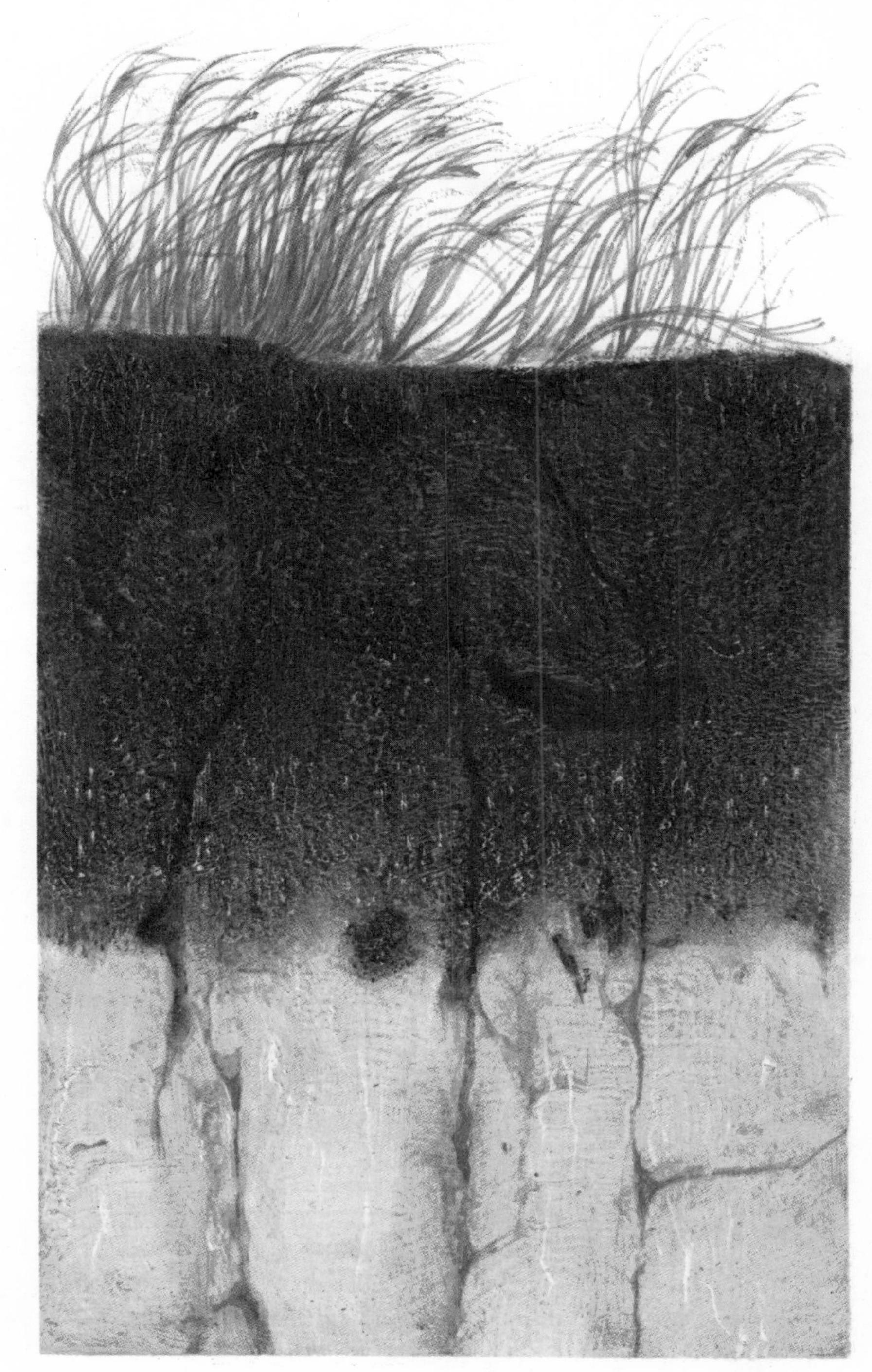

E

F

finely balanced the Earth's systems are at the junction between the lithosphere and the atmosphere. There will be a great deal more to say about this area later on. For the time being we can take a look at the atmosphere — the Earth's gaseous outer layer. Most of the gases in the atmosphere — a good 80 per cent — are concentrated in the troposphere, that is in that part of the atmosphere in which 'weather' is formed, where aircraft fly, and which extends from the Earth's surface up to 10—12 km/6.25—7.5 miles at high latitudes, and up to 18 km/11.25 miles over the Equator. The troposphere is characterized by a pro-

G

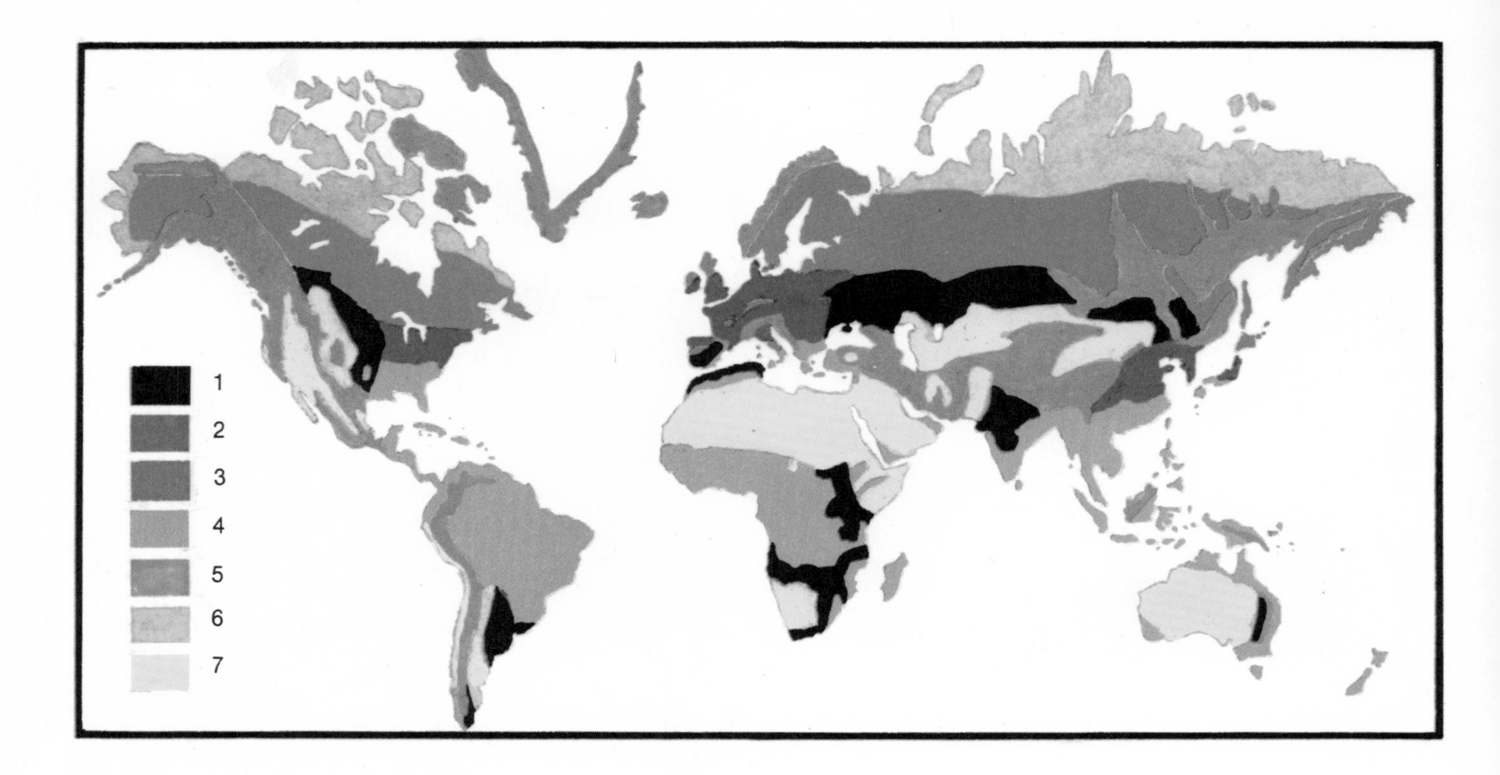

gressive upwards decline in temperature, and by a constant chemical composition. Only the carbon dioxide content changes not in relation to altitude, but according to the time of day.

Above the troposphere is the stratosphere, which has an identical composition of atmospheric gases and a relatively constant temperature, and still higher the mesosphere and the thermosphere. The latter two have a low mass compared to the troposphere. The mesosphere differs from the stratosphere in its low atmospheric pressure, as well as in its temperature, which declines with increasing distance from the stratosphere. There are also differences in composition, with an increase in the proportion of light gases and a change in the concentrations of ozone. This is highest at the upper boundary with the stratosphere. The composition and ratios of other gaseous molecules, however, remain constant. Whereas in the mesosphere the temperature drop is even more marked, in the thermosphere, on the other hand, the temperature rises, as its name would suggest. The thermosphere then meets the exosphere, which has an extremely low concentration of gases, and where gaseous molecules can escape the Earth's gravity field.

The boundaries of another gaseous sphere, the ionosphere, are flexible, as this sphere is defined by neither temperature nor composition; its existence and boundaries are dependent on the concentration of free electrons and ions, which varies from day to night, as well as on the intensity of cosmic radiation. Thus the ionosphere forms part of both the mesosphere and the thermosphere. Atmospheric pressure here is so low that it could almost be termed a vacuum compared to surface conditions. Its physical properties also differ substantially from other atmospheric layers, as this is a region of the Earth itself. In the lower layers of the atmosphere and part of the ionosphere, nitrogen and oxygen predominate. At altitudes of over 90 km/56.25 miles the short-wave component in solar radiation brings about the disintegration of oxygen and nitrogen molecules. These two gases are therefore present in the form of atoms and ions. Ionization brings about the high electrical conductivity of this part of the atmosphere, and hence its capacity to reflect electromagnetic waves. This capacity forms the basis for short-wave radio broadcasting.

The atmosphere is that part of the Earth's shell which we can most easily imagine being affected by human activity. Sulphur dioxide and carbon dioxide, as well as chlorofluorocarbons can easily destroy ozone molecules.

Neither the individual layers of the atmosphere nor the atmosphere as a whole have precisely defined boundaries. At about 800 km/500 miles above the surface of the Earth, in a region known as the exosphere, the atmosphere merges with space through the escape of individual molecules or atoms of lighter gases such as hydrogen and helium. The Earth's gravity is not strong enough to retain them. The exosphere itself is a vacuum. Further into surrounding space, evidence of the Earth's gravity is seen by the presence of a magnetic field which attracts its own satellite – the Moon – and by the existence of belts of radiation (Van Allen belts). These contain electromagnetic particles and protect the Earth from cosmic radiation, forming a perfect shield.

Pictures which show the Earth as a sphere divided into clearly defined layers, with various clearly defined gaseous layers surrounding it, are correct up to a point, although not entirely. The Earth's layer are permeable and

◁
68 Distribution of principal soil types:
1 – black soil (chernozem)
2 – brown soil
3 – podsol
4 – latosols
5 – mountain soils
6 – tundra soils
7 – desert soils

69 The gaseous envelope of the Earth, the atmosphere, is a highly dynamic system. All its components circulate in the atmosphere, the lithos-phere, the hydrosphere and the biosphere, it is a very lived and, consequently, higly homogeneous system, in a state of dynamic equilibrium. The composition of the atmosphere changes. Lighter gases, such as hydrogen, tend to escape to higher strata, while heavier gases concentrate in the lower strata of the atmosphere. (That is why, for instance, extremely high concentrations of carbon dioxide, CO_2*, can be found at the bottom of unventilated wells or caves.) The stratification of the atmosphere is not only due to the effect of the gravity field. Cosmic radiation, which causes ionization of gases, also influences the composition of the atmosphere. (Well known is, for instance, the 'ozone layer', the place of higher ozone concentration, or the fact that at high elevations, where low temperature prevails, the air is dry, devoid of water vapours.) There is a profile from the Earth surface up to a height of 10,000 km/6,213 miles. These components which characterize the concentration of the given atmospheric stratum, are marked: A – nitrogen and oxygen stratum, B – oxygen stratum, C – helium stratum, D – hydrogen stratum.*

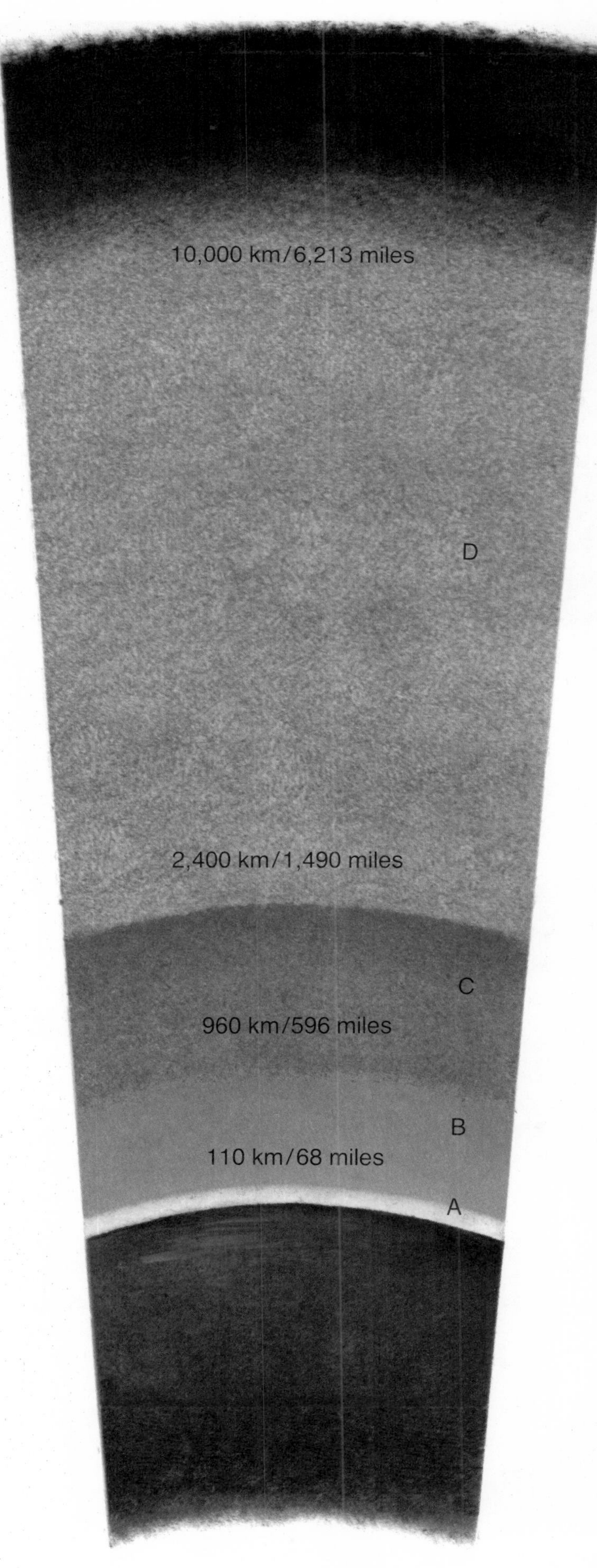

open, with no clear and constant boundaries. This is what, in fact, makes the Earth a habitable, living, dynamic planet: the processes which are at work in and among its various spheres. These spheres are illustrated to make it easier to describe and classify the Earth's components. From the point of view of one single carbon dioxide molecule, however, such 'boundaries' are meaningless. One single molecule which was once part of the Earth's upper mantle may, by the way of the volcanic processes, have reached the atmosphere. From here, it may have been used by animals to construct a nest of some sort, thereby becoming part of the biosphere. Later, it would be possible for it to become part of the lithosphere, when, perhaps, it may have been washed into a stream by rain. Eventually the molecule may settle on the river bed as sediment, and over many years, become sedimentary rock. Over a period of time – perhaps the river may have dried up or changed course – the rock may have weathered and the molecule reached the surface. This example shows all too clearly the importance of the study of all terrestrial spheres and their interrelationships.

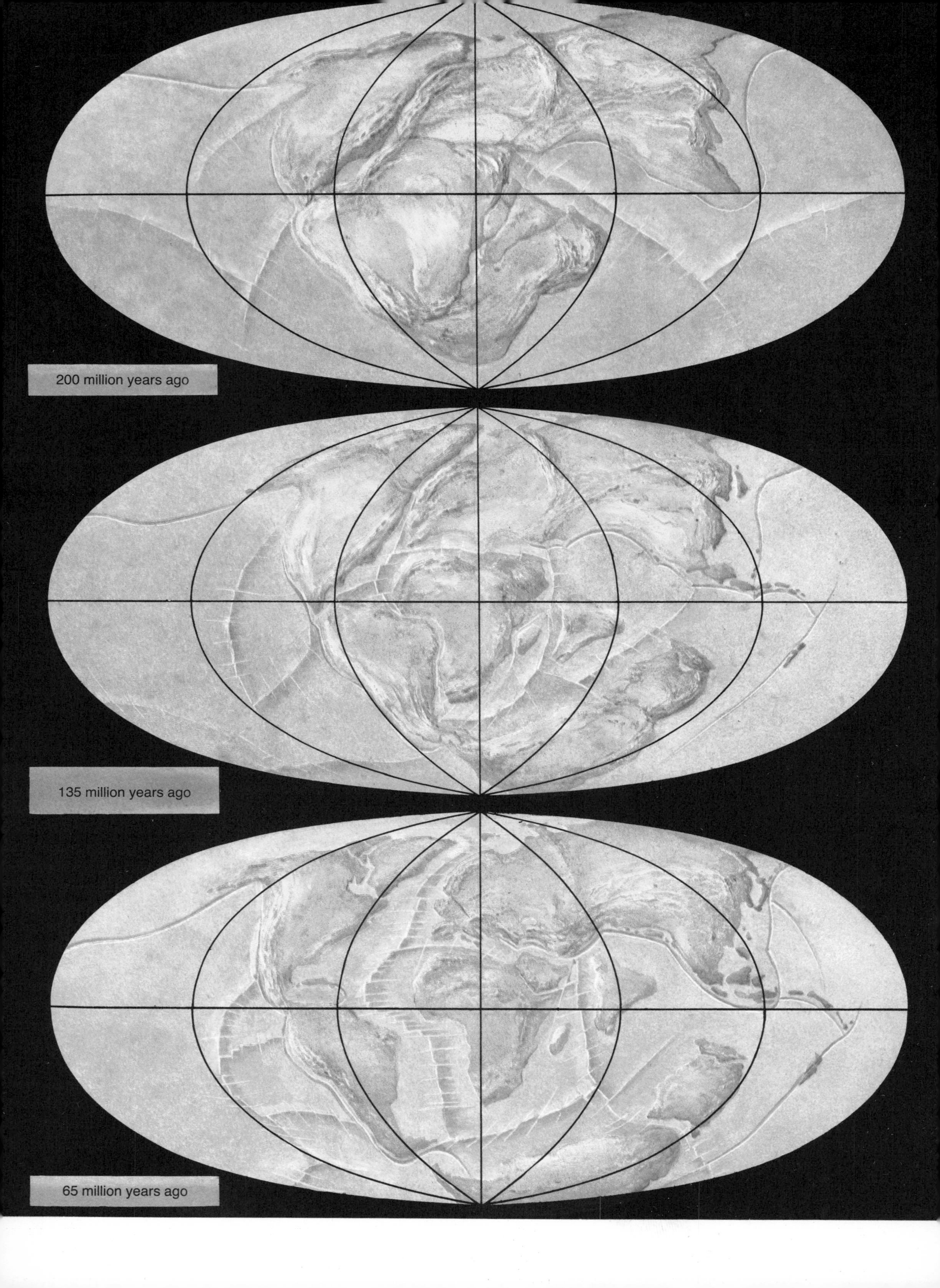
200 million years ago
135 million years ago
65 million years ago

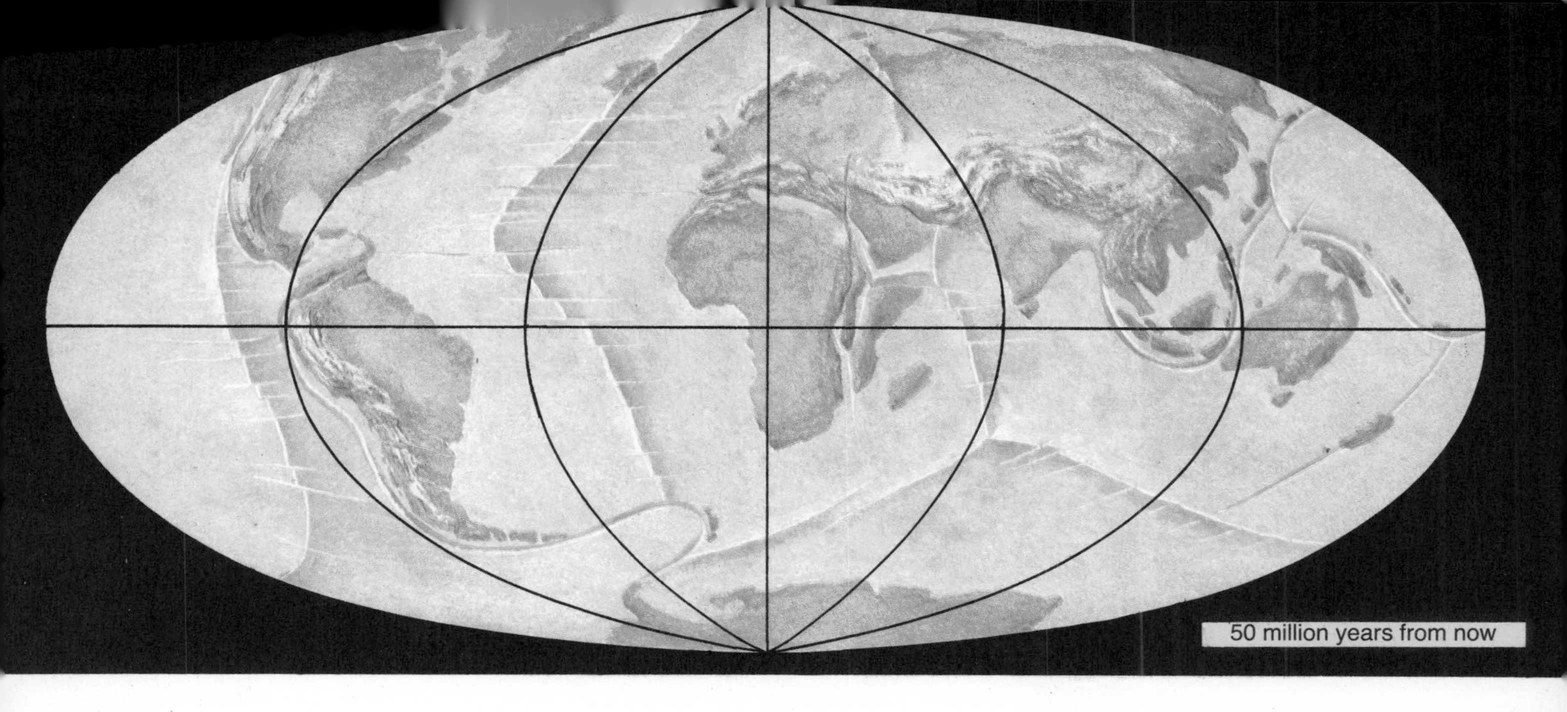

THE STABLE AND RESTLESS PLANET

Anyone with a penchant for detective stories knows that a reconstruction of the case usually brings about the final solution. A similar method can be used to uncover the history of the Earth. The idea of reconstructing the processes whereby terrestrial geological formations came about is as old as the science of geology itself. It is a very straightforward method, and already over a century old, stemming from the time of the British naturalist and geologist Charles Lyell. It is based on the assumption that current processes taking place on the Earth and in its interior mirror those which have gone before. In other words, the present is the key to the past. This can be demonstrated by using quite a simple example. Let us look at a stream down which large lumps of rock are moving during a heavy downpour which has caused the stream to swell and flow freely. If similar large rocks can be found nearby in places where water no longer flows, it is logical to suppose that water did once flow there. The same applies to glaciers, seas, volcanoes and ocean beds. So if we want to know what happened in the past, we look at how a glacier, sea, volcano or ocean floor behaves today. Comparison of this kind between the geological past and present has helped to produce some of the more revolutionary ideas in the history of the study of the Earth.

As has already been noted, the Earth has changed in the course of its evolution. It was once without an oxygen atmosphere and was once heavily bombarded by meteorites. Its heat generation used to have a different pattern: the Sun produced less radiation and the heat output from the Earth's interior was greater. It is therefore necessary to qualify all past geological processes, but at the same time to be aware that in terms of the Earth's history what was to be found 200 million years ago is almost the same as what would be found today. Given that the land masses we are studying present us with two thousand million years of history, with older formations accounting

70 The analysis of the Earth's geological history is one of the most interesting problems that the geologists have to deal with. It is not merely an academic exercise, because this knowledge may possibly bring about practical results, i.e. the discovery of raw material deposits. First place among theories on continental drift is occupied by Wegener's theory which integrates best the achievements of geology and biology and is most acceptable for its simplicity. The modern variant of continental drift in the past is shown in the periods of 200, 135 and 65 million years ago. The upper left hand part of the picture represents the oldest period. It shows Palaeozoic mountain ranges and two supercontinents, Laurasia and Gondwanaland. Some 135 million years ago Gondwanaland disintegrated and drifted away in several directions (central picture). Laurasia broke in half and formed Asia and North America. The last picture shows the situation 65 million years ago, i.e. the approximate time when dinosaurs became extinct. India broke off and drifted northwards and the Mediterranean was still a large ocean, opening into the Indian and Atlantic oceans which were still very small.

One predicted future for the configuration of the continents in 50 million years is illustrated in the upper right hand picture. Africa and Europe collide, and Australia and New Guinea have drifted northwards. The distance between Africa and South America has increased by more than 1,000 km/621 miles. East Africa has separated from the central part of the continent.

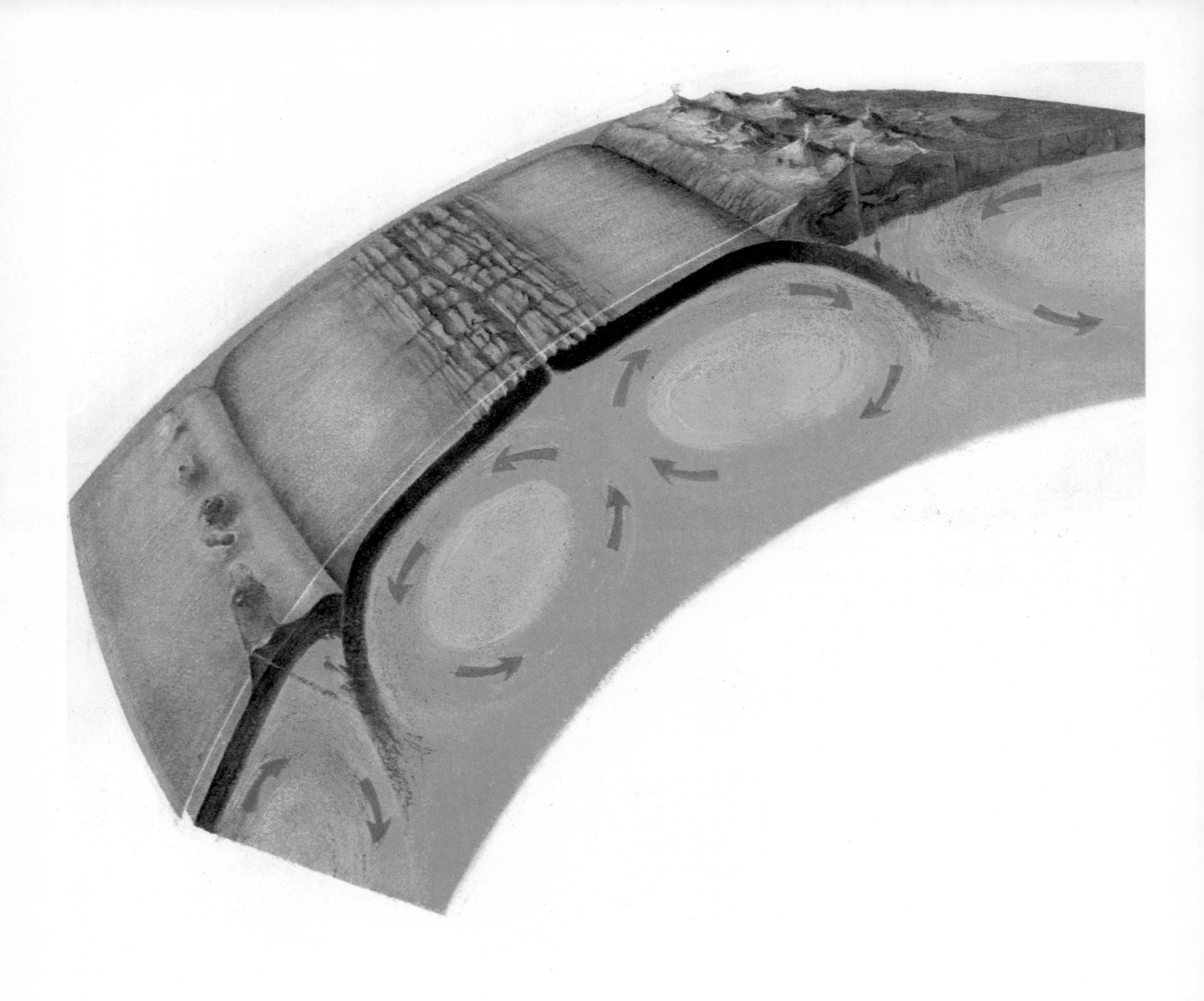

72 If one plate on the Earth's surface starts to move, all the others begin moving, too. The movement of the plate can be described as rotation around an axis. It is vital when demonstrating such a theory by way of experiment (the Euler theorem) the dimension of the sphere must remain constant. The description of the movement of lithospheric plates on the Earth's surface is based on similar principles; therefore, Euler poles are defined for every plate movement. If the dimensions of the Earth are to be preserved, it means that if a new crust originates anywhere on the planet, a corresponding quantity of the old crust must be disposed of elsewhere. Shown here is the formation of an oceanic plate (with red lines representing the mid-ocean ridge) and its movement evidenced by the age of individual extinct volcanoes on the ocean floor. Remnants of the old plate can be seen in the trench (movement of other plates is not shown).

◁
71 According to the plate tectonics theory the cells of the softer, more plastic mantle move by convection (indicated by red arrow in the picture); these are the principal cause of plate movements. The dark blue colour represents the oceanic plates with the red band of lava erupting in the mid-ocean ridge. The oceanic plates move from the mid-ocean ridge and after cooling down they sink back into the asthenosphere (red). The deep sea trenches form in places where an oceanic plate comes into contact with either a continental plate or another oceanic plate. The process beginning in deep sea trenches by which the lithospheric plate is forced down into the asthenosphere is called subduction. Subduction results in volcanic activity. Magma forms in the upper part of the subducted plate. It occurs on the surface in volcanic island archipelagoes. A similar process takes place in the active continental margin.

73 The preceding picture is supplemented with the hot spot profile. According to contemporary opinions the hot spot forms part of the asthenosphere (lower area coloured brown) and, consequently, is relatively firmly fixed in the deep parts of the mantle (marked by arrow). It is the origin of most volcanic activities in the oceans.

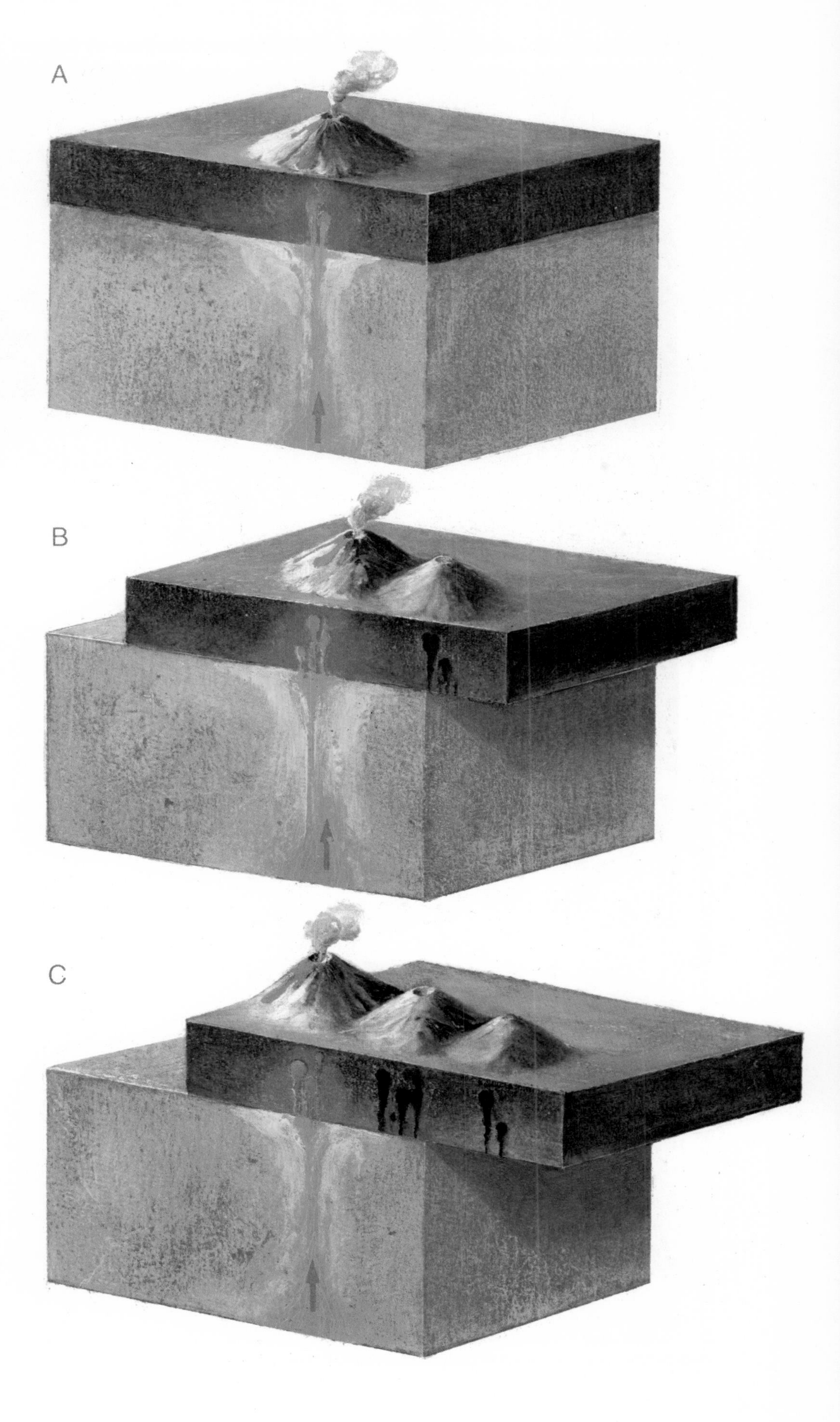

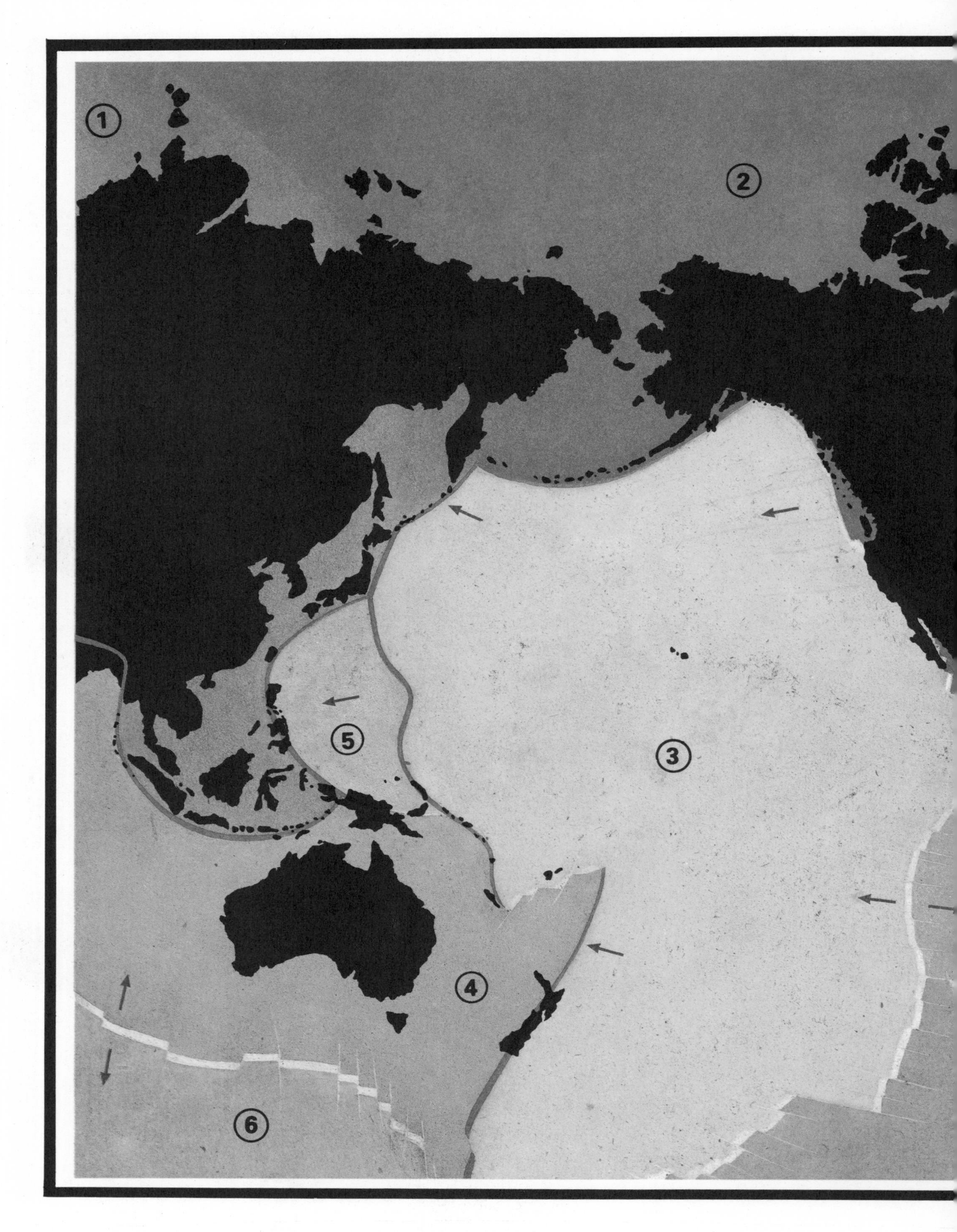

74 The Earth is divided into plates whose boundaries are defined by the foci of contemporary earthquakes and the occurrence of volcanic rocks: 1 – Eurasian, 2 – North American, 3 – Pacific, 4 – Indoaustralian, 5 – Philippine, 6 – Antarctic, 7 – Nazca, 8 – Cocos, 9 – Caribbean,

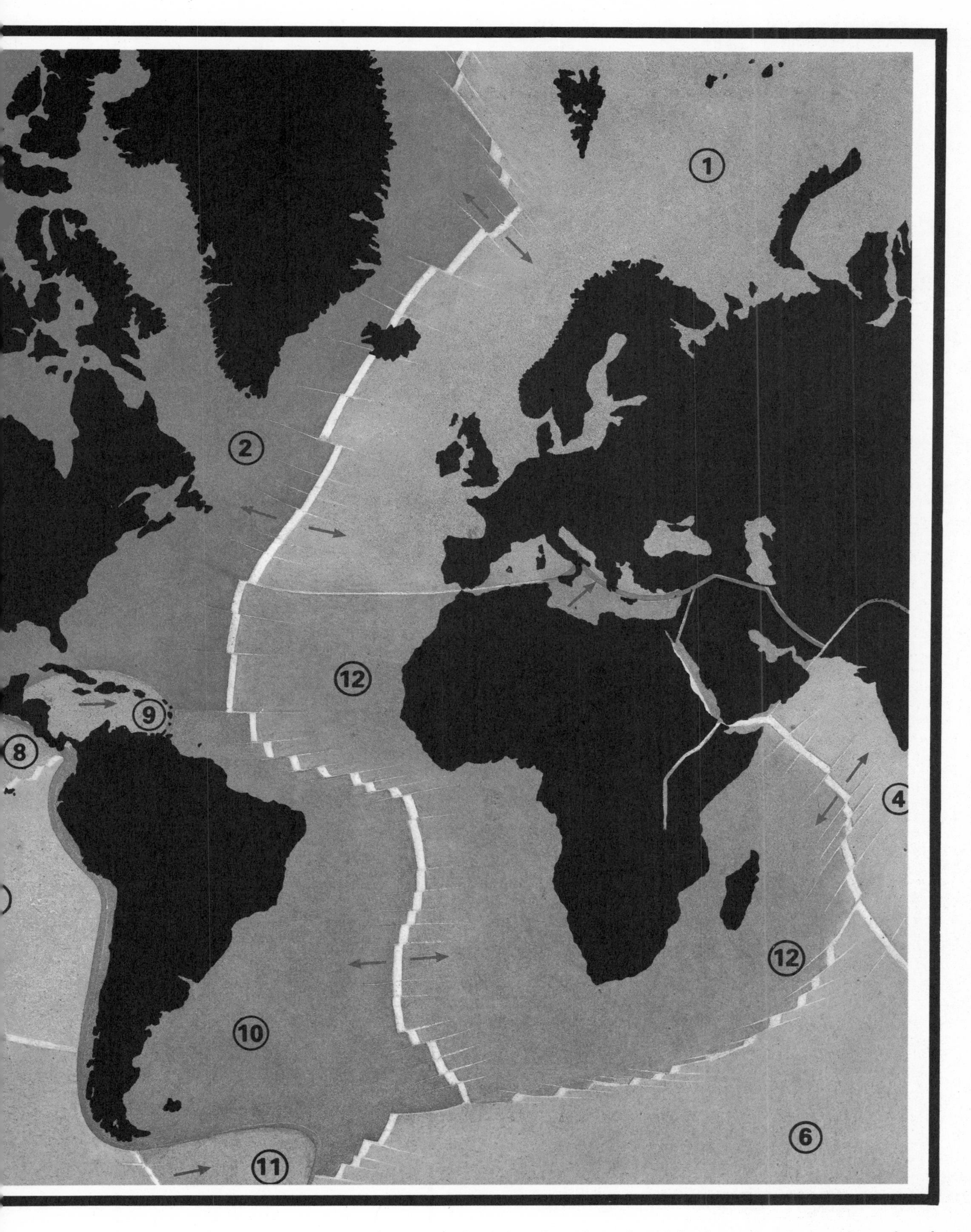

10 – South American, 11 – Nova Scotian, 12 – African. Apart from these the geologists have defined a number of minor plates, often of local significance only, as a means of explaining particular tectonic phenomena relating to local geology.

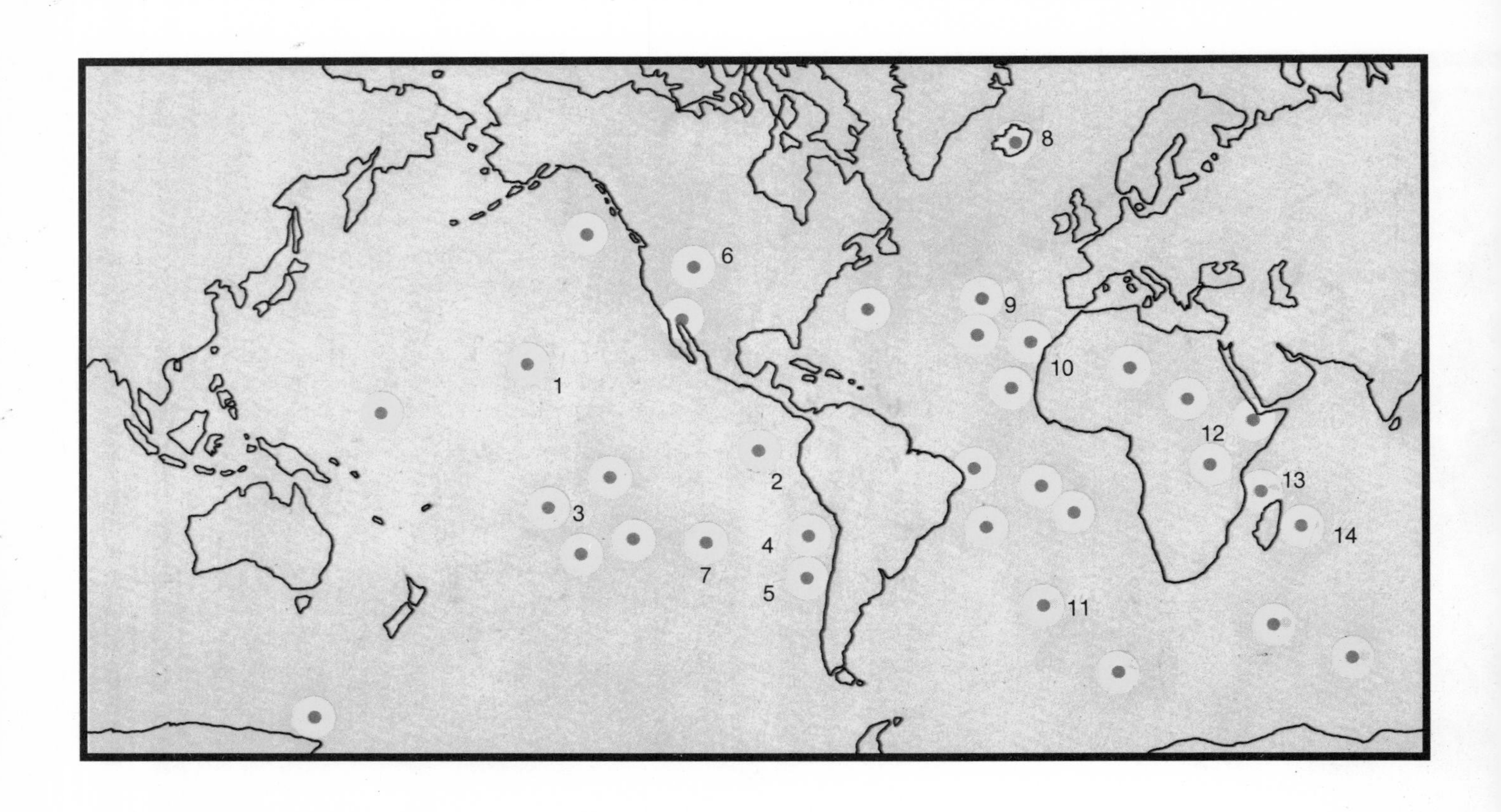

75 Where the internal (geothermal) heat flows from the interior of the Earth to its surface, magma from the mantle accumulates. In such places linear formations, such as mid-ocean ridges, are often formed. Local formations are called 'hot spots'. Scientists are still not sure of their origin. Nevertheless, it is evident that there is 'convection' in the upper mantle and its structure is characterized by the fact that it is composed of many unrelated parts; the movement of mass inside the Earth is very complex.

Here we see the most significant hot spots on Earth: 1 — Hawaii, 2 — Galapagos Islands, 3 — Tahiti, 4 — San Félix, 5 — Juan Fernandez, 6 — Yellowstone, 7 — Easter Island, 8 — Iceland, 9 — Azores, 10 — Canary Islands, 11 — Tristan da Cunha, 12 — rifts in eastern Africa, 13 — Comoros Islands, 14 — Réunion Island; and a number of other spots indicating the places of ascending mantle masses.

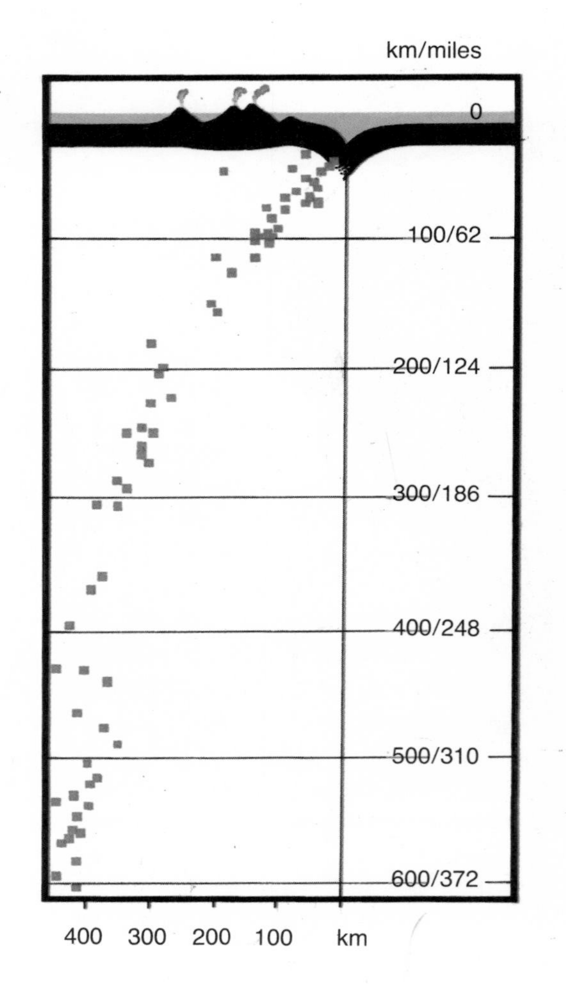

76 Accurate measurements taken in the location of earthquake foci and their registration give us an insight into the depth of the subsurface strata of the Earth. The cross section of an island archipelago shows the earthquake foci extending from the bottom of a deep sea trench to depths of some 600 km/372 miles. The foci indicate the surface of a subducting oceanic plate. Similar profiles of the majority of island archipelagoes and continental margins are used when documenting interaction of plates in convergence margins.

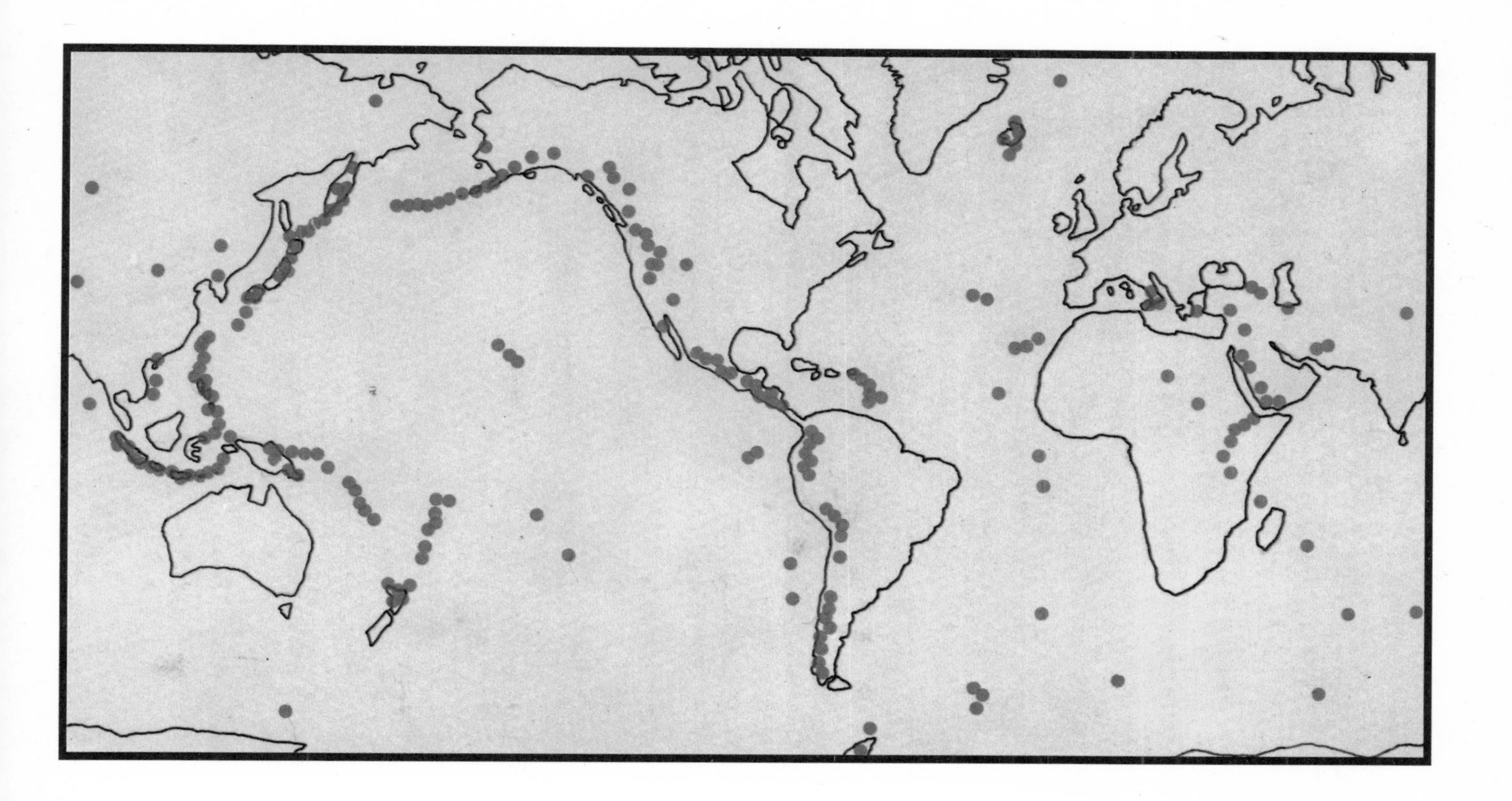

77 There are more than a thousand volcanoes on the Earth's surface. Further volcanoes are concealed below the surface of the oceans. The map shows the most important volcanoes visible on the surface. There are both the volcanoes of active geological margins (Pacific Ocean margin) and the volcanoes of continental rifts (East Africa), the hot spot volcanoes (Hawaii, Galapagos Islands) as well as those visible above the surface of the mid-Atlantic ridge.

for only relatively small sections of the crust, current geological events can be safely taken as a model for past ones.

Reconstruction of the geological past is not just an academic exercise: it also has practical uses. If, for instance, we are able to understand the conditions in which copper or zinc ore forms nowadays, we are then able to search in geological formations for rocks which formed under similar conditions in the past. This knowledge of course facilitates the search for these ores. Similarly from the ecological viewpoint, the study and reconstruction of the geological past, with all its evolutionary progressions and setbacks, is of paramount importance. Palaeontology, a science originally confined to the classification and description of extinct organisms and once regarded by many laymen as science for the sake of science, has since acquired enormous prestige. Nowadays it is concerned with the causes behind evolutionary changes and catastrophes, and the reaction of organisms to them. It has also played a major role in the development of new disciplines such as evento-stratigraphy, i.e. the study of the sequence of major events, or bio-events.

Numerous geoscientists have attempted to account for the processes taking place in geological evolution on our planet, striving to collate knowledge from various scientific fields and use it to explain volcanic activity, earthquakes, the formation of mountain ranges and abrupt changes or ecological catastrophes.

Many theories and hypotheses have arisen. It was once thought, for example, that the Earth was shrinking because it was cooling. According to this view, the folding and uplifting of mountain ranges occurred in a manner similar to that on an aging, dehydrating apple. Others assumed that the Earth was increasing in size, but this has been refuted by palaeontological evidence, which embraces 600 million years of terrestrial history (micro-palaeontologists have pushed this boundary back a further thousand million years). If the Earth were larger or smaller today than in times past, the parameters of its orbit would inevitably change, the days and years differing substantially from their previous forms. The study of corals 400 million years old, however, indicates that in the Devonian period of the Palaeozoic era, the Earth had virtually the same number of days in a year as it does today. It follows from this that the Earth's dimensions have not changed in the course of its geological history.

On account of discrepancies of this kind, many great hypotheses have had to be abandoned, while others have been retained to form the basis for further hypotheses. One of these, known as 'plate tectonics', caught on around the world towards the end of the 1960s. This hypothesis

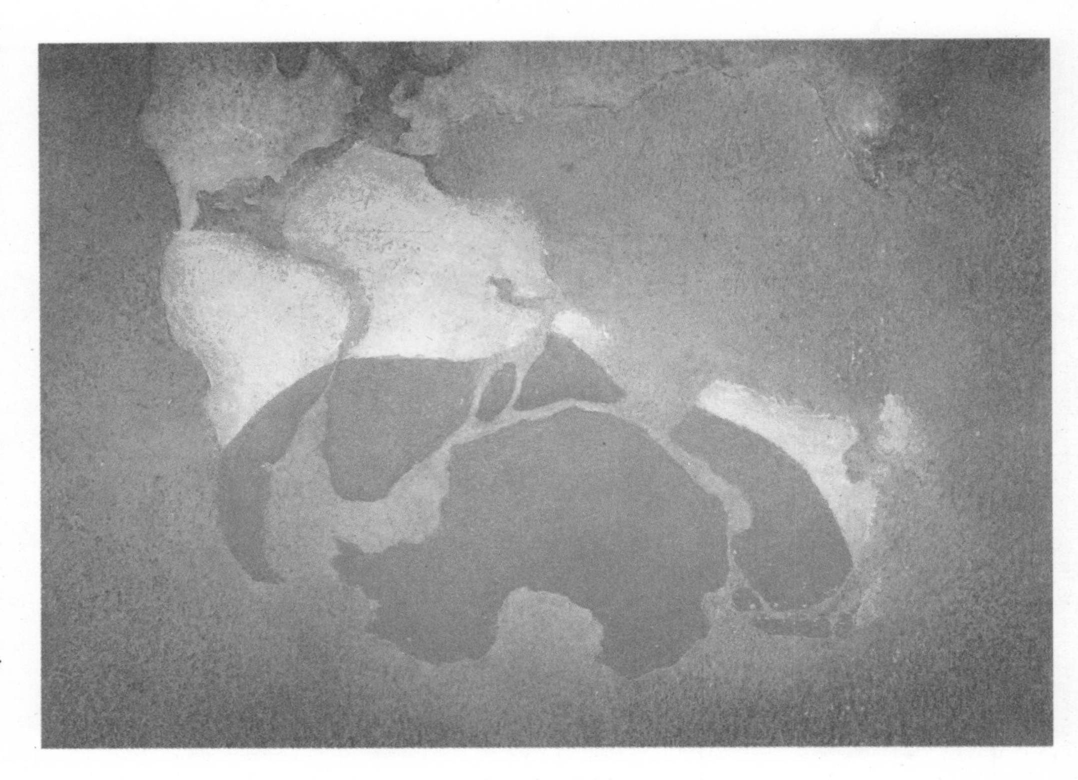

78 When studying the origins of the Himalayas, we must go back in time, to the end of the Palaeozoic Era, when the supercontinent of Gondwana disintegrated. It was at that time that the very beginnings of the Indian peninsula probably appeared and began drifting northwards. A few million years ago it collided with another supercontinent, Laurasia. Proof of the existence of these supercontinents has been furnished by palaeontologists. The one time existence of Gondwana has been proven by finds of identical plant fossils in many different parts of the world. Among these are ferns of the genera Glossopteris *and* Gangamopteris *which occur in South Africa, South America, India, Madagascar, Antarctica and Australia. The green colour in the picture represents the simultaneous distribution of the fossilized remains of these plants.*

79 By studying various fossils, the artist has been able to create an illustrative reconstruction of a plant of the genus Glossopteris *which once existed all over Gondwana.*

▷
80 This strange-looking animal, the herbivorous Lystrosaurus, *which lived in shallow waters, is further proof of the fact that Antarctica, Africa and India were once joined. It is one of the most important pieces of evidence in proving the existence of Gondwana.*

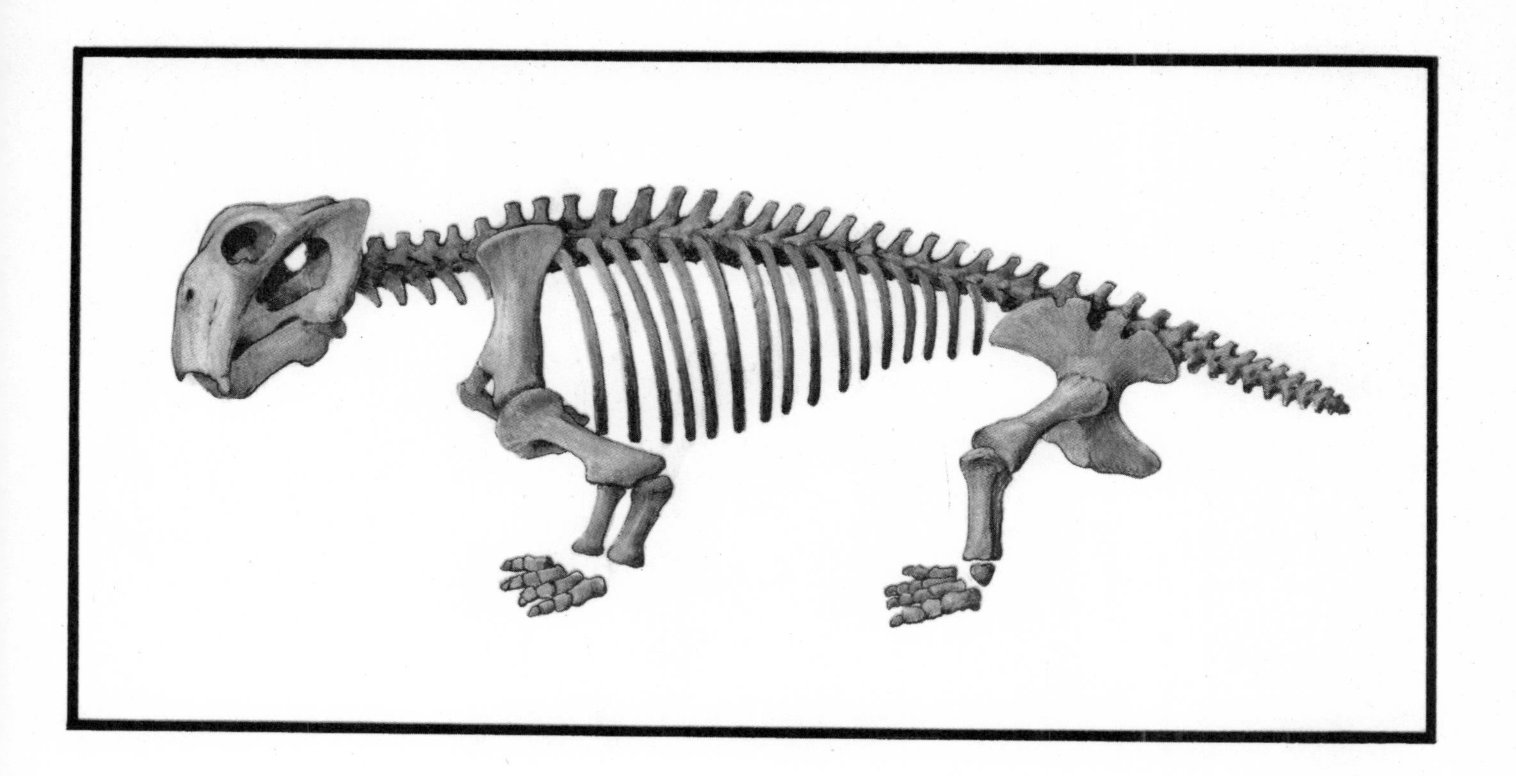

represents an attempt to collate many separate geophysical and geological observations. In this book it is used as a framework for describing the Earth's metabolism, as well as to describe the present 'geological' world with the aid of arguments drawn from it. As early as the 1920s, a simple form of this hypothesis already existed among some researchers, the most frequently quoted of whom is the German scientist A. Wegener. While it does not constitute the ultimate solution to all geological problems, it does seem to provide the best means so far of drawing contemporary observations together. It was rapidly taken up among geoscientists in the Anglo-Saxon countries, perhaps because it was so simple and easy to understand, but partly also because it is rooted in the observation of current events on the Earth's surface and in its interior. Elsewhere, for example in Russia and other parts of Eastern Europe, its route into geology textbooks and the offices of geological forecasters was a more tortuous one. The fact that it could be used in the search for sources of useful raw materials, as well as the way it links the geology of the ocean floor with that of continents, has added to its appeal.

It may be possible, therefore, to draw an organic and adequate picture of contemporary geological events and to form a judgment about, or at least consider, whether Man is capable of affecting it. The problem is that we have too much available data and too many observations. It will probably be no mean task to find among all this the most accurate, appropriate and key aspects. It would be useful at this point, therefore, to recap on what has already been noted about the planet, its face and its anatomy:

— terrestrial earthquake and volcanic activities are concentrated for the most part in narrow belts;

— the ocean floor is very young, the youngest part being at its centre, where there is considerable heat flow and where volcanic activity currently occurs;

— shifts in the magnetic field are registered in older volcanic rocks of the ocean floor, revealing a symmetrical magnetic pattern running along the mid-ocean rift axis. The oldest parts of an ocean floor are those closest to a continent;

— the oceanic basin is poor in sediment, even the deep ocean trenches do not contain much, with sediment disappearing either in the trenches themselves or their vicinity;

— in deep sea trenches, shallow earthquakes occur, the depth of focuses increasing to as much as 700 km/440 miles towards the continents;

— every deep sea trench region has its own region of active volcanoes, either on the edges of continents or in structures known as island arcs;

— volcanic rocks occurring on island arcs differ both from those of the mid-ocean ridges and from those occurring in continental regions;

— the continental crust differs from the oceanic not only in composition, but also in age, the continental crust containing substantially older rocks than the oceanic;

— the upper part of the terrestrial body is rigid and solid (lithosphere), whereas its lower part, the asthenosphere, which starts from depths of 120—200 km/75—125 miles, is ductile.

These observations may be augmented by several general and well-known physical ones, for example that on a sphere constructed of plates, movement in one plate leads to movement in them all. The border outlines of the South American continent in the east and the African continent in the west largely correspond to and fit into each other.

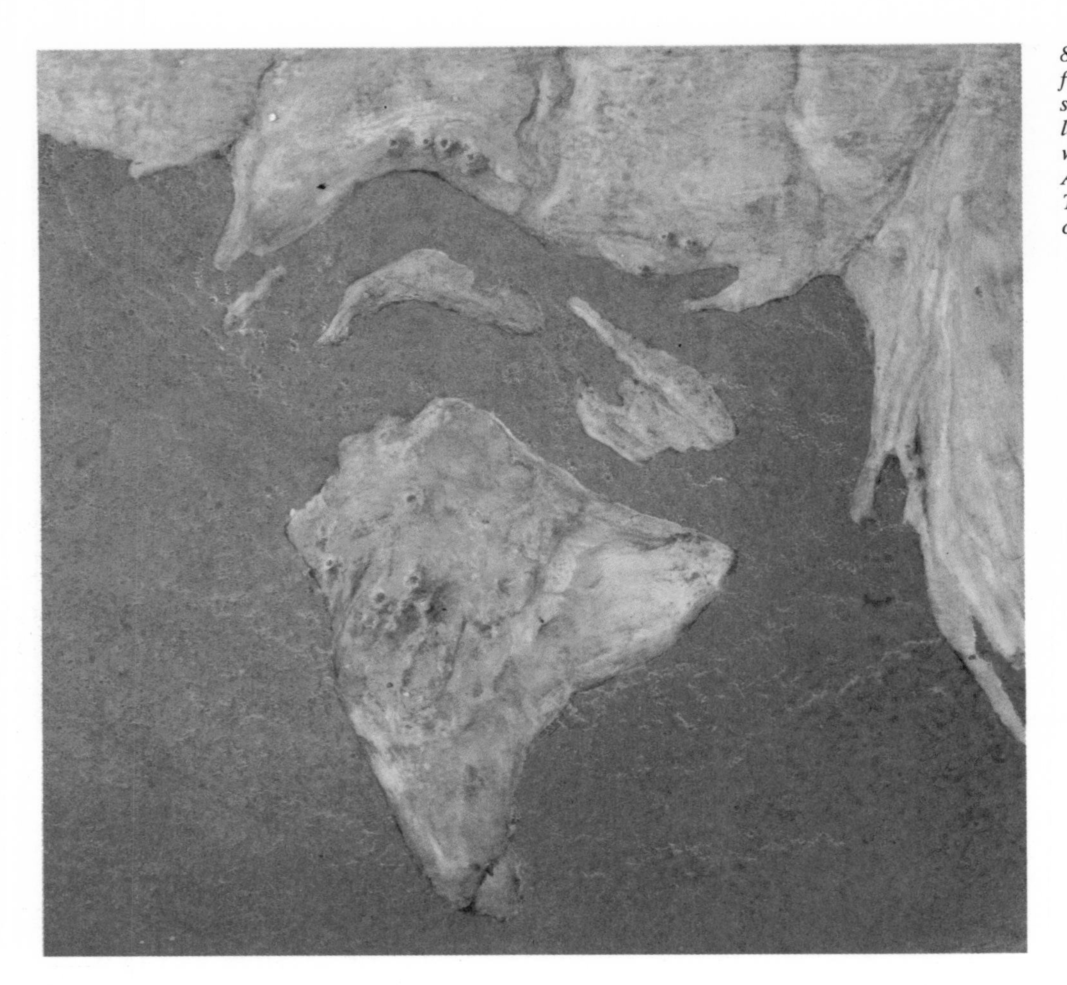

81 The end of the Mesozoic Era found the present Indian peninsula still as a micro-continent or large island drifting northwards (above), while in the Tertiary period India and Asia had already collided (below). The present situation with stress indications is shown in the next picture.

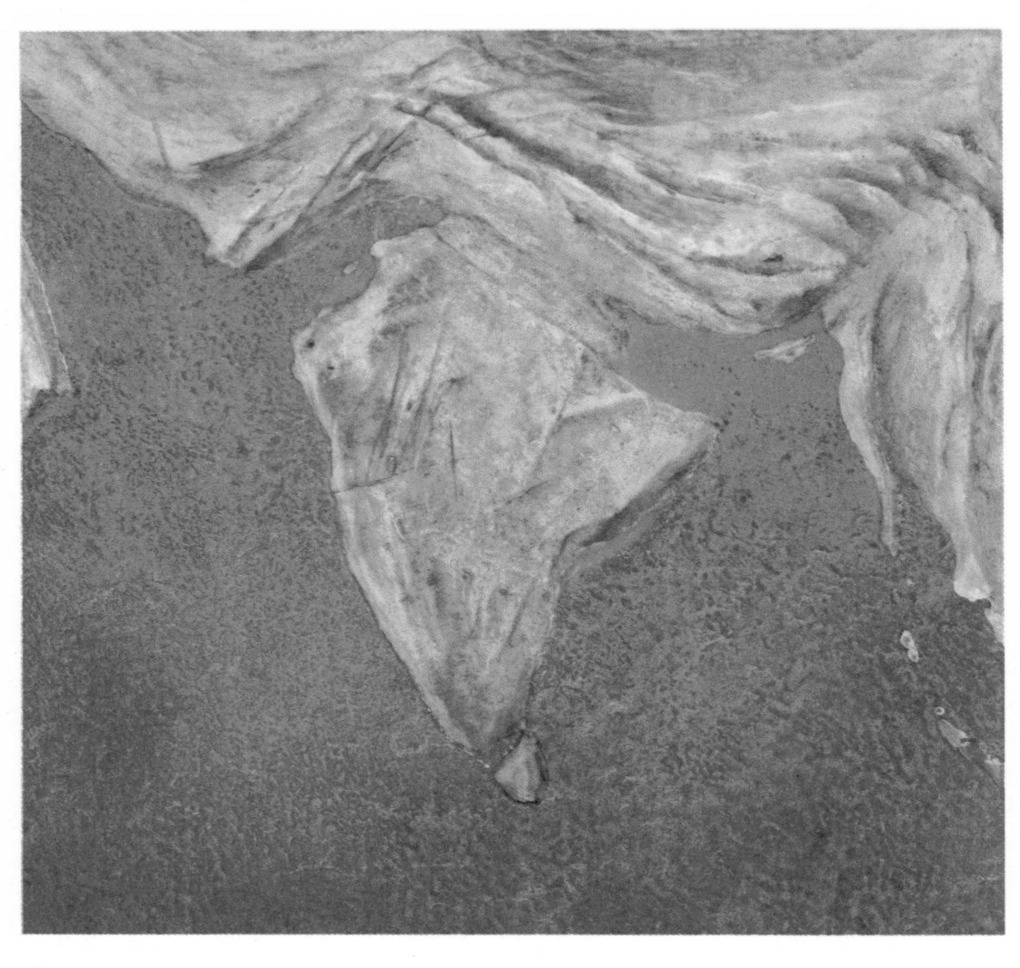

The following is a possible scenario of how the Earth has behaved up to the present; it may be assumed that it will continue to behave in the same way for some time, since if this dynamic behaviour were to cease it would spell the beginning of the end for our planet.

In this scenario, the terrestrial mantle is in motion. The asthenosphere is ductile, since it contains unequally distributed sources of heat, so that the mantle is in massive constant flux and motion. 'Convection cells', cell-like entities with dimensions of several thousand kilometres/miles, come into existence. In the location of today's ocean ridges, there are convection cell outlets on the surface, so that these ocean ridges have increased not only heat flow but the production of igneous rocks, in the form of basalts, which occur through repeated melting-down of the mantle. Since these convection cell outlets are constantly acquiring new material, the older, consolidated material is pushed aside. In the ductile asthenosphere, which reaches the surface at these points, a solid, rigid lithosphere, an ocean plate, comes about as a result of cooling. It moves around the asthenosphere and migrates from the mid-ocean ridge towards the continent, cooling and becoming stronger and more rigid on the way. Its motion is not slow: measurement has shown that the plate covers 5–10 cm/2–4 inches a year. A deposited layer of sediment forms on its surface. At a certain distance from the mid-ocean ridge, by which time it has chilled considerably or encountered another plate, some shift in movement occurs, which may take the form either of the simple bending and sinking of the rigid plate into the ductile mantle, a collision of two plates or withdrawal.

Where an oceanic plate collides with a continental plate (the latter generally being lighter and consisting of material rich in silicon and poor in iron), the oceanic plate slides under the continental. Because of the alteration in thermal and pressure conditions, changes occur in the plate. Rocks are formed with a high specific density and perhaps because of this, they sink into the upper mantle. Before the rocks begin to submerge, however, many more important changes occur throughout the plate in the course of their formation and their journey away from the oceanic ridge. The outflow of lava on to the ocean bottom causes a turbulent reaction with the sea water. The lava splits, releasing gases, and reacts with the sea water. The composition of igneous rocks changes as they chill, as does that of the surrounding sea water.

Even hot springs can occur here on the ocean floor with seawater heated by the warmth of the Earth. These springs bring many mineral substances to the surface from the depths of lava flows, including some capable of forming ore deposits. The ocean bed in mid-ocean ridge regions and on abyssal plains illustrates the importance of energy

△

82 Here we see a picture of an earthquake where the accumulated stresses were suddenly dispersed. A detailed study of earthquake foci in the Earth's crust carried out by seismologists over several years shows clearly the point at the contact of the Indian plate and Eurasia, where stresses originate.

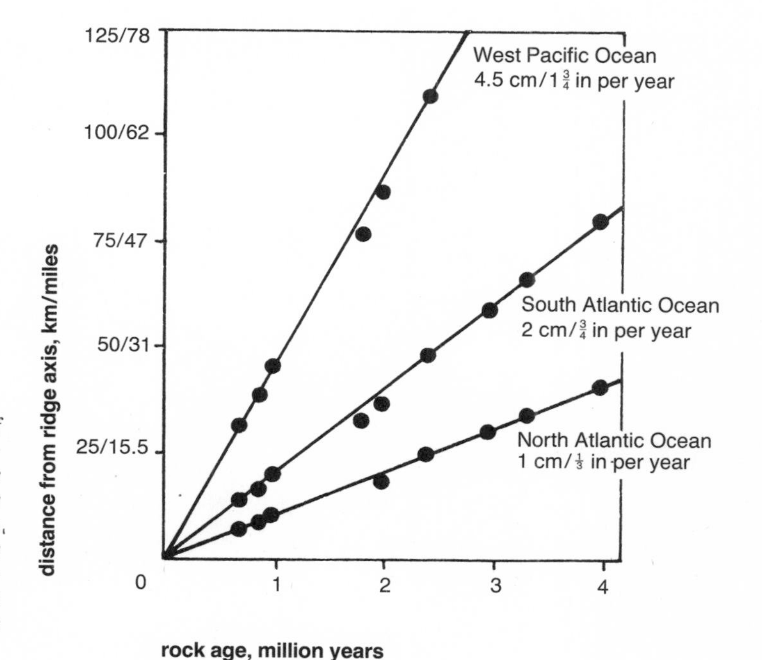

83 Radioactive measurements taken of the geological age of rocks on the ocean floor provide proof of its movement. Theoretically, the rocks of the mid-ocean ridge should be the youngest; the further away rocks are situated, the older they are. Also their speed of movement away from the mid-ocean ridge can be determined from this distance along with the age of the rocks. In the diagram the measured distance in kilometres is plotted against the geological age of the rocks. From this data the velocity of movement of the ocean floor can be calculated. The highest velocity is in the Western Pacific.

and matter exchange between the lithosphere, the hydrosphere and the atmosphere. We should recall at this point that Man has a significant effect on changes in the composition of river water and so also on changes in the composition of seawater.

Only relatively small number of rock deposits occur on the ocean bottom and these are very young. Rocks which have formed part of the crust do nevertheless reach the deep ocean trenches along with those which have erupted on the mid-ocean ridge. These crustal rocks have previously undergone a weathering process, having been swept into the ocean via rivers, once again becoming part of the Earth's 'internal' metabolic process. Material from land masses can in this way be conveyed into the depths together with the plate, undergoing changes and sometimes even becoming part of the magma of newly-forming islands. Some shortsighted people have suggested we dispose of toxic or radioactive waste in deep sea trenches. It would only be a matter of time before it was brought to the surface, as part of the natural cycle. This continental material bears isotopic evidence of several metamorphic pro-

▷
85 Significant progress in the study of the continentlal crust can be made through indirect observations and geophysical measurements taken from deep boreholes. One of these pioneer experiments is the borehole in Oberpfalz in Germany. On its completion it should reach a depth of 16 km/10 miles and should penetrate two geological units important from the European point of view. On the borehole site these units are mutually superimposed: the Moldanubian (right) and the Saxothiringian (left). Below both units there is the mantle, which will not be interfered with by the borehole.

84 The collision of two continental plates may result in a zonal mountain range. This example is from a point of contact between the Indian and Eurasian plates. The Himalayas — a collision mountain range. The Indian plate (on the left, coloured brown) carries sedimentary rocks on its surface (yellow) and collides with the Asian plate (light brown and reddish). Great masses of continental crust accumulate and the sedimentary rocks are drawn, together with the subducted Indian plate, deep below the Himalayas (shown by the arrow). The subduction of such a great quantity of such material to great depths results in a continental crust of great thickness, which may lead to the formation of granite magma. In the case of the Himalayas the thickness of the continental crust in the collision areas is estimated, on the basis of seismological measurements, at 60—75 km/37—46 miles, which is approximately double the mean thickness of the Earth's crust in the shield and plateau areas.

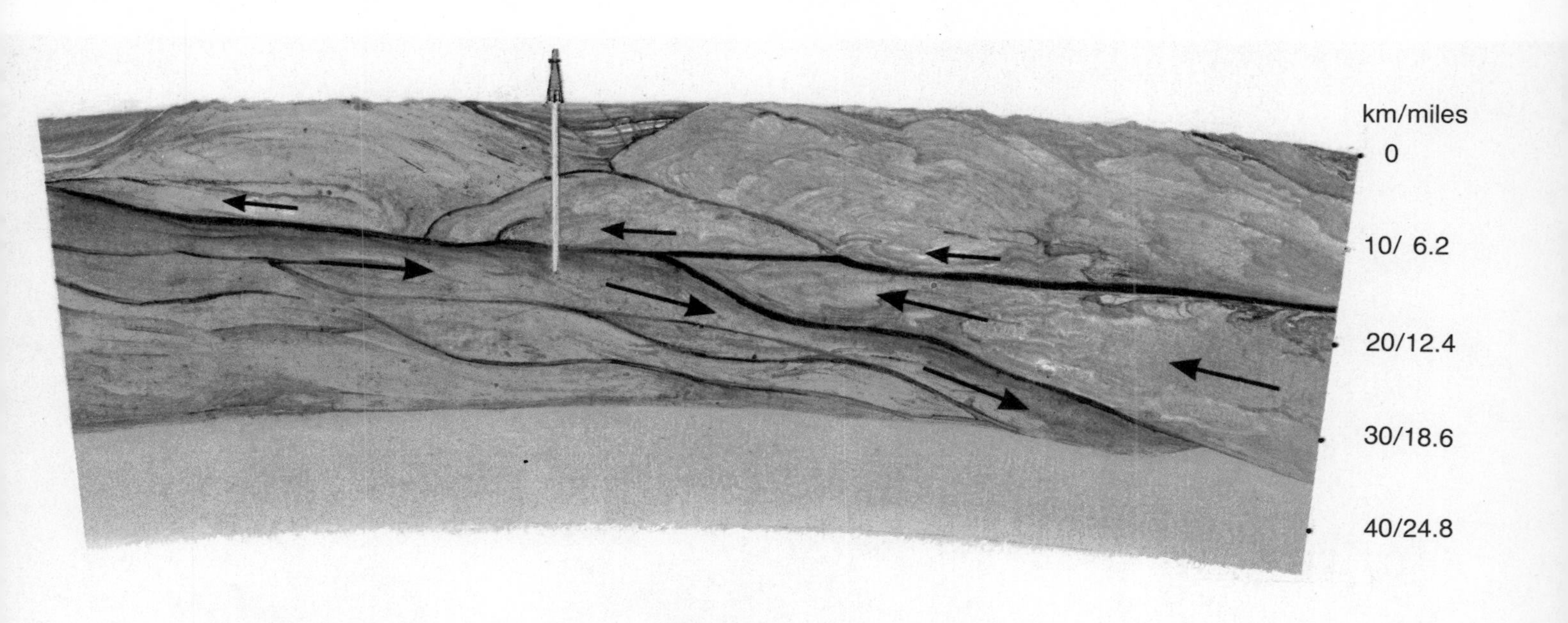
km/miles
0
10/ 6.2
20/12.4
30/18.6
40/24.8

Mount Everest
8,848 m/29,028 feet above sea level
Tibet

◁
86 Information gained by submarine investigation has shown that hot water springs containing enormous quantities of metal ores and sulphur well up on the ocean floor. They were called 'black smokers'. On such sites deposits of non-ferrous metals, such as copper, zinc and lead are found. This discovery not only assisted in the explanation of the origin of non-ferrous metal deposits, often connected with deep-sea sediments, but also showed how different forms of life were able to develop in areas of little oxygen.

87 Lava formations on the ocean floor are reminiscent in many respects of recent lava formations on dry land. On the sea floor cushion-like or loaf-like forms occur. Geologists studying older geological formations are familiar with these.

88 Boundaries between lithospheric plates may be divergent *(upper two pictures) or* convergent *(lower two pictures). The arrows indicate the movement of the individual segments. One example of a divergent boundary is the mid-ocean ridge; the first picture shows a very simple diagram of a divergent boundary. Real examples, however are as a rule more complex: the ridge of the divergent boundary may be broken by a series of 'transform faults' (second picture from the top). A convergent boundary may have formed by* subduction *where one plate is forced below the other (third from the top), or by* obduction, *when one plate slides over another (fourth from the top). Collision boundaries, particularly between continental plates, are often indistinct.*

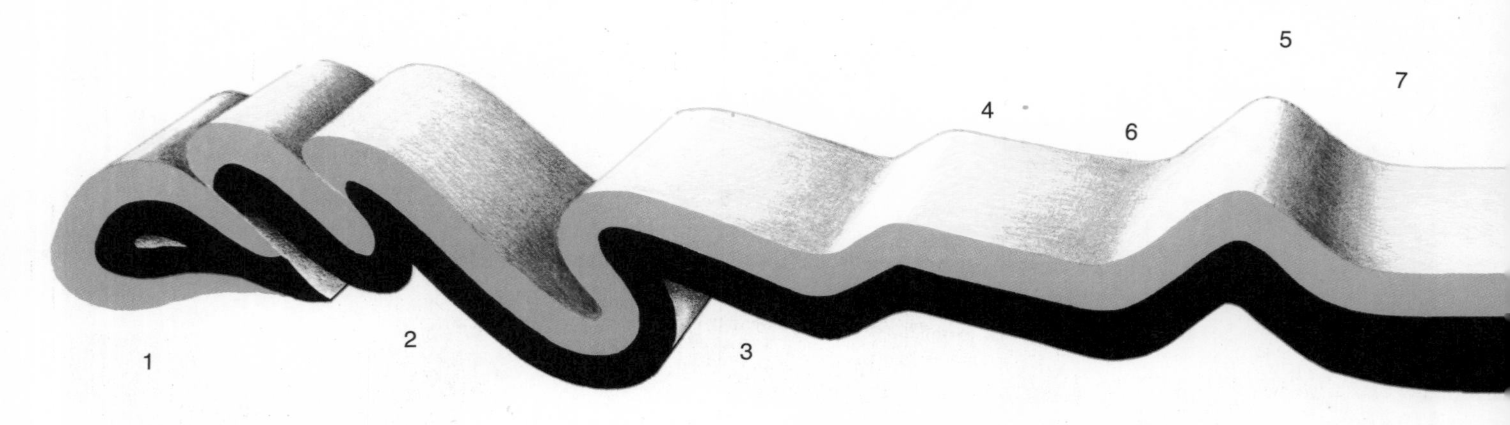

89 A glossary of terms concerning strata deformation by lateral pressure:
1 — fold nappe
2 — overlap (overthrust)
3 — overturned fold
4 — flexure
5 — fold
6 — syncline (synform)
7 — anticline (antiform)
8 — drop
9 — uplift
10 — horst
11 — graben

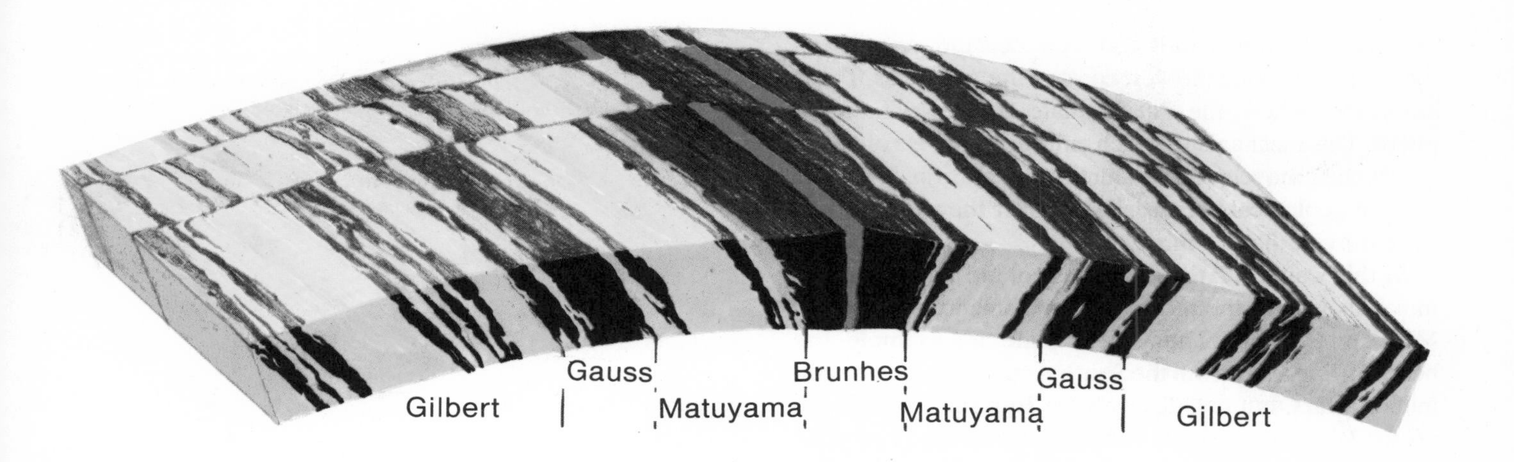

90 A block of oceanic crust in the mid-ocean ridge area, showing magnetic anomalies on the ocean floor. In the course of the Earth's history, the positioning of its magnetic field changed several times. The North and the South Magnetic Poles swapped places. This is known in scientific terms as a 'magnetic reversal'. Rocks which formed from magma, when the old 'North Magnetic Pole' was situated in the north, are shown in black, while these rock complexes which formed when the old 'North Magnetic Pole' became situated in the south are shown in yellow. Methods of determining the age of rocks, based on radioactive decay, resulted in the conclusion that the further away rocks occur from the mid-ocean ridge (coloured red) the older they are. Studies of the ocean floor have shown that almost 100 magnetic reversals have taken place in the geological history of the Earth. Each such change is given a name; some of these names are shown in the illustration.

cesses which appears in the igneous rocks of volcanoes on the ocean periphery. This can be demonstrated by any geochemist studying the chemical element content and the atomic weights and nuclear properties of igneous rocks in island arcs or on ocean peripheries. In some ten million years' time, geochemists may find traces of what our civilization has deposited on the ocean bottom in the products of repeated melting around subducting plates.

Subduction and the collision of two plates are not straightforward processes. Specific density alters during subduction, together with the escape of water and other volatile components: there is a great deal of water in the rocks of an ocean plate. This loss of water brings about changes in rocks which form the upper part of the ocean plate. This can, in turn, lead to movement in the material of the mantle, and sometimes, especially in what is known as the 'overlying wedge', to melting. In this way, volcanic centres are born. These can be seen in areas adjacent to the Pacific Ocean, extending from Kamchatka across the Kurile Islands, Japan, the Philippines, Papua-New Gui-

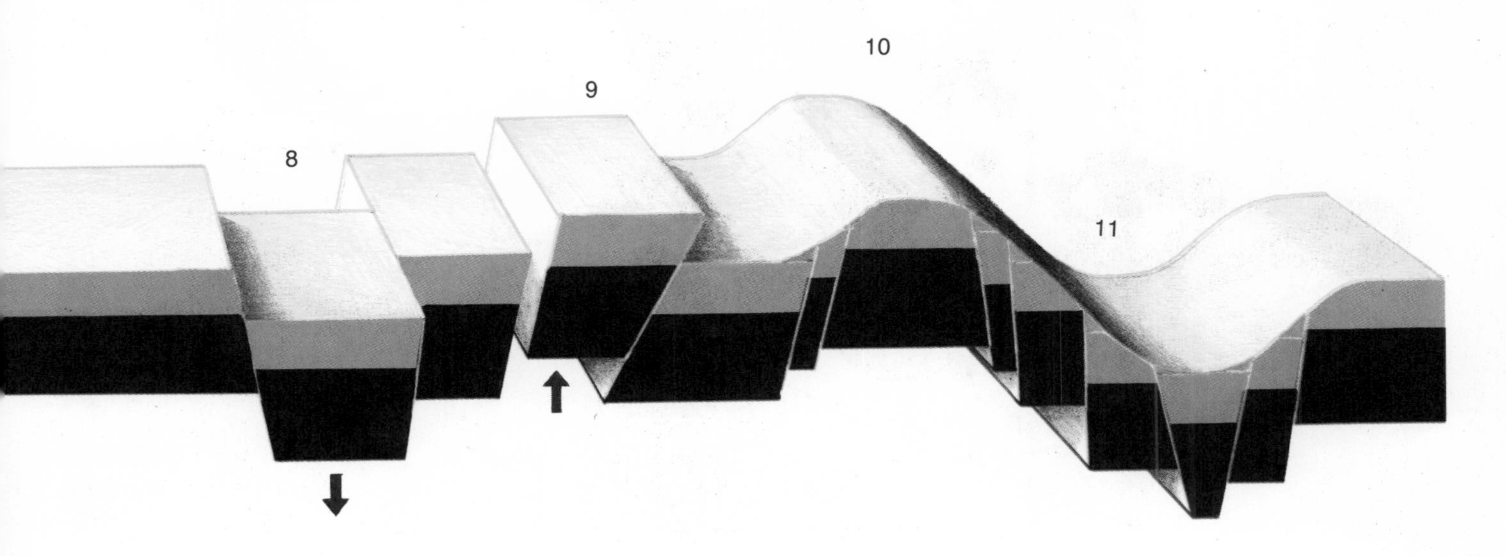

nea, the Solomon Islands and New Zealand, running on the other side along the west coast of the Americas. These are places where the Pacific plate collides with other plates. This mechanism, which embraces the rise of ocean plates, their movement, subduction or collision, forms the basis of geological occurrences all over the world: if one plate moves, they all move.

In this way the Atlantic, Eurasian and African plates move, as well as the more exoticly named ones, such as Nazca or Coconut. The African plate, for example, has been drifting away from the South American plate for 200 million years, but collides with the Eurasian plate to the north. We may distinguish between two types of plate junction: *divergent,* where plates drift apart, and *convergent,* where they collide. There is a divergent junction in mid-ocean ridges, and a convergent one in the island arcs, active continental margins and 'collision zones' in mountain ranges.

Looking at the map of the world, we can see that volca-

91 Iceland is an unusual phenomenon of the land surface. It is part of the Mid-Atlantic Ridge appearing as dry land. Within only a few hundred kilometres there is a great deal of volcanic activity. Here lava fields are shown black, glacial areas white; the names indicate the most important centres of volcanic activity.

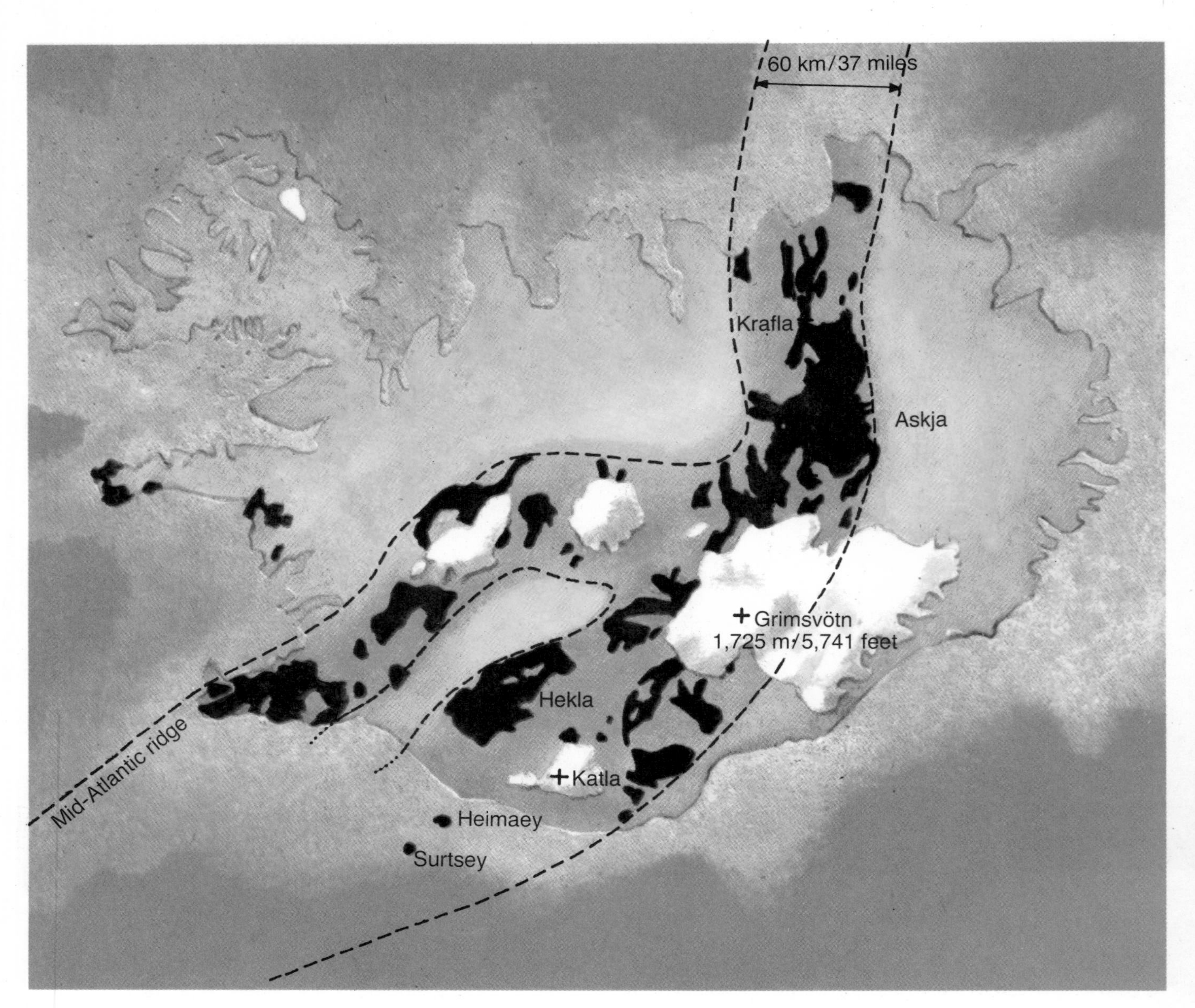

noes occur at both divergent and convergent junctions. In all these places there is an outflow of molten matter from the mantle. However, there are also two other very important volcanic regions apart from the junctions of lithospheric plates. This may at first sight appear to speak against this seemingly convincing hypothesis. Yet if these points are examined more closely, it can be seen that the first is located around the great African lakes, that is, in the East African continental rift. There are numerous volcanoes in this region, the most famous being Kilimanjaro; but why there? This is because the situation is similar to that of the mid-ocean 'rifts'. It has been discovered that in the continental rift region the ductile mantle rises up towards the surface, and where molten material has been very active it has formed the rift structure of the Red Sea, which differs only slightly from the mid-ocean rift proper. This means that in about ten million years or so it is possible that the eastern part of African will split from its western part and the two plates, which nowadays manifest themselves as a rift with a thinned continental lithosphere, will begin to drift apart. Both the strength and the weakness of a hypothesis may lie in such predictions.

Volcanoes can also occur in places where one would least expect them. These places are known as hot spots, and there are about twenty of them in the world, the most important being the Hawaiian Islands, Tahiti and, as has already been mentioned, the Galápagos Islands. According to the lithosphere plate hypothesis described, a volcano occurs in a part of a certain plate junction, not at the centre of a plate. In fact, however, these apparently 'chaotic' volcanoes have provided superb proof of the validity of the hypothesis. They are better viewed from a cinematograph than described in words. A hot spot is firmly anchored in the lower mantle, somewhere deep in the asthenosphere. The mobile, rigid ocean plate 'travels' above this spot, and the magma flowing out to the surface keeps forming new volcanoes, the old ones drifting away together with the oceanic plate.

The chapter on the Earth's face described how the highest mountain ranges, such as the Alps, the Caucasus and the Himalayas, are composed of very young rocks, and that high mountains in fact uplifted relatively recently, only a few million years ago. Measurement has revealed that high mountains are in fact growing, but that, simultaneously, they are being lowered by current erosion. Let us take a look at a special geological map of the world, showing rocks of the same age and origin. Like the Andean ridge, the Eurasian high mountain ridge also has many volcanoes. In the not too distant past, there were a great many in the Carpathian Mountains, and the highest peaks in the Caucasus today are also volcanoes. Asia Minor (Turkey), as well as the northern slopes of the Himalayas and the Tibetan high mountain plateau, all have currently active volcanoes. As in the case of volcano chains, these high mountains similarly constitute regions of contact between two plates in an active, geologically young area. Geologists conclude that volcanoes in these regions stem from a collision between two lithospheric plates, and in the case of the above mentioned European and Asian high mountains between two continental plates. The volcanoes of the Pacific Ocean involve either a collision of two oceanic plates of 'island arcs' or, in the case of South America, of an oceanic plate with a continental plate.

Continental plates are generally composed of sedimentary, igneous and metamorphic rocks. Not only volcanic and magmatic activity, but also interaction between the atmosphere, hydrosphere and lithosphere have played major parts in rock formation in the continental plates. To this also should be added the role of tectonic movement and the fact that rocks vary in their mechanical properties: some deform in a brittle way, that is splitting, while others deform through being ductile. Great amounts of such characteristically diverse material, worked on by water, wind, sedimentation and metamorphic processes, go deep into the crust when continental plates collide, reaching places where high pressure and high temperatures prevail. Rocks change under such conditions, each reacting in its own way. Take, for example, a clay-based sediment containing wood fragments. The pressure caused simply by the sediment acting upon itself would be enough to squeeze out the water. Combine this with a little heat, and you have wood coal. Rocks and rock components behave in a similar way to wood, changing their structure and internal composition. Molecules of water and other building molecules regroup, resulting in new minerals and new chemical compounds that are in equilibrium with the conditions prevailing at depth. This process is known as 'metamorphosis', which, when applied to rocks, means their adaptation to altered conditions – either increased temperature or pressure, or decreased or increased water levels. Metamorphosis also takes place if the rock is penetrated by hot flows, if water comes near molten matter, or if rocks lose their water and other volatile components.

In an environment where continental lithospheric plates collide and crush against one another, it may also happen that circumstances arise in which rocks melt down. Molten material then appears on the surface in the form of magma. Most rock nevertheless remains solid, deforming and adapting to constantly changing conditions. Volatile components such as water, carbon dioxide and sodium and chloride ions leave the rock complex and release other minerals on their way up to the surface, bearing these minerals in the form of fluids. In many instances they reach the hydrosphere and atmosphere and then become part of it.

Rocks react to movements within the crust and within specific, even small plates. They can break up and slip over one another like scales in horizontally arranged faults. Tectonic processes are, therefore, of particular significance for the geological structure of continents. This is easy to see on the illustration showing the situation in the Himalayas, where the Indian subcontinent (shown here in brown and yellow) collides with the Asian plate. The subcontinent is moving northwards, transporting a thin layer of sedimentary rock on its solid part. At points of contact, these scrape and fold, the major part of the material being dislocated under the Himalayas to places where there are high temperatures and pressure creating the possibility of molten matter. Little is known about what happens at such depths. It is possible, however, to simulate conditions such as heat and pressure, as well as the water content and composition of rocks, in the laboratory. A great deal of information is gained in this way. It has taken millions of years of erosion to expose the roots of high mountain ranges like this. This is shown in the second illustration, of the Bohemian massif, a collision of continental plates somewhat older than the current one.

Molten material, together with the gaseous phase and water, play a special role in the metabolic processes of the Earth's interior. For molten matter to arise in the conditions of the terrestrial crust, not even extremely high temperatures or pressure are necessary, at least not very high in geological terms. Granitic rocks, which are among the most frequent on the surface, occur quite commonly within the crust. A temperature of around 600–700 °C/ 1272–1484 °F and pressure of around 5,000 atm (0.5 GPa) is sufficient. Where suitable material, such as sedimentary rock and water, is available, molten granite can form. This mixes readily with other rocks, intruding into folding complexes. The formation of granite is a chapter in itself, not only within geology, but even within ore geology, since granite is accompanied by a number of minerals used by man, the tin and molybdenum dominating among them. The processes of granite formation are perhaps the most important metabolic processes taking place within the crust, often where continental lithospheric plates collide – today probably somewhere deep under the Himalayas, the Andes in South America and the western part of North America.

It may be supposed that most of the processes described in this chapter can be accounted for by deep, internal forces, such as the heat of the Earth. However, we should also bear in mind the important role played by a compound as abundant as water, which is a medium for the exchange of matter and energy. Without water from the hydrosphere and the sedimentary basin, without flowing water in general, there would be no granitic rocks, and therefore, no continental crust.

It is water, therefore, that makes the continental crust and the lithosphere what they are. This involves a cycle of lithospheric water, which is an integral part of the workings of the Earth's surface, its depths, and its upper and lower crusts. Water is involved in erosion, weathering, the transporting and deposition of rocks. It also plays a crucial role in rock metamorphosis and ore formation, being the most active component in the melting process which takes place within the continental crust. Without water in crustal rocks there would be no granitic magma. Even within these processes, water is involved at depth in cyclical processes. As soon as granitic magma moves close to the Earth's surface and cools, it crystallizes. When minerals form a solid crystalline granite, only a small proportion of the water remains, dissolved at high pressure in the molten magma. Most of the water which does not become part of the rock returns to the hydrosphere, sometimes in the form of hot springs. This water may then in turn become part of the surface waters of the meteoric cycle. Isotopic studies of water contained in igneous rocks have shown that at least part of the water present has already undergone a surface cycle. Most of the water on the surface, either in underground springs, clouds, lakes or the sea, also evidently originated in the upper mantle, having been brought to the surface by volcanic rocks at some early stage in the Earth's evolution. Since that time it has become part of the lithosphere, but may have returned to the mantle (e.g. during subduction or plate collision), in the same way as the single carbon molecule previously mentioned.

Observing the natural water cycle, in which water circulates among clouds, rain, the runoff into rivers and seas and later evaporation into clouds, we ought to be aware that this is a short-term cycle. Water is able in this way to reach the deeper parts of the mantle, particularly during the subduction of the oceanic crust, as well as into the deep parts of the continental crust. So far only rough guesses can be made at the amounts of water involved. It can take millions of years for this 'geologically captured' water to find its way back into the hydrosphere.

Using the example of water, we have shown that it is not altogether appropriate to divide the Earth's metabolism – its cycles of material and energy exchange – into superficial and internal processes. Water is not the only substance that migrates between the hydrosphere, atmosphere and the depths of the lithosphere. Other substances are carried along with the water, which, after all, is one of Nature's best solvents.

We are now familiar with the Earth's metabolism, in which the oceanic crust, and later the continental crust, form as a result of convection in the mantle. We have also seen that there is a dynamic exchange of matter and energy between individual spheres of the Earth. Plate tectonics provides a good explanation of the cycle of matter within the Earth. The Earth is a living, moving, changing organism, admittedly over many millions of years, in which the human life-span is like a blink of an eye. This kind of cycle was observed by our forefathers, for example the Scottish geologist J. Hutton, who showed in the 19th century how rocks undergo a complex cycle during the Earth's evolution. Magmatic activity accompanies mountain-building. After this comes the weathering of rocks, their erosion, runoff into sedimentary basins, the subsidence of sedimentary basins accompanied later by metamorphosis and melting, and yet another magmatic process. This completes the cycle, and then it starts all over again.

It should be remembered, however, that even within these vast cycles, operating apparently independently of Man, there are still elements affected by human activity: the amount of sedimentary material and its chemical composition. The Earth is like a giant sponge – at some point in the future its pollution levels will reach saturation point – and then?

92 The East African lakes are situated in a geologically active region, called the East African Rift. The connection with other rift structures, e.g. the Gulf of Aden, the Red Sea and the Dead Sea rifts, is easy to see. In the area of the East African Rift the continent begins to break by the separation of two lithospheric plates. It is highly probable that in a few million years the eastern part will have become totally separated from the central part and that a sea, similar to the Red Sea, will replace the present-day lakes. As in the majority of other rifts, the East African Rift has a central 'valley' (rift) in which volcanoes occur (marked with triangles. The valley is separated by two faults (the incline of the fault is indicated by the zigzag lines). Such formations are called 'grabens'. As the area of upper mantle beneath the continents has a different composition from the mantle of oceanic areas, so the composition of volcanic rocks in the East African Rift is different from that of rocks from mid-ocean ridges. The geological roles of both rifts, however, are identical.

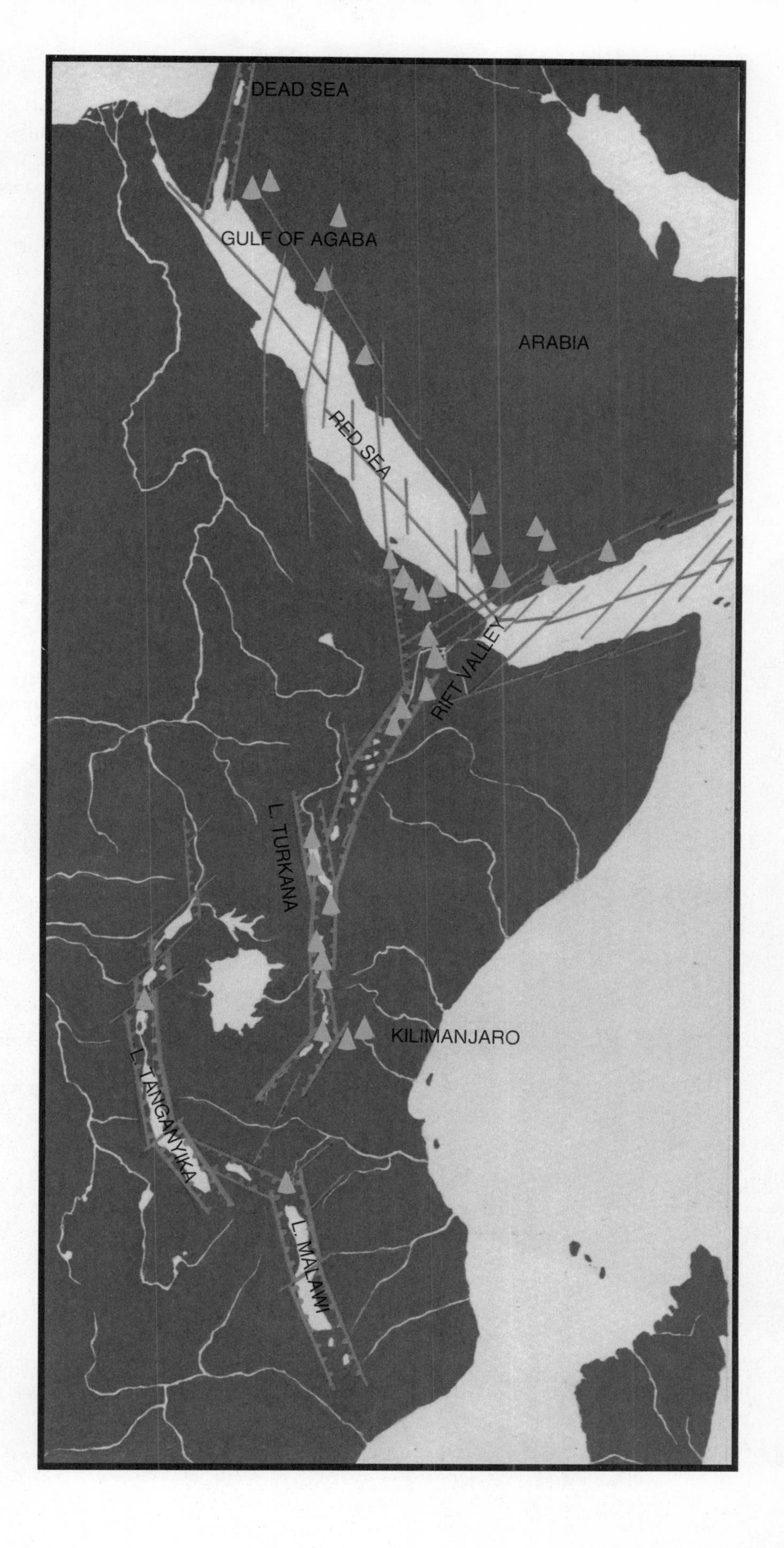

Solar radiation 100 %

4 % reflected from the surface of the Earth back into space

47 % received by the Earth and converted to heat

19 % absorbed by the atmosphere

From the energy received from the Sun 0.0022 % is used in the process of decomposition, photosynthesis and directly by animals; part of this energy is stored by the Earth in the form of fossil fuels.

30 % reflected from the atmosphere back into space

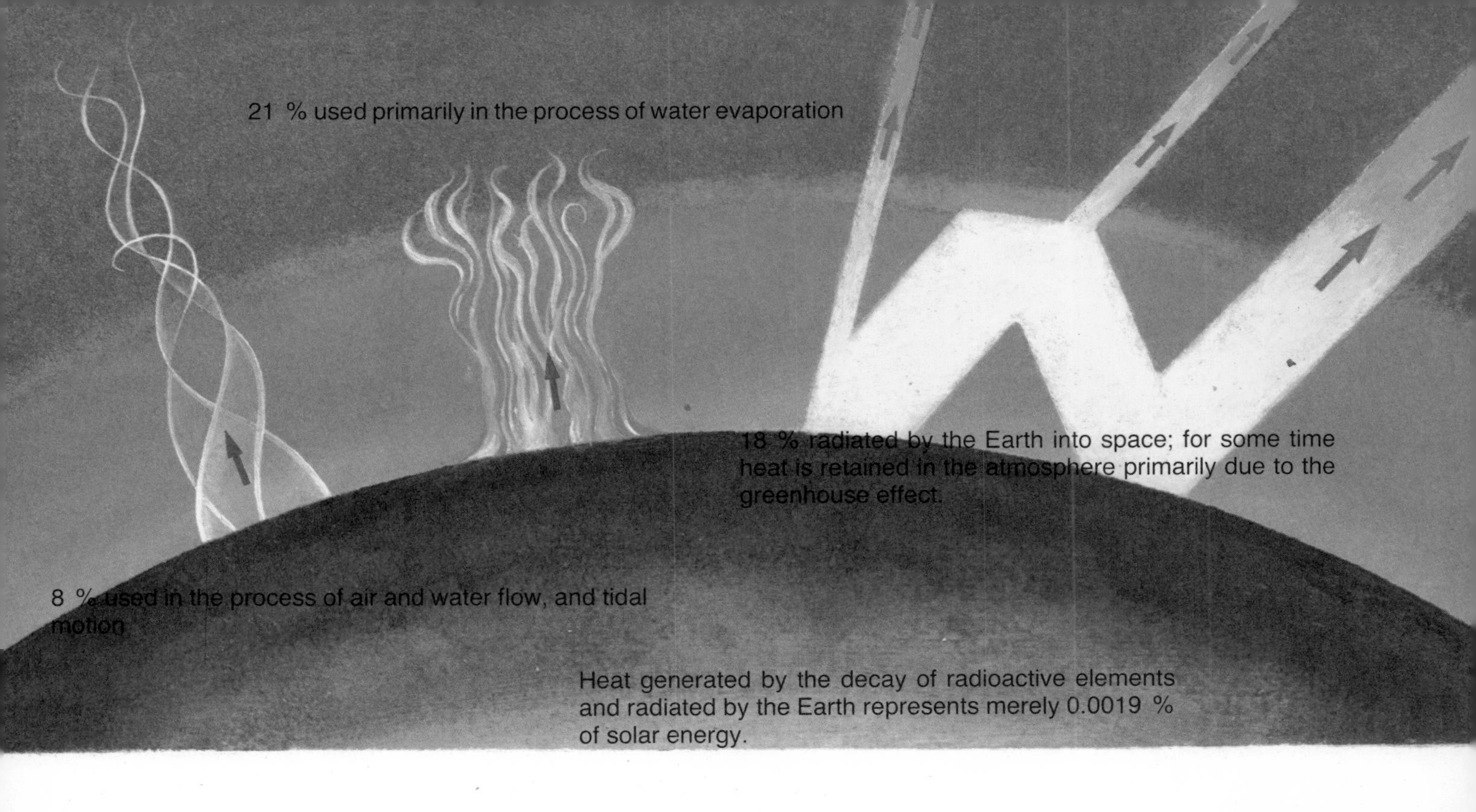

WHAT MOVES THE EARTH

Examining the surface and geological make-up of the Earth reveals a lively picture, and we don't need an exceptional capacity for observation to notice that the Earth is an unusually active planetary body. Whole lithospheric plates are in motion, as are the waters in the oceans; lava erupts from volcanoes, and enormous masses of air move around in the atmosphere. High mountain ranges rise, ocean floors form, boulders split, rocks are weathered, mineral structures are transformed and new minerals form. These processes consume a lot of energy. The Earth is neither in perpetual motion nor is it a clockwork device which will run forever once it has been wound up. So what does move the Earth, and what keeps in motion the processes taking place in its interior and on its surface?

The preceding chapters have tried to give a 'potted' history of the Earth and show the present-day situation from an historical perspective. Now let's try to do the same with the Earth's energy system. The Earth's history is rather like our own personal memories: the further we go back, the less precisely are we able to recall. In this way specific events, although quite separate, overlap and become blurred. Difficult as it is to decipher events in the history of the Earth, it is more difficult to decipher its thermal history and to draw up a 'balance-sheet' of its energy intake and expenditure. The Earth is like a child building castles in a sand-pit. The child will knock down the old castles in order to build new ones, yet will still be playing with the same sand. From time to time, new sand will be brought in to replace that which has been washed or blown away. The evolution of the terrestrial crust takes place in much the

93 The Earth, as a whole, represents energywise a perfectly balanced system. The quantities of heat absorbed, reflected and emitted have been the same for a period of at least 3 billion years. During the course of the Earth's history, there have been, as well as temperate periods, both colder and warmer periods. During colder eras (glacial periods) parts of the Earth were covered with ice, in warmer eras (interglacial periods) the majority of glaciers melted and, consequently, the ocean level rose. The Sun is over one thousand times more powerful than any other energy source affecting the Earth. It is, therefore, understandable to look to the Sun for clues about the origins of the Earth. One solution of the Earth's future energy problems is also sought from the Sun, in the form of solar energy. All other sources, such as the radioactive heat of the Earth (the source of geothermal energy), or the energy produced by the gravitational pull between the Sun, the Moon and the Earth, are negligible when estimating the energy balance of the Earth. However, in spite of this they are still energy sources which will have to be managed economically in the future.

same way, with old rocks and geological formations being used to build newer ones. This too makes the task of reconstructing the Earth's thermal history a more difficult one. We shall try, however, to follow the course of the Earth's energy balance from its beginnings up to the present day. We shall take the same approach as before, in which the present is the key to the past. First, let us look at the Earth's present energy system.

The Earth has two basic energy sources – an external (exogenous) and internal (endogenous). We experience the beneficial effects of the Sun's radiation daily, while volcanoes remind us of the Earth's interior heat. Let us concentrate upon these two energy systems separately. Although the endogenous energy system is vast, it comprises a mere fraction of the exogenous one. Nevertheless, we are primarily concerned with the inanimate aspects of the Earth, and so shall deal with its interior energy first.

Most of the energy used by the Earth comes from the Sun, the amount of heat produced from the Earth's interior representing a mere fraction of its overall heat energy system. The effects of these two energy sources, nevertheless, ultimately overlap. The amount of heat radiating from the Sun on to the surface of the Earth is tens of thousands of times greater than the amount of heat which reaches the Earth's surface from its own interior. Of the heat radiated by the Sun to the Earth, approximately 30 per cent is reflected back into space, and 19 per cent is absorbed by the atmosphere. A further 4 per cent is reflected by snow and ice. The amount of heat received naturally varies from place to place, and heat flow does not remain constant in one place.

The same applies to heat from the Earth's interior. There are places on the Earth with a high heat flow, for example regions of current volcanic activity in the mid-ocean ridges, the island arcs, rift regions or hot spots, just as there are also places with very low heat flow.

The temperature of the Earth increases from crust to centre; the closer to the Earth's centre the higher is the temperature. This is known as the geothermal gradient and is given in degrees per kilometre. This amounts to 20-30°C/68-86°F in upper, crustal parts. At depths greater than 10 m/11 yd the temperature remains constant, unaffected by either the annual or the daily temperature changes of the Earth's atmosphere.

A particular contribution to the temperature balance of the Earth is played by radioactive elements – uranium, thorium and potassium isotopes. Different rocks have different heat-producing properties, depending on the individual concentration of radioactive elements. Since these elements are concentrated in upper crustal rocks, these

94 Of four glacial periods which took place during the Earth's history the coldest was the last but one, and was called the 'Riss'. This satellite view of Europe shows the area covered by continental glaciation in Northern Europe and the extent of continental mountain glaciers in the Alps, Carpathians and Pyrenees. Water which froze during the Riss glaciation caused the ocean level to fall and, consequently, exposed part of the continental shelf. The present situation of global warming threatens the opposite: the thawing of northern and Antarctic glaciers and, consequently, a significant rise in sea level.

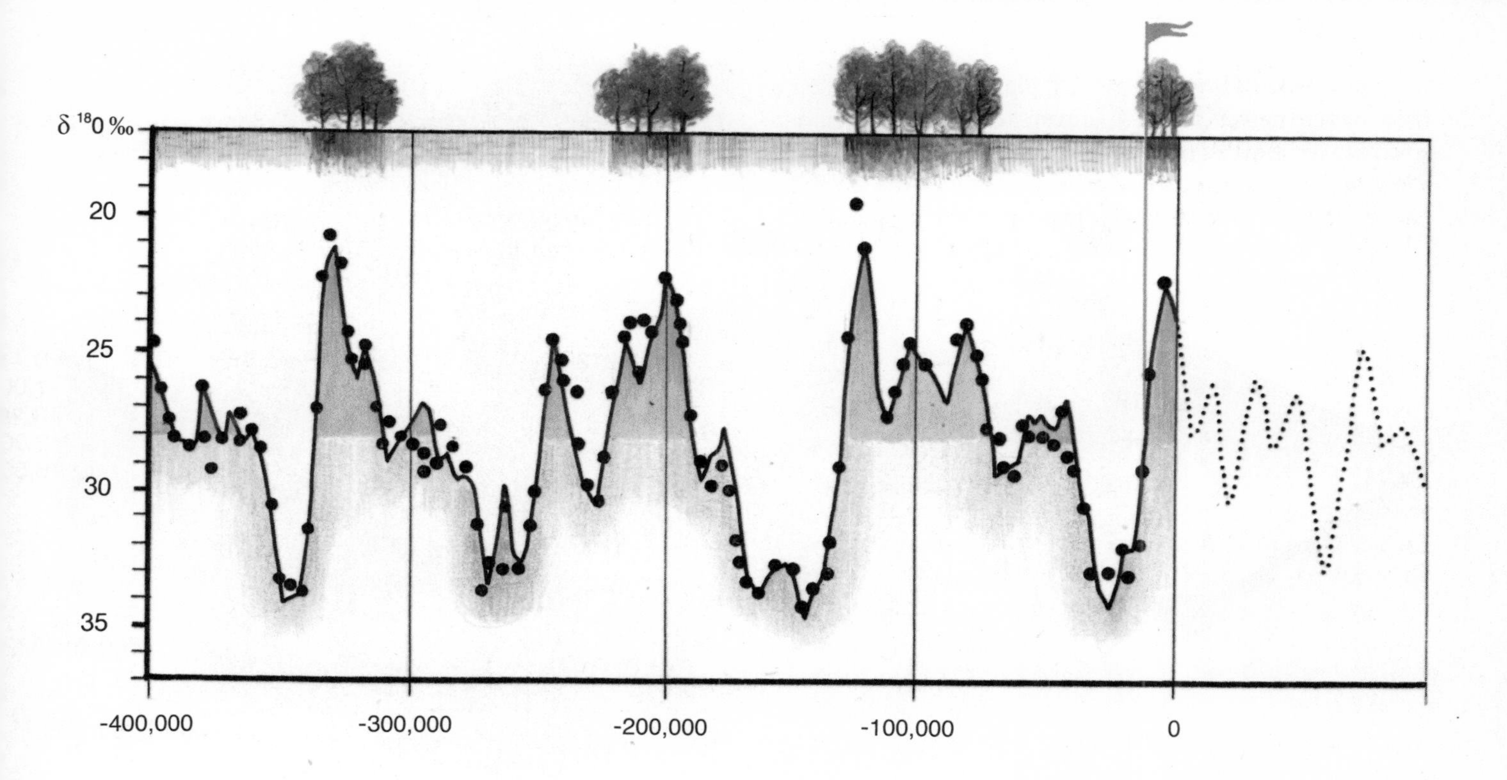

95 Modern research into the ocean floor, boreholes into undersea sediment and its subsequent laboratory analysis has helped not only in determining lengths of individual glacial periods, but also in measuring temperature fluctuations. A curve plotted on the basis of the distribution of oxygen isotopes, which reflects temperature fluctuations, shows regular oscillations. Similar oscillations appear also on a smaller scale, e.g. in the eleven-year periods corresponding with the maximums of solar activity. The present period is marked 'O'. The red flag represents 12,000 years ago, when the last glacial period ended and the current warm period began. Such warm periods are called interglacial periods and are characterized by heavy forestation and soil generation, while in the glacial perioods the soil in the northern temperate zone is frozen and the vegetation is limited to the sporadic occurrence of some 'leaf' trees, such as hazels and birches.

rocks produce the most heat. Heat emission from granite, for example, is considerable compared with that of basalt, situated at a greater depth, or mantle rocks, whose heat-producing capacity is an order lower than that of basalt. It is for this reason that heat flow from different types of rock is so diverse in character, even in regions where the Earth's structure is reasonably stable, and not subject to rapid change. Nonetheless a heat flow map shows a number of other factors, e.g. the relationship between the Earth's surface and its deeper parts. Along with all the other factors there are to consider, we should bear in mind that rocks make good insulators. So long as there is no water flowing through or alongside rocks, their ability to conduct heat is minimal and this, therefore, leads to an accumulation of heat deep inside the Earth.

A look at a world map showing measured heat flow values, i.e. the heat output from the Earth's interior, would seem to confirm popularly held beliefs regarding the division of the Earth's lithosperes into plates. Mid-ocean ridge areas have very high flows. The same also holds for regions where there are rifts and collision vulcanism, whereas regions of old ocean floor, deep sea trenches and shields display perceptibly lower heat flow values. This would seem to confirm the supposition that a significant proportion of heat from the Earth's interior reaches the surface not only by means of conduction, but also by convection combined with the movement of matter.

It is assumed that from the nature of radioactivity itself, as can be seen from the illustration, radioactive elements decay in the course of time, and as a result of this, the heat-production of radioactive sources is reduced. This would seem to indicate that, at least from the point of view of radioactive elements, heat activity of the Earth in ancient times was far more turbulent that it is nowadays. The role played by radioactive elements with a short half-life is unclear: the difficulties associated with their existence have already been touched on. These elements do, nevertheless, play an important part in some theories concerned with the early evolution of planetary bodies.

With regard to the Earth's history, it is not possible to use present-day criteria. The early history of the planet, the development of its organic life forms and its own particular gravitational force clearly constitute an exceptional series of events.

One way towards solving these problems is to study the nearby planets of the solar system, i.e. Mars, Venus and Mercury, as well as the Moon. These are less dynamic planetary bodies — a lazy child in our imaginary sand-pit, who builds only one castle, and then goes away. These planets, therefore, are 'frozen in time', retaining evolutionary features which may give us an insight into an earlier stage

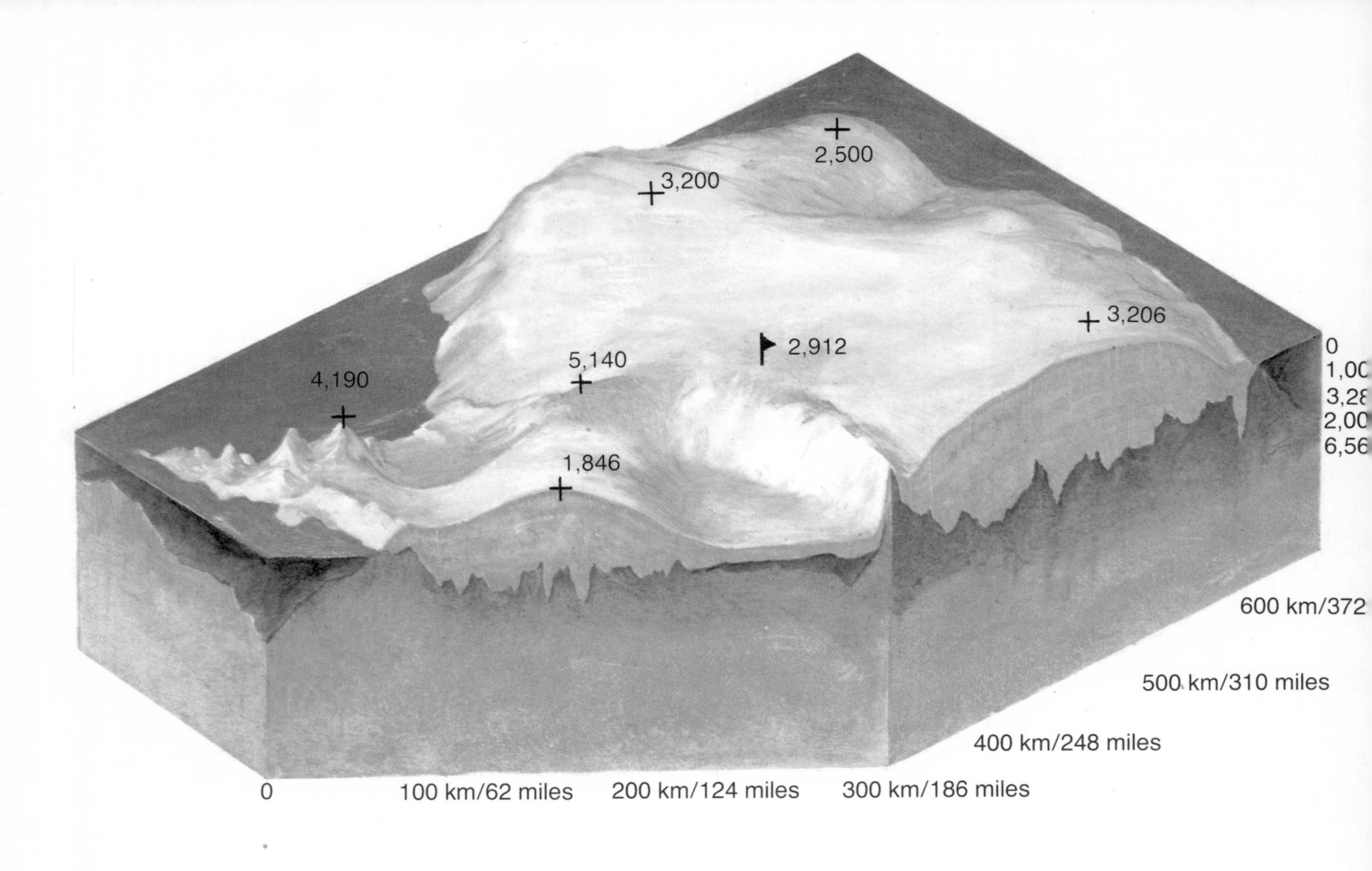

in the Earth's development. Geologists, who only in exceptional circumstances are able to uncover the secrets of archaic rocks, i.e. those which are more than two billion years old, were all in favour of the space programme. They believed that the study of planetary and lunar surfaces would further knowledge of their early history and, as a consequence, of the history of the Earth itself. Evidence of the correlation between the Earth and space geology was not long in coming, and with it brought quite a few surprises. Where the scientists had anticipated finding a cool planetary body (the Earth's Moon), they discovered that early in the history of the Moon, and probably of the planets of our solar system, there occurred high temperatures, followed by the incidence of molten rocks over almost the entire planet.

Let us try to imagine the earliest stages in the evolution of a planetary body. Fragments of matter from space travel at extremely high velocities, and in the process wrap themselves around some kind of gravitational centre: the nucleus of a planet in the making. The kinetic energy within these rapidly moving components is converted into heat. This is one of the commonest physical processes; the heat produced in this phase is known as accretion heat.

The matter which wraps itself around the planetary body, thus giving it form, has a number of properties. It is primitive matter, being of cosmic origin and with little differentiation. It contains metal, sulphide and siliceous components, as well as isotopes of radioactive elements: uranium, thorium and potassium. Within the heated planetary body, metallic and sulphide components separate from siliceous components (a process similar to that inside a blast furnace). Being heavier, the metallic component has a higher specific density, therefore sinking to the centre of the planet, for example the Earth. A certain amount of heat, known as gravitation heat, is also released during this process. Many scientists suppose these processes of separation of metal from silicates within the Earth still to be continuing, and that they will go on for another two billion years, the gravitation heat produced contributing to the Earth's interior energy balance.

Examining the heat balance in the Earth's evolution, we can see that this planetary body has an exceptional degree of equilibrium, with a balance between intake and output. It is, furthermore, also able up to a point to regulate its intake of external heat energy. The magnitude of the interior heat energy source within this regulation process is negligible. Whilst it is a fact that the Earth has had, for much of its geological history, water on its surface, and that temperatures have ranged within limits capable of sustaining life, it is nonetheless clear that these two energy sources complement each other. This is shown in the illustration, from which it will be seen how much the amount of energy

◁
96 Antarctica is the largest continental glacier on Earth, the biggest reservoir of drinkable water in the world. It is also one of the greatest potential dangers known to Man. The thawing of all or part of the Antarctic glacier due to the greenhouse effect could result in global catastrophe caused by a rise of several metres in world ocean levels.

97 Alternating warm interglacial and very cold glacial periods are also recorded in the soil horizon. Richer, more bountiful and therefore more significant soil horizons originated in warmer periods, while during glacial periods soil generation is very slow and poor. An example from Central Europe shows a relatively poor brown earth (A) with underlying potter's clay. The presence of loess indicates a dry, cold period, a landscape with sparse vegetation and eroded by wind. Horizon B illustrates a poorly developed soil generated during a temperature fluctuation in the glacial period. Soil horizons C, D and E represent warmer interglacial periods.

originating from interior sources has in fact changed.

Chance was undoubtedly a factor in the history of the Earth. Let us pause to consider that for a long time the Earth did not have the kind of atmosphere it has today, that there was no oxygen, only compounds containing oxygen (oxides) and molecular nitrogen. We now know that minute changes in atmospheric composition can and do affect the Earth's heat balance. A reduction or increase in the amount of a certain gas in the atmosphere, e.g. carbon dioxide or methane, can alter it to a significant extcent. Each increase can mean a rise in temperature in the lower atmospheric levels. Nowadays, therefore, we use the term 'gases with a greenhouse effect'. The temperature balance in geological history scarcely seems credible, knowing as we do that the amount of heat produced by the Earth itself has declined considerably. We should therefore ask ourselves the question to what extent the amount of energy reaching the Earth from space has changed, and how it has been heated by the Sun during the course of its long history. Comparable situations known from the evolution of other suns (stars) suggest that at the beginning of the Earth's history the heat output of the Sun was 40 per cent less than it is today. However, the heat output of the Earth and the heat left over after the formation of the planet (known as residual heat) was probably able to compensate for this low solar heat output, and the planet, therefore, did not extinguish. It was evidently during this period that the self-regulating system which exists between the Earth's lithosphere, atmosphere and hydrosphere evolved and eventually settled into a state of equilibrium. It is possible that the greenhouse effect, which is causing many people concern today, in fact played a positive role in geological history.

If we take a look at early geological history, for example

◁
98 The French coast at Mont Saint Michel shows the relation between Earth temperature, glaciation and sea level. The granite knob or 'monadnock' jutting out of the sea is 78 m/256 ft high, the church tower is 80 m/262 ft high. This shows the possible sea level during the thawing of the Antarctic glacier.

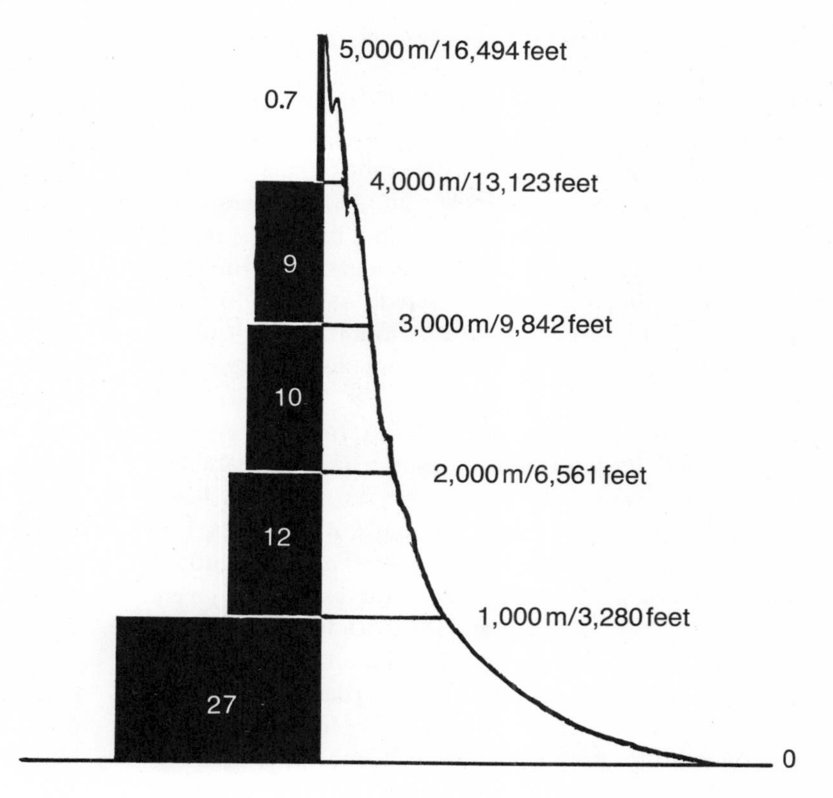

99 The catastrophic consequences of a significant rise in sea level are heightened by the fact that at lower elevations above sea level the population density is substantially more than at higher elevations. The figures on the left represent population density per 1 square km/0.3 square miles, those on the right represent the elevation.

100 Temperature record of a typical sunny summer day in Europe. The curve in the yellow field indicates the overall amount of solar energy occurring on the Earth's surface. The red curve indicates the actual history of air temperature which slightly lags behind the maximum influx of energy.

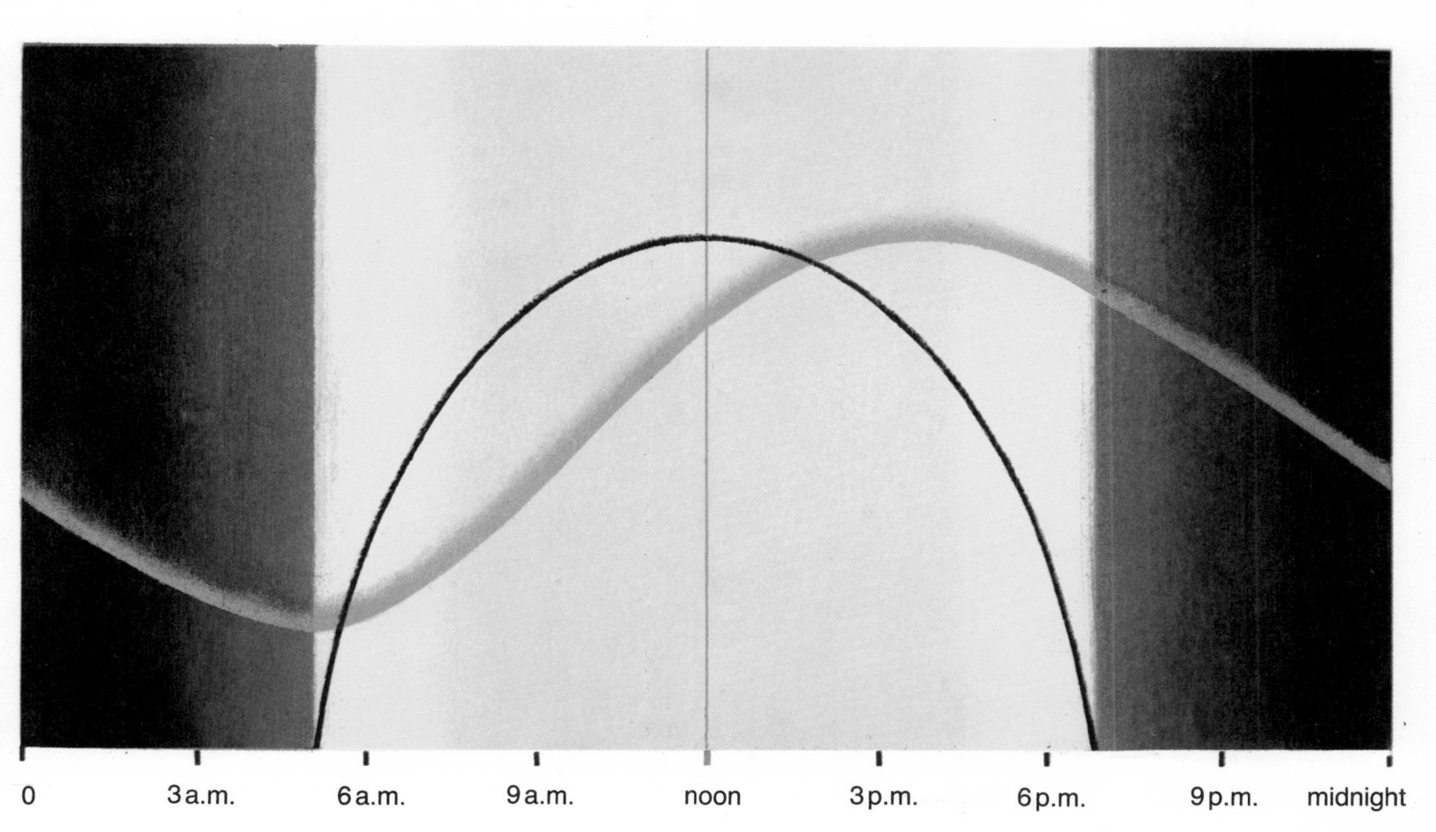

the Mesozoic era, we find only slight deviations in the temperature of seawater from that of today. It is possible that this is also the case for the temperature of the Earth's surface, the oxygen system and the capacity of the planet's organisms to regulate the amount of carbon dioxide. Similar changes may also be observed from briefer time-spans, for example the Quaternary era. It can, therefore, probably be assumed that the Earth, with a certain amount of delay and inertia, reacts to solar activity as well as to periodic deviations from its orbit. Most important of all, however, is the capacity of the planet's organisms to regulate the energy balance.

The intake of energy into certain terrestrial regions, together with its geographical position and the character of subjacent rocks, determine a number of things. They determine the way in which the landscape evolves, the type of landscape into which it evolves, and the kind of ecosystems that will be capable of survival in the given conditions. There are links and feedback between the atmosphere, hydrosphere and lithosphere from which develop certain processes such as the way rocks weather and the formation of certain types of soil — loess, black soil (chernozem), podzol or laterite. Evidence of temporary surpluses or shortages of energy are therefore apparent from changes in landscape type. Where there is a surplus of energy, there is, under favourable conditions, also a surplus production of organic matter, or biomass.

Such timespans have occurred in the geological history of the planet, for example in the Carboniferous period at the end of the Palaeozoic era. Organic surpluses of worldwide geological significance formed in favourable heat conditions: coal reserves formed which could reasonably be termed 'conserved solar energy'. At other times the Earth had to compensate for energy losses, hence those eras in its history which we term 'ice ages', in which glacial regions spread, the average temperature of the oceans dropped and the Earth's energy intake was less than its output. An ice shield formed around the poles, thawing out slowly when there was sufficient energy. The amount of energy needed to thaw ice is considerable, so that glaciers, and large masses of ice in general, serve as an energy barrier against the Earth overheating. In glacial or ice ages such as these, the temperature fell by 5°C/41°F compared with the interglacial ages (such as the age in which we are now living). In such eras, however, not only the temperature, but also the composition of the atmosphere changed. Scientists have provided evidence that in interglacial ages the atmosphere contains over 25 per cent more carbon dioxide and over 100 per cent more methane than in ice ages.

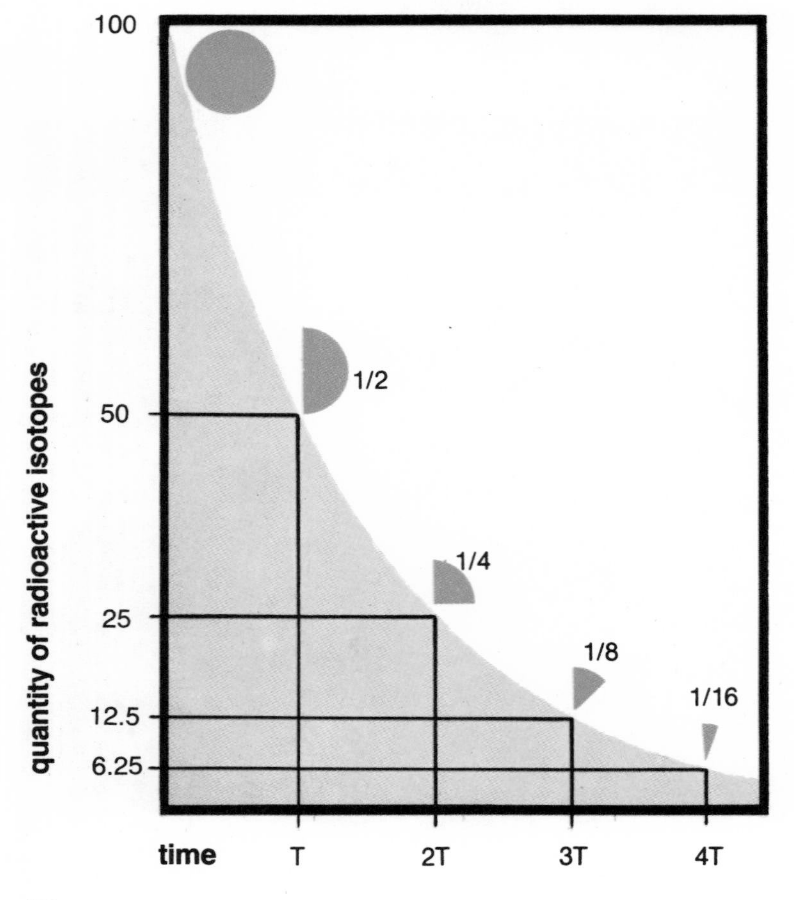

101 Radioactive isotopes are used to measure the ages of rock complexes and, as a consequence, the age of the Earth. The 'half-life' is a period taken for half the atoms of the given radioactive isotope to disintegrate. For this reason information regarding half-life forms the basis of the estimate of rock age. Illustrated here is the half-life of any radioactive isotope. At the same time it shows how the quantity of heat produced by the Earth varies with time. During geological periods not only the number of radioactive elements decrease, but so, too, does the quantity of heat produced by these elements and, consequently, the overall amount of geothermal heat of the planet.

102 Gases such as carbon dioxide and methane, as well as water vapour, markedly influence the climate of the Earth on both global and local scales. In urban areas the greenhouse effect occurs in sunny weather coupled with high air pressure. Poor air circulation causes the temperature to rise and carbon dioxide, water vapour and other gases form a shield which prevents the exchange of air between cold upper strata of the atmosphere and the heavily heated lower stratum.

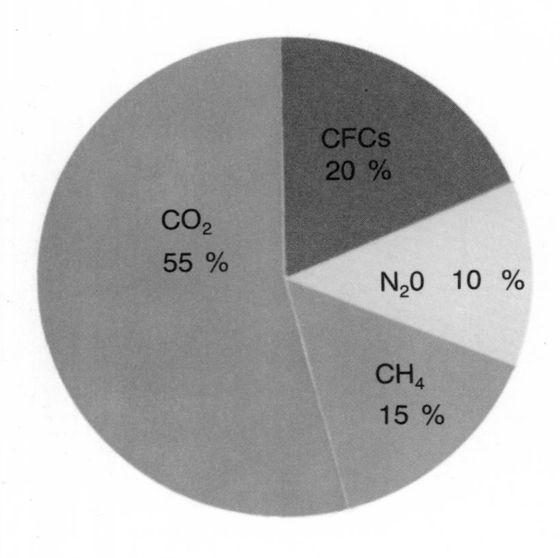

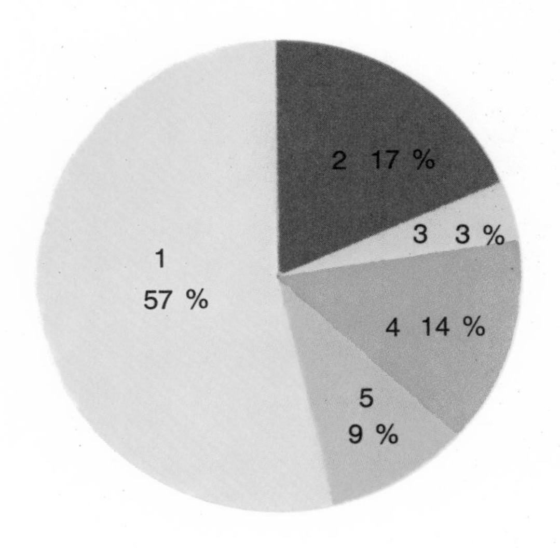

103 Global warming is no more merely a subject of scientific interest. Forecasts are now so alarming that even politicians have begun to take the matter seriously. Before any action is taken it will be necessary to collect large amounts of reliable and specific data on the greenhouse effect while atmospheric gases are still in measurable quantities. There are, however, intermediate estimates made from time to time. The largest percentage is carbon dioxide, followed by chlorofluorocarbons (CFCs), methane and nitrogen oxides.

104 The major portion (57 per cent) of compounds responsible for the greenhouse effect are as a result of power generation (1). The second largest portion comes from normal domestic use. Chlorinated and fluorinated hydrocarbons (2), used as coolants in refrigerators or as compressed gases in aerosol sprays, are responsible for 17 per cent of the temperature increase on Earth. Next in line are agriculture (4), deforestation and changes in land use (5) and industry (3).

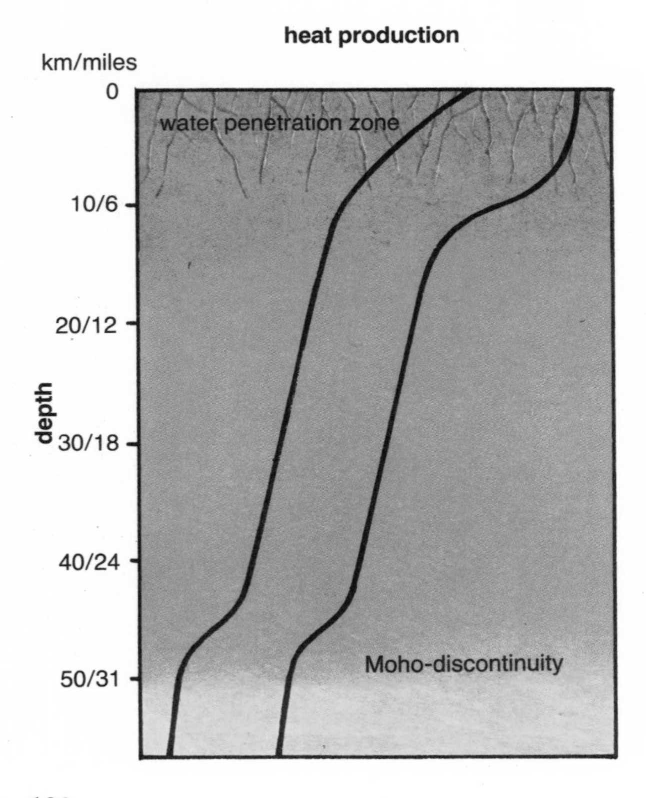

105 Heat escaping from the Earth comes from several different sources. The most significant is from the radioactive, heat-generating elements in the upper part of the Earth's crust. The proportion of these elements contained in the lower part of the crust is somewhat smaller and there is less still in the mantle. The amount of heat produced by each tonne is dependent on the proportion of elements it contains. The way in which heat is transmitted is also very important. In lower zones most of the heat is transmitted by conduction; in upper zones, particularly where surface waters penetrate, most of the heat is transmitted by convection.

The Earth's current energy levels appear to be balanced but this depends on how accurately we interpret the information we are given by Nature. Man has recently begun to intervene into energy systems which previously operated in an automatic, self-regulatory way. He has all too quickly tapped and consumed vast solar energy reserves in the form of coal, crude oil and natural gas. This not only causes atmospheric warming of the environment from the burning of these fossil fuels, it has serious polluting side-effects as well. The amounts of waste discharged and emitted are undoubtedly increasing, and the Earth's atmosphere is now suffering under excess of sulphur, nitrogen and carbon dioxide. Because of pollution many areas of the world are becoming too dangerous for man or animals to live. Cities are choking on exhaust fumes and sea birds are dying as a result of huge oil spills. The latter may not be as a result of burning the fuel, but it is, nevertheless, a direct result of our desire to make use of it. Only comparatively recently scientists believed additional carbon dioxide in the atmosphere to be harmless, arguing that it is consumed from the atmosphere by plants during the process of photosynthesis. There was, apparently, a thousand times more of it in the primordial atmosphere than there is today. It was only in 1957 that two American scientists R. Revelle and H. E. Suess drew attention to the fact that through the emission of carbon dioxide in Nature, man was conducting an experiment that could have grave consequences. The current level is 25 per cent higher than is normal in interglacial periods — the situation is serious.

In recent decades it has become all too obvious that the world's energy resources are finite. There is no straightforward answer to this problem, although nowadays we are all aware that it will be necessary to find alternative forms of energy. Of course any such forms of energy should, ideally, be non-pollutant; our planet cannot stand any more punishment. Perhaps we should learn to take our clues from the Earth itself, adapting natural energy forms to our own design. Perhaps if we learn to listen, we will hear.

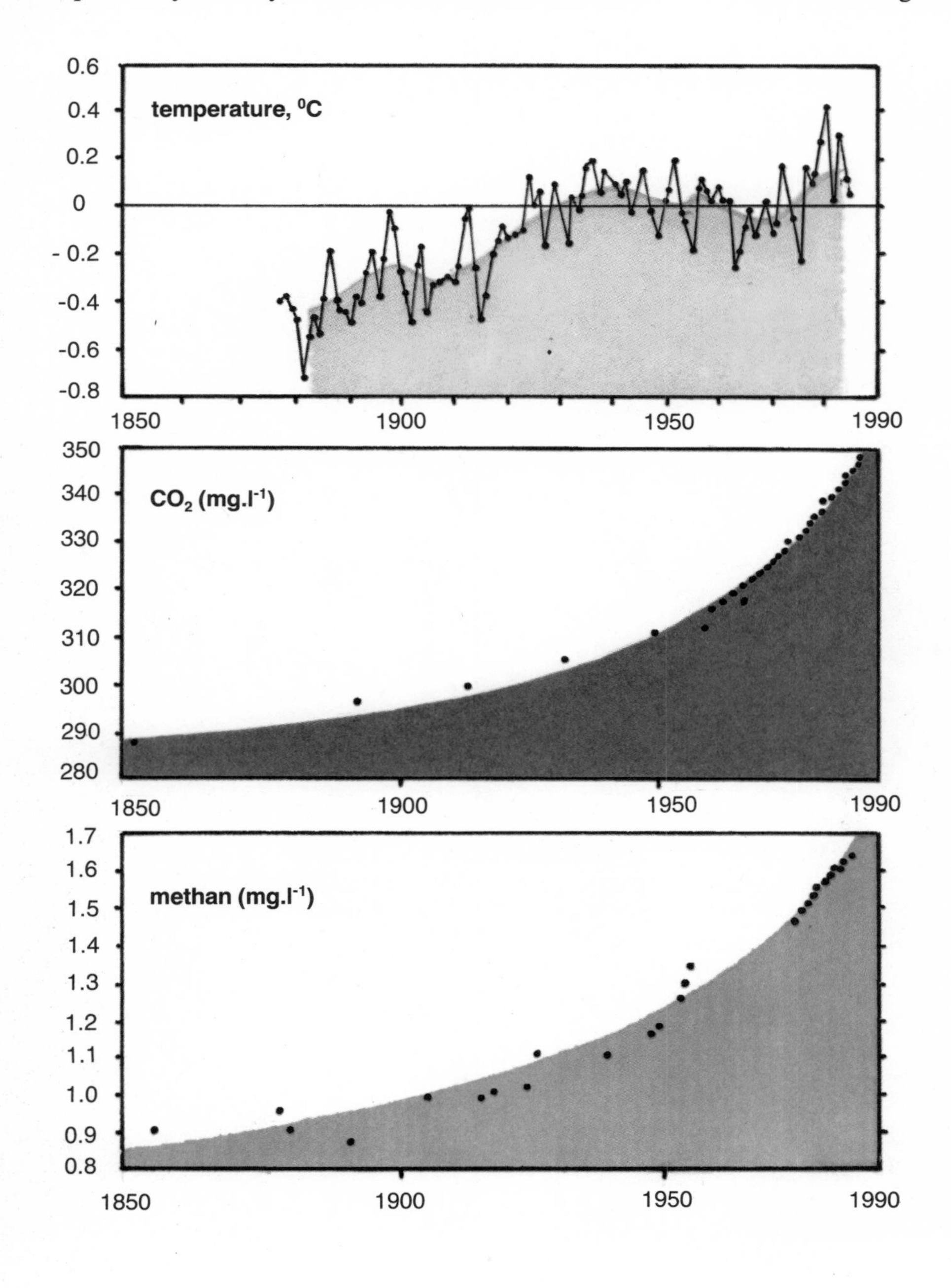

106 Three warning pictures: carbon dioxide and methane which have a marked greenhouse effect on the atmosphere are increasing. Also the mean temperature on the Earth is increasing, although not markedly. This is either a true global evaluation indicative of change which has taken place throughout the entire history of the Earth, or it is an indication of the fact that our measurements cover only a very short and so far unrepresentative period of time. The second possibility would be more preferable; however, scientists are of the opinion that it is high time to ring the alarm bells.

CYCLES

107 The principal steps of Hutton's rock cycles comprise: erosion, transport, sedimentation, diagenesis, metamorphosis, magmatic activity and uplift. In denuded rocks this cycle begins again with erosion. The picture presents this rock cycle in simplified form. The weathering of the volcanic cone and the spectacularly moulded sandstone valley in the upper part of the picture both represent erosion, the ravines on the volcano slopes are transport routes. In the lower part of the picture the rocks settle, bend, and are pressed into the deep parts, where they undergo metamorphosis or melting. On the surface they often appear in the form of lava. The whole cycle may take billions of years. The cyclic character of the process may be observed on every part of the Earth. Often only certain parts of the cycle can be observed, such as sedimentation or magmatic activity. The questions, What makes such a cycle run? How do the rocks from the Earth's surface get to its centre? Where are they melted or metamorphosed?, are the most fundamental questions of geology. In the past it was thought the answers lay in the geosynclines — long, deep basins in which many rocks are deposited. The weight of these rocks and of the material lying above them along with the effects of horizontal forces cause these rocks to be pushed deep down into the Earth; from here they are later uplifted to form folding mountain ranges (see Fig. 111). In the past thirty years, however, the theory of horizontally moving lithospheric plates has prevailed, the mutual interaction of which pushes the rocks far into the Earth. Thus we can see that older, more accepted theories have acquired a newer, simpler, and therefore perhaps also more acceptable interpretation.

A glance at an overflowing river, a seething ocean or the wind bearing tiny grains of dust should leave us in no doubt that erosion is one of the most powerful factors in geology. If we add to this list the effects of glaciers, green plants and the effects of chemicals such as carbon dioxide in rainwater, we can then form a picture of erosion damage. Most of the material from solid rock that is released in this way ends in the sea in the form of fine sand, clay, mud or dissolved substances. The salt content in seawater comes from land masses alone, and theoretically through the evaporation of the sea this salt, over millions of years, should become more concentrated and dense. However, leaving aside exceptions such as the Red Sea and the Mediterranean, which both have a higher salt content than the world's major oceans, the concentration of substances dissolved in seawater has remained constant throughout all these eras. This has been proved both by isotopic studies and the observations of palaeontologists. Since, therefore, there is a constant runoff into the oceans of materials dissolved in the waters of streams and rivers, there must be some mechanism whereby this excess salt is elim-

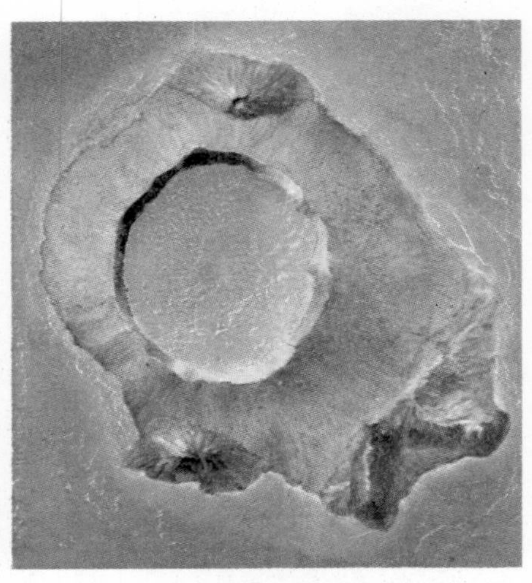

1.6—1.0 million years ago

1 million—100 thousand years ago

100 thousand years ago

inated from the oceans. If such a mechanism did not exist, there would be no salt deposits on the land masses. Just as chlorine and sodium ions are removed from seawater, so are other ions such as magnesium, calcium, potassium, iodine, bromide, iron and phosphorus. This means that all these ions remain in seawater for a limited time; this is known as residence time.

The amount of material borne by rivers and carried to the oceans is vast. Sedimentologists and geochemists have calculated the amount of such material for the last 600 million years on the basis of the amount of sedimentary rock there is. If such a runoff rate were to continue for a long period, all the high mountains, mountain ranges, highlands, and even lowlands, would be swept into the oceans. In 1.6 billion years the land masses would cease to exist. In Greenland, however, geologists have discovered rocks that are 3.8 billion years old, while rocks in Canada and southern Africa are of similar age. Those in the Brazilian shield are only slightly younger. This seems to indicate that the land mass crust has been in existence for a long time, at least 4 billion years. If we are to follow the erosion theory, this would mean that the continents have been in existence for nearly twice as long as they should have been. Several explanations suggest themselves as a solution to this paradox. The speed of erosion may not have been as great in the past as it is now. This is highly unlikely, however, since the geological structure of older formations would appear to indicate that mountain ranges were at least as high, if not higher, in the past, and the sedimentary basins were of the same depth. The conditions for erosion determined by the altitude differential, therefore, were either the same, or even more favourable. It may also be assumed that the continents were much larger, therefore taking longer to erode. From observation of the small amounts of sediment on the ocean bottom, as well as of the structure and composition of mountain belts, we may arrive at the conclusion that the continents are still being formed and are, in fact, extending.

The term 'extending', however, should not be taken too literally. The mere process of the recycling of rocks which has already been described in previous chapters could be seen to explain this problem — and yet even on this point there is not unequivocal agreement among researchers. It is in fact one of the fundamental 'vexed questions' of geology.

One hypothesis rests on the idea that in the beginning, when the Earth was separating into its various layers, and the core and mantle were forming, the crust also formed. Its size has neither increased nor decreased since that time, thus remaining the same and recycling within the rock cycle of orogenesis (the formation of mountains) — weathering — erosion — sedimentation — anatexis (melting) — metamorphosis — orogenesis. In this first stage of the 'Earth's major differentiation', the hydrosphere and atmosphere also formed. Let us deal with the atmosphere first. For the process of abrupt emission of gases from inside the planet, scientists use the somewhat vulgar term 'big burp'. This 'burping' of the Earth, however, is actually accompanied by the release of a large amount of material. It would appear to be a simple mechanism, which solves the problem both of the formation of the atmosphere and of the continental crust. However, observations made in the study of radiogenic isotopes in particular tend to refute rather than support this hypothesis. Studying the gases in volcanic eruptions or in deep fault regions, we ascertain that many of them originate from the mantle and never, in fact, formed part of the atmosphere. For example, it is known that the isotopic composition of helium in the Earth's atmosphere results from the interaction of cosmic rays with atmospheric helium. Helium escaping from the mantle, on the other hand, has an entirely different composition and ratio. We are therefore able to measure how much of the Earth's helium emissions have been recycled from the exisiting atmosphere and how much originates from the mantle itself. Moreover, since helium from the mantle occurs most frequently in the vicinity of great faults or heavy volcanic activity it can be taken as proof that the upper mantle is still emitting gases into the atmosphere. The fact that the existing atmosphere is augmented by new gases may be an indi-

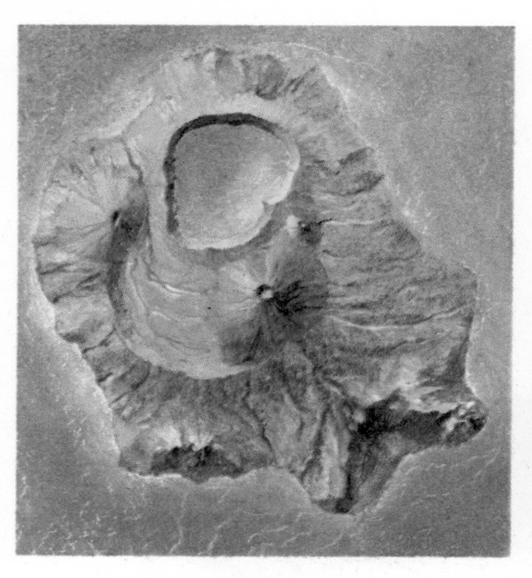

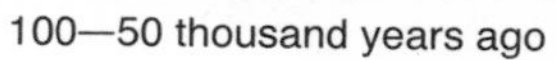

100—50 thousand years ago

50—18 thousand years ago

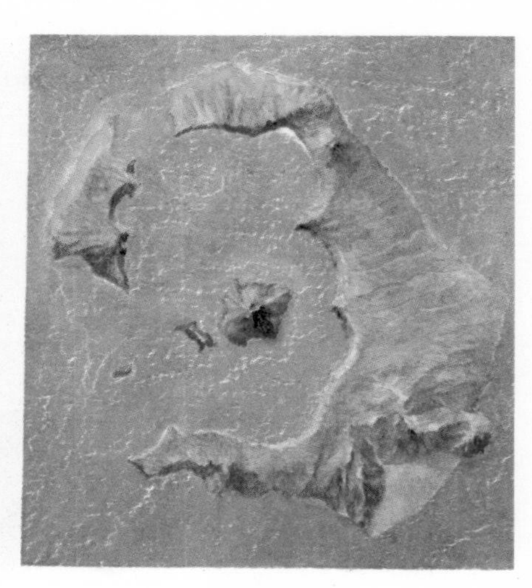

present

◁
108, 109 The development of the Earth's surface is particularly volatile in areas where various sources of energy come together. This example, the Santorini volcano in the Aegean Sea, is illustrated by a series of pictures. It is a testimony to the fact that the growth of a volcano is not always the result of accretion. The destruction of this volcano and, simultaneously, the whole island was caused by external factors — erosion coupled with an enormous eruption. A new volcanic cone appeared between 1707 and 1950.

110 Erosion plays a significant part in carving the face of our planet. It is caused by climatic conditions. The effects of erosion are immediately apparent, particularly in areas characterized by large morphological differences, such as that illustrated, where a volcano protrudes from the sea. The picture could be considered a continuation of the preceding illustrations of the Santorini volcano in the Aegean Sea. A few thousand years are enough to turn a freshly formed young cone into a wrinkled old cone.

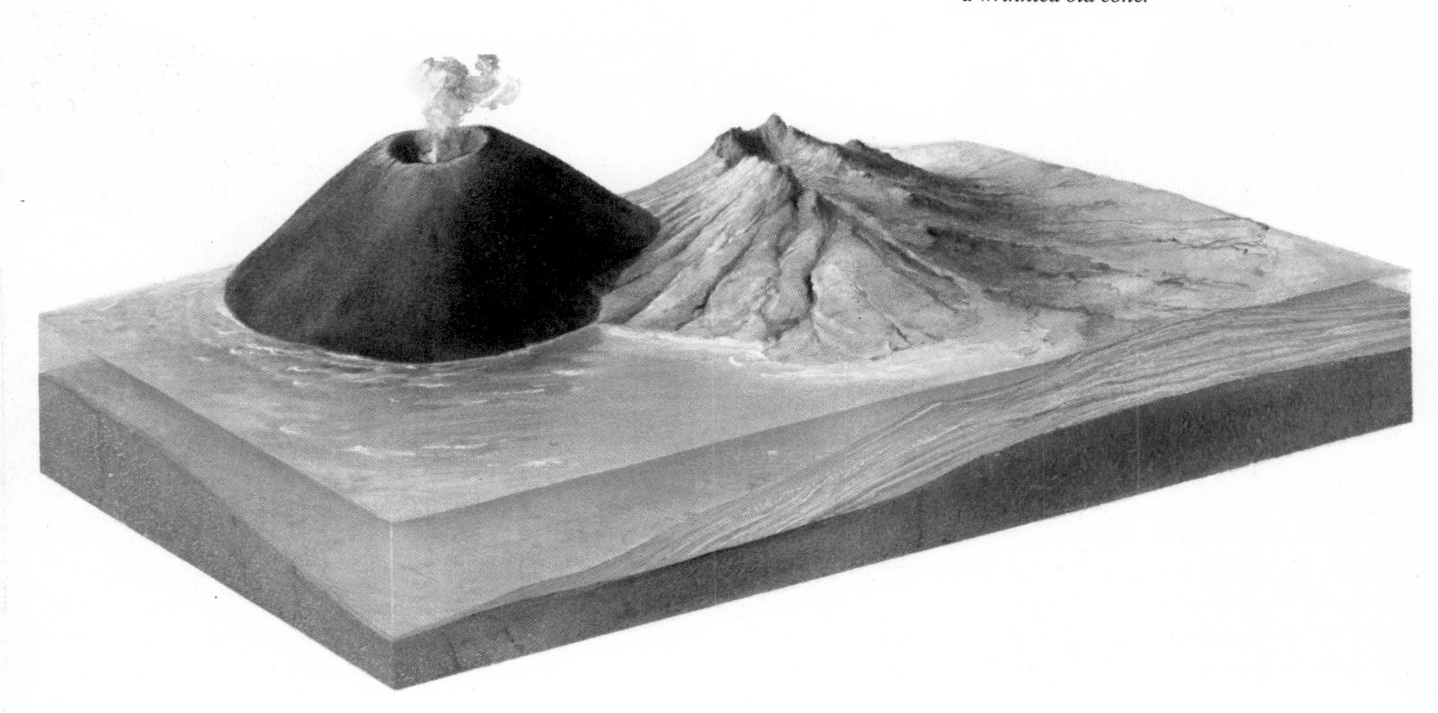

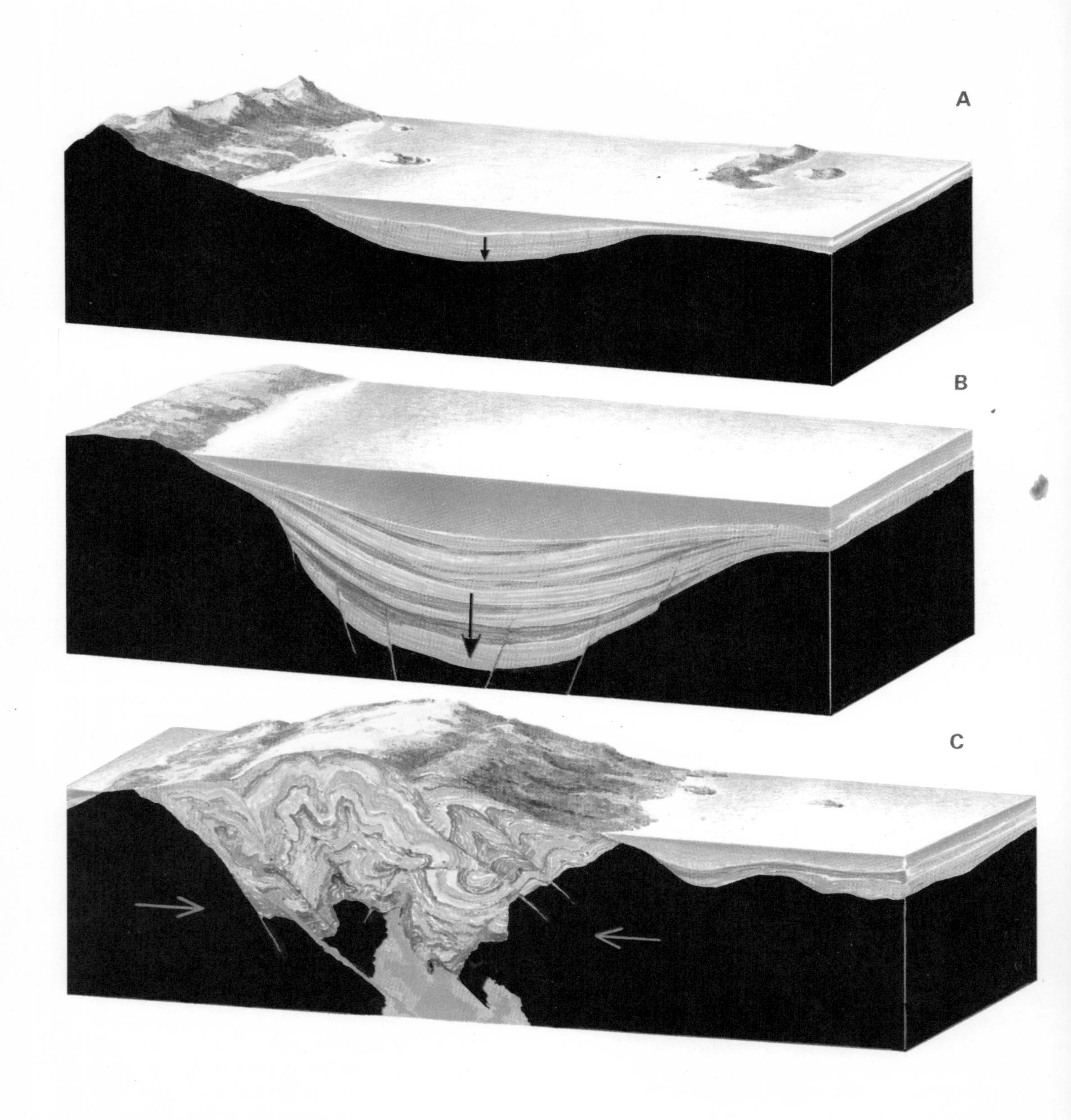

111 The three main stages in the formation of a folded mountain chain according to the hypothesis of geosynclinical development of the Earth's crust. The first picture shows erosion and sedimentation in a relatively shallow basin. In the second the mountains are eroded, but the basin is becoming deeper. In the third picture the layers of rock have been 'folded' and shallow seas have formed.

112 In the tectonic process of obduction the 'heavier' oceanic plate (green tones) slides over the continental plate (red). It is a process characteristic of active geological margins, and is the opposite of the process of subduction. As a result of obduction geologists are able to find on dry land complete sections of rock which originated on the ocean floor. The ocean floor consists of peridotite in its lower part, on top of which there are gabbroes, covered by a layer of basalt with a thin stratum of sedimentary rocks on top. Ocean floor obduction is considered a process of continental crust accretion, similar to the accumulation of sedimentary rocks and volcanic activity in island archipelagoes.

cation that even continents can grow — not only through the recycling of rocks, but also by the upper mantle providing them with new 'portions' of continental crust.

Scientists have made repeated attempts to explain how the continental crust grows, from the observation that cosmic material assists in the process, as it did when the Earth was first forming. The Earth, they say, formed from falling meteorites. Nowadays, however, only a small number of meteorites fall to the Earth — certainly not enough to enlarge the Earth by any noticeable amount. Moreover, the composition of the material they contain differs considerably from that of the continental crust.

It will be necessary to look elsewhere, therefore, for an explanation of how the continental crust grows. It was a great surprise to Renaissance scientists to discover the fossilized remains of ancient sea creatures in rocks found in the Alps and the Carpathians. It can be assumed, therefore, that there are forces in the Earth which uplift the ocean bed, together with pieces of already existing continents, and in the process massive mountain ranges form. This mountain-building process, known as 'orogenesis', has been known to geologists for many years. It is one of the most basic geological processes, and yet scientists have modified their explanation of it many times. Most researchers today believe that orogenesis results from a collision between two, usually continental, lithospheric plates. This theory, however, assumes that the process is cyclical, whereby rock is dispersed by weathering, swept by rivers into the sea, forms sediment and then forms mountains in the mountain-building process. Then the whole cycle begins again — weathering, sedimentation, orogenesis. Some process of this kind was assumed to exist by scientists in the last century. They even formed a theory to show how weathered rocks made their way to the deeper parts of the terrestrial crust, where they melted down and eventually erupted back onto the surface. This is the well-known 'Hutton's' or 'rock' cycle.

Geochemists have come to the conclusion that the continental crust recycles, but a proportion of primary matter originating from the mantle can be detected in rocks. This means that the upper mantle feeds not only the atmosphere, but also the hydrosphere and the continental crust. This is a feasible concept, since growth can also be observed in rocks from the geological past. This is depicted on geological world maps where it can be seen that progressively younger orogenic belts occur around continental cores. By looking at the illustration of North America, it is easy to picture the actual growth.

Modern geochemists, equipped with sensitive instruments, are able to determine the ratios of recycled to new material. Armed with this information it is possible to determine the true amount of 'growth' as opposed to a change of state.

Similarly, examination of the properties and composition of igneous rocks from the terrestrial crust allow us to look at links between the 'used' and 'new' material involved in their construction. Rocks from mid-ocean ridges appear to come from the upper mantle, being largely of 'primary' origin. This cannot be said of all rocks in the archipelagoes, where there is evidence of a small proportion of used material, and in some places the proportion of recycled material is considerable. This is even more true of rocks from the continental periphery, which consist predominantly of material which has already undergone the sedimentary cycle, that is weathering, erosion and sedimentation, one or more times.

Processes on the terrestrial surface leave such distinctive traces in rock material that these do not disappear even after melting. Geochemists, trying to work out how the mantle originated, find in the course of their detective work mantle rocks lacking in certain components. These have gone to form the continental crust. In this case the

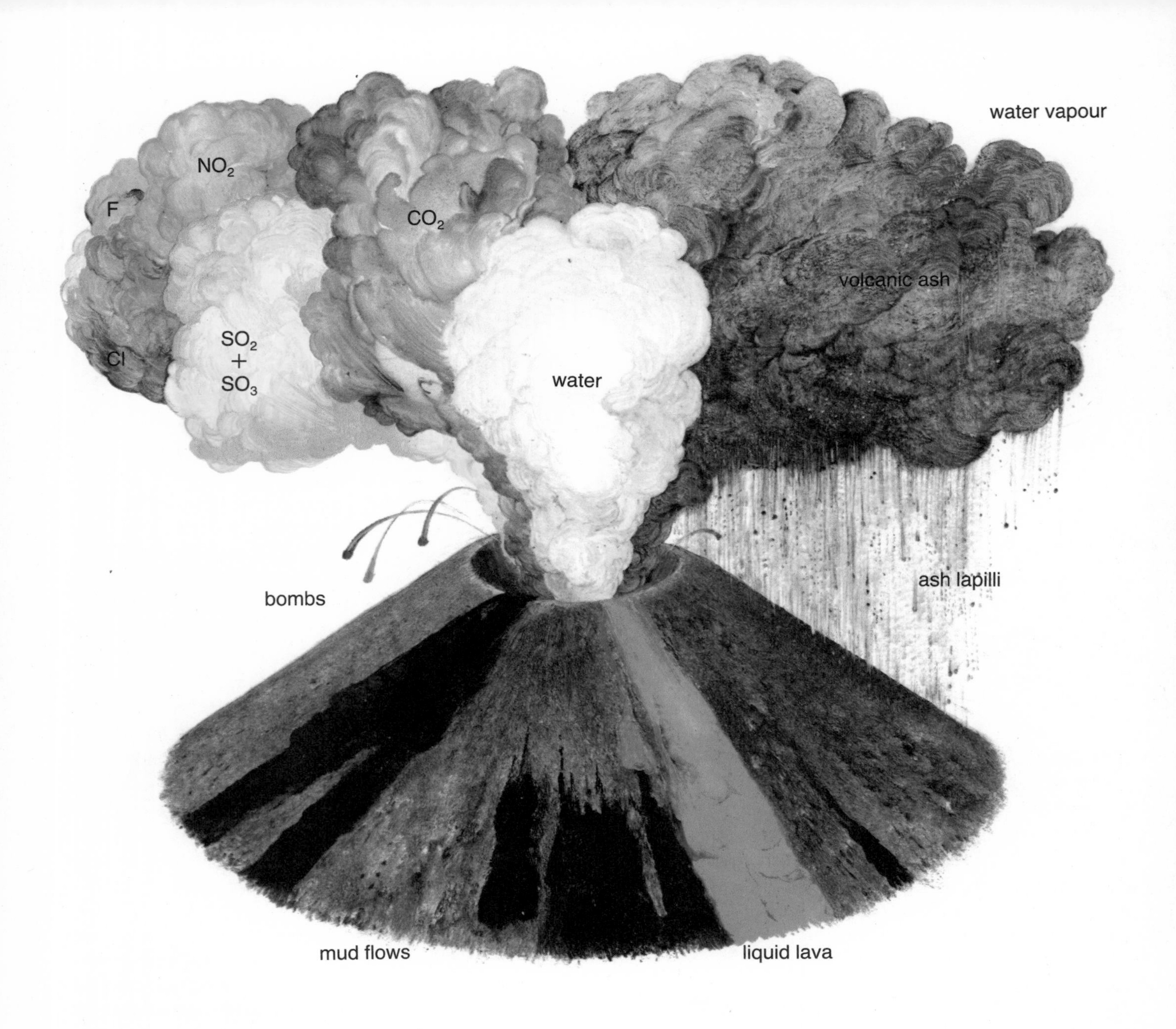

113 Magmatic activity (represented by the volcano in the picture) is the chief agent and means of transporting various components involved in the formation of the Earth's different layers. Lava and volcanic ash, which help form the new lithosphere, water (the future component of the hydrosphere) and gases (the future components of the atmosphere) are produced; all these factors contribute to the growth of the planet.

mantle is said to be impoverished or depleted, unlike fertile mantle material, which, through melting, is still able to contribute to continental growth. Geologists did once hold the view that depletion of the mantle occurred mainly under continents. However nowadays, through the observation of convection flow, it is known that this is only true of a small part of the mantle which, together with the crust, forms the solid, rigid lithosphere.

Now that we have had a general, overall look at the continental crust, we shall move on to look at one of the most commonplace crustal components which, unlike sandstone and other rocks, is mobile: water.

The sight of the Earth from space has earned it the title of the Blue Planet. The Earth is exceptional in comparison with other planets for the presence of an entire layer of surface water, known as the hydrosphere. Like the continental crust, however, the hydrosphere is also a result of geological evolution, having come about through a release

114 In areas where active endogenic geological processes are 'complete', geologists try to decipher the sequence of continental crust accretion. In this section of the Eurasian plate the crust formation was brought about not only through geological processes which took place over two and a half billion years ago, but also by processes only a few dozen million years old; even now, these are slowly fading away. In geology the process of accretion includes not only the increased volume of the continental crust, but also volcanic activity, collision of enormous continental masses and the repeated periods of weathering, sedimentation, folding and metamorphoses.

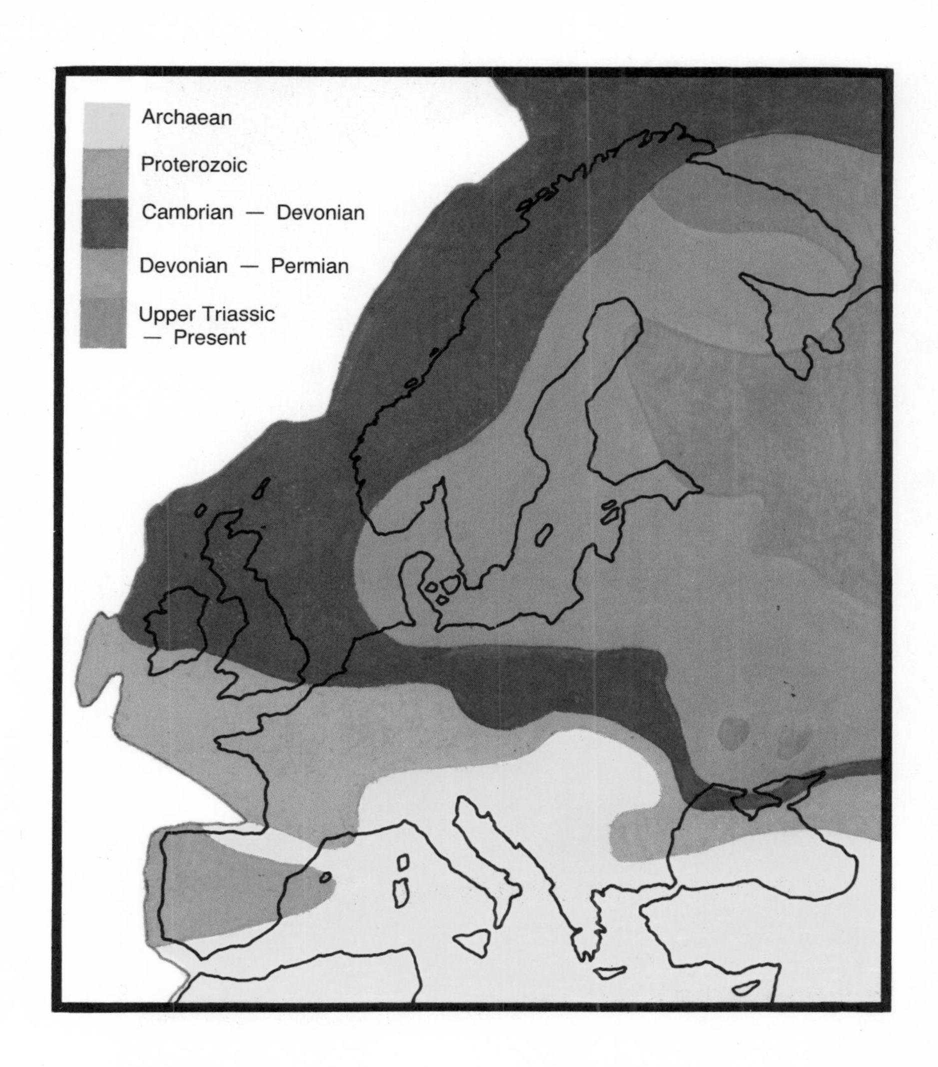

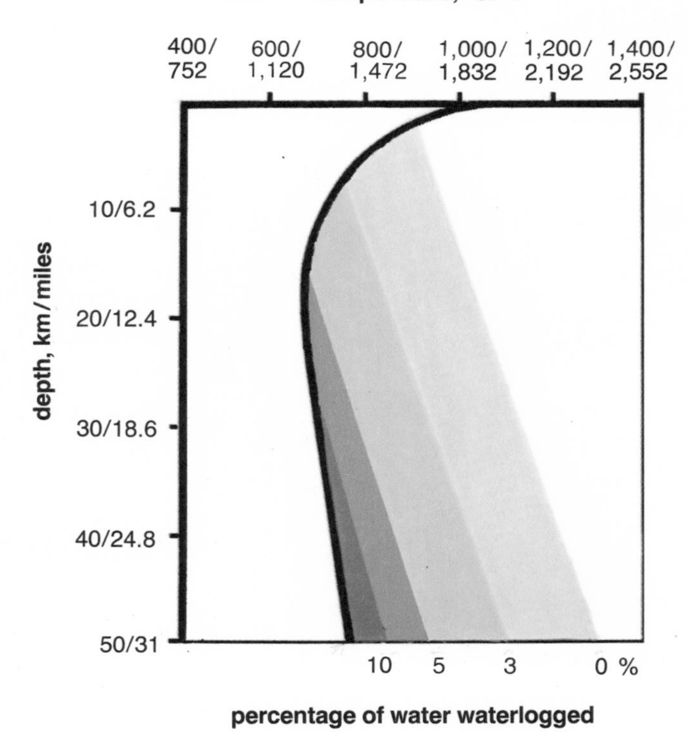

of gases from the mantle. The hydrosphere has been retained as a result of gravity. If the Earth were smaller, its gravitational force would not be sufficient to enable the Earth to retain its water. We have already seen how the continental crust grows by using both secondary and primary raw materials. The same applies to water. Water is recycled not only within the small water cycle — rain, infiltration, river, sea, evaporation — but also by penetrating the deep surface cycle. In this way there are two types of

115 The presence of water trapped deep underground, at great pressure, reduces the temperature of rocks at the beginning of melting. Geologists speak of 'wet' melting, i.e. melting in the presence of water, or 'dry' melting, where water is totally absent or present only in negligible quantities. The temperature of granite at the beginning of melting is reduced by between 300 and 500°C/672 and 932°F by the presence of water, that is, from 1,200 to 700°C/2,224 to 1,292°F. It is a small miracle of energy. Here we see how the melting point of granite changes according to the amount of water present and the depth at which it is located. Problems occur when the water-rich magma reaches the surface or when it crystallizes at depth and the accompanying water cannot be accommodated in the crystalline structure of the minerals. Sometimes water is forced from the depths of the Earth under such great pressure that it can cause an eruption. Many volcanic eruptions, particularly the dangerous ones, are actually powered by steam and gases released from the magma.

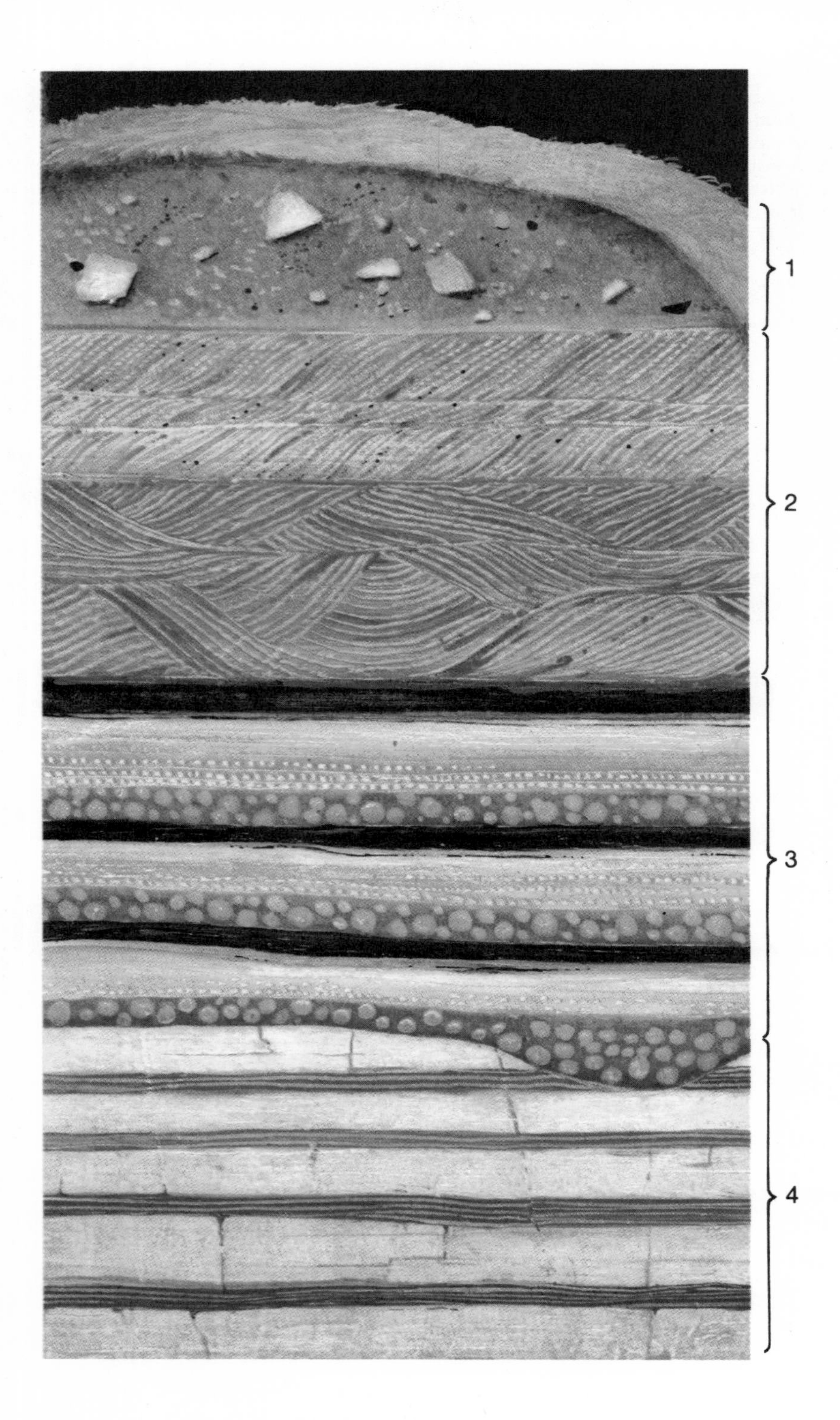

116 Sedimentary rocks clearly indicate changes in the land surface from millions of years ago; they even show changes in weather, seasons and climate. A section of sedimentary rock shows glacial deposits (tillites) in its upper layer; they are unclassified, sharp-edged chips alternating with fine-particled material (1) which indicate that wind and water did not take part in the sedimentation of this rock. Below the tillites there are slanting and crossing sandstone strata (2), which may have originated in an environment of alternating streams of water. Below these deposits there are regularly alternating groups of gravel beds, coarse at the base, alternating with finer gravels, sand and last, very fine-particle deposits combined with a proportion of organic components (3). The way in which these sediments appear to cut into the bedrock indicates that they are the remnants of a river where flood water alternated (perhaps seasonally) with mild flow; the lowermost strata of rocks (4) is similar. Regular layers of sedimentation — alternating coarse and fine-particle strata — suggests seasonal variations, perhaps even connected with change in solar activity and alternating conditions on Earth.

117 The water cycle: evaporated continental or sea water or water released by magma crystallization travels through the atmosphere in the form of vapour, forms clouds and finally falls to the surface of the Earth in the form of rain. Here it evaporates again, flows through permeable rocks and away in water courses or soaks deep into the ground, where it seeps. The surface water thus becomes ground water. The activating forces in the water cycle are solar energy, gravity and geothermal heat. Neither the amount of water reaching the sea as ground water, nor that travelling through the underground hydrothermal systems, i.e. heated ground water, have been estimated accurately so far (red arrows), because outflows to the ocean floor were discovered only recently. It is also difficult to determine how much water has already been through the water cycle, and how much is coming into it for the first time. The figures in the picture illustrate that the quantity of rainwater falling on to the oceans is only slightly lower than that which evaporates from them. The cycle volume may be expressed in millimetres per year (as in the picture) or in units used to convey description of enormous quantities of matter — tens of thousands of cubic kilometres per year.

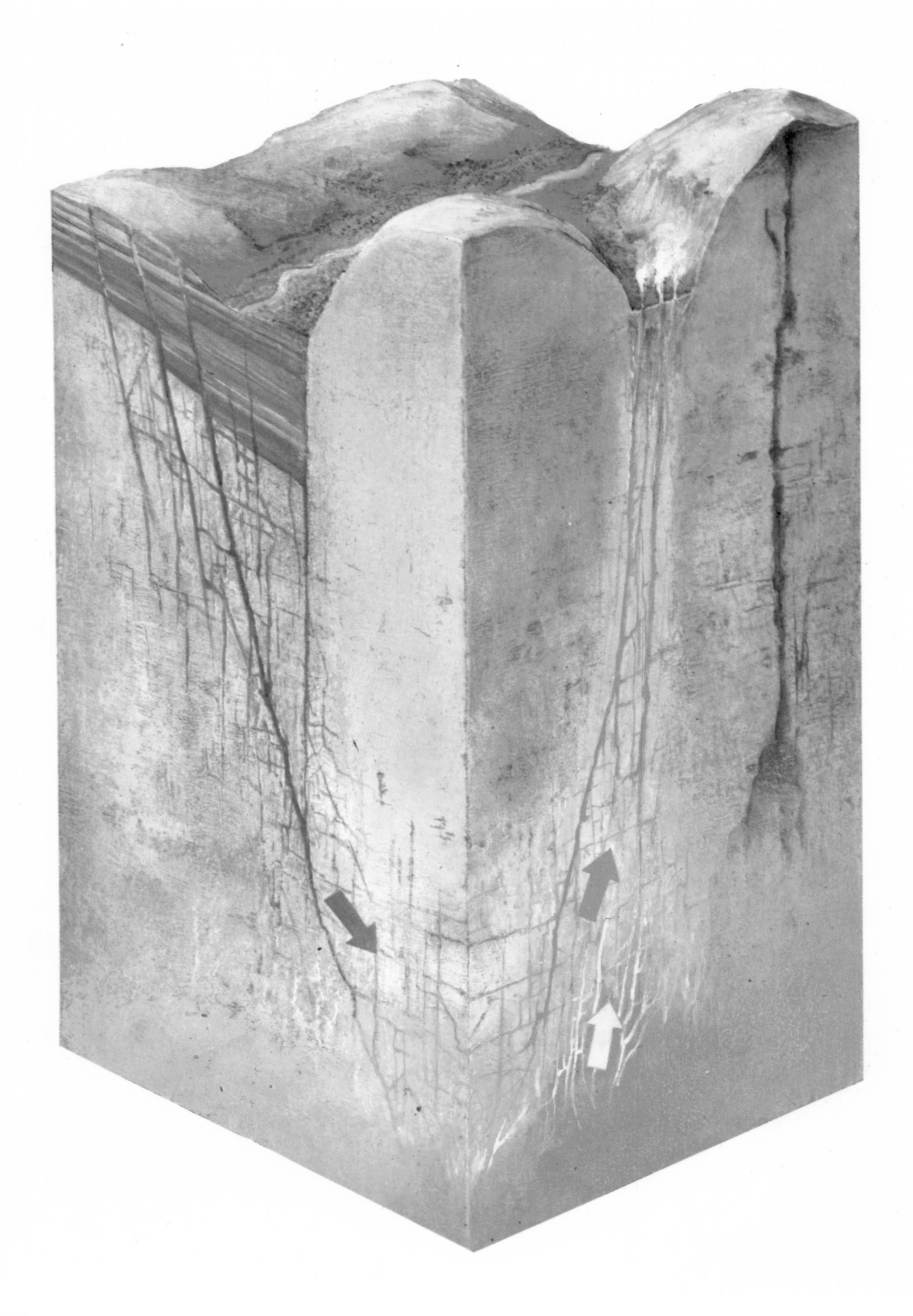

◁
118 Hot springs occur relatively frequently on the Earth's surface. Often they have a high content of dissolved mineral substances. Most hot springs contain ordinary rain water which has been heated deep in the Earth. From the fluvial plain, rich in water and waterlogged sedimentary rocks, water seeps deeper into the Earth, where it is warmed. During its ascent to the surface it washes out and takes with it many different types of minerals, may even be saturated with gas, and flows out on to the surface in the form of hot springs.

119 Carbon, the element most essential for all life on our planet, occurs in nature in two principal forms: that of carbon dioxide and that of organic carbon. Carbon dioxide is present in the atmosphere in relatively small concentrations, but a considerable quantity of this compound can also be found in the waters of the oceans — approximately one hundred times as much as in the atmosphere. Carbon dioxide is also found in carbonaceous rocks (chiefly in limestone), animal shells and fossil fuels. Carbon moves in nature with relative ease; in the biosphere as the result of biochemical oxidation and reduction of solids and gases (and vice versa). Also the exchange of carbon dioxide between the atmosphere and the ocean is very fast. Man contributes to this cycle with 5 billion tonnes of carbon in the form of carbon dioxide every year by the combustion of fossil fuels, and with another billion tonnes through deforestation. It is almost absurd that the element which is most needed for life causes the biggest problem at present, i.e. the global warming of the planet. Carbon dioxide, whose ratio in the Earth's atmosphere has been increasing since the industrial revolution at the rate of 1.5 PaAS per million per year, produces a strong greenhouse effect.

water on the surface: water which has been bound into the terrestrial mantle since the Earth formed, and water which has already participated in the surface cycle. It is therefore probable that even the amount of water on the Earth's surface is 'growing'.

Since the time water first appeared on the Earth, which was around 3.8 billion years ago, it has become an important agent in most geological processes. The Earth's water surface acts as one huge planetary thermostat. It serves to prevent the Earth becoming either too hot or too cold. No water on the surface of the Earth would mean the end of evolution — just look at Mars or Venus!

It may seem that there is no cause for concern. After all, the water in the crust is completed by that from the mantle. Nowadays, however, there is hardly any untouched water on Earth. It exists only in abandoned places and below the surface of the Earth, but most water has already been adversely affected by human activity. It is through water that Man affects the rock formation cycle and the internal workings of the Earth. The amount of material borne by water into the seas and oceans, and changes in the composition of seawater and rain, is altering the established behaviour of chemical elements in the lithosphere. Take, for example, aluminium, which was until recently a subject of indifference to geochemists. They had not even bothered to study its cycles. In the course of the weathering of rock

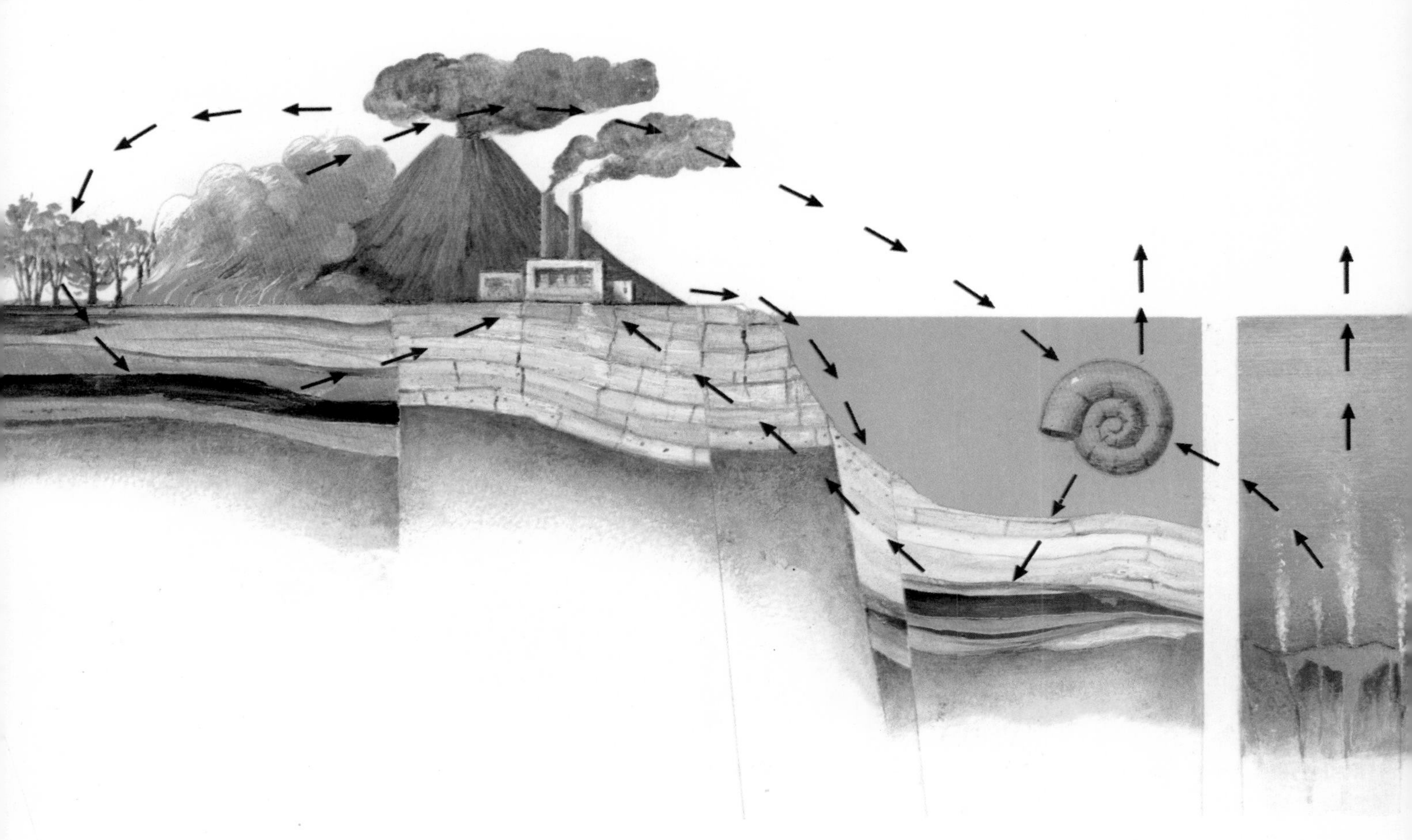

120 The oxygen cycle is so complicated and so little understood that it is almost impossible to illustrate in only one picture. The role of oxygen in animate nature and in geological processes is not limited merely to oxidation and reduction, but includes much more complex processes, such as photosynthesis, respiration, and metamorphous reactions between minerals. Weathering of minerals in nature uses oxygen, but the reduction in the deposition of organic matter and the oxygen originating during photosynthesis make up for this loss. Measuring the amounts of oxygen used in any of these processes is difficult in the present state of knowledge. Similarly, it is not possible at this point to state categorically that the oxygen balance is becoming more precarious from the burning of fossil fuels, which consumes enormous quantities of oxygen.

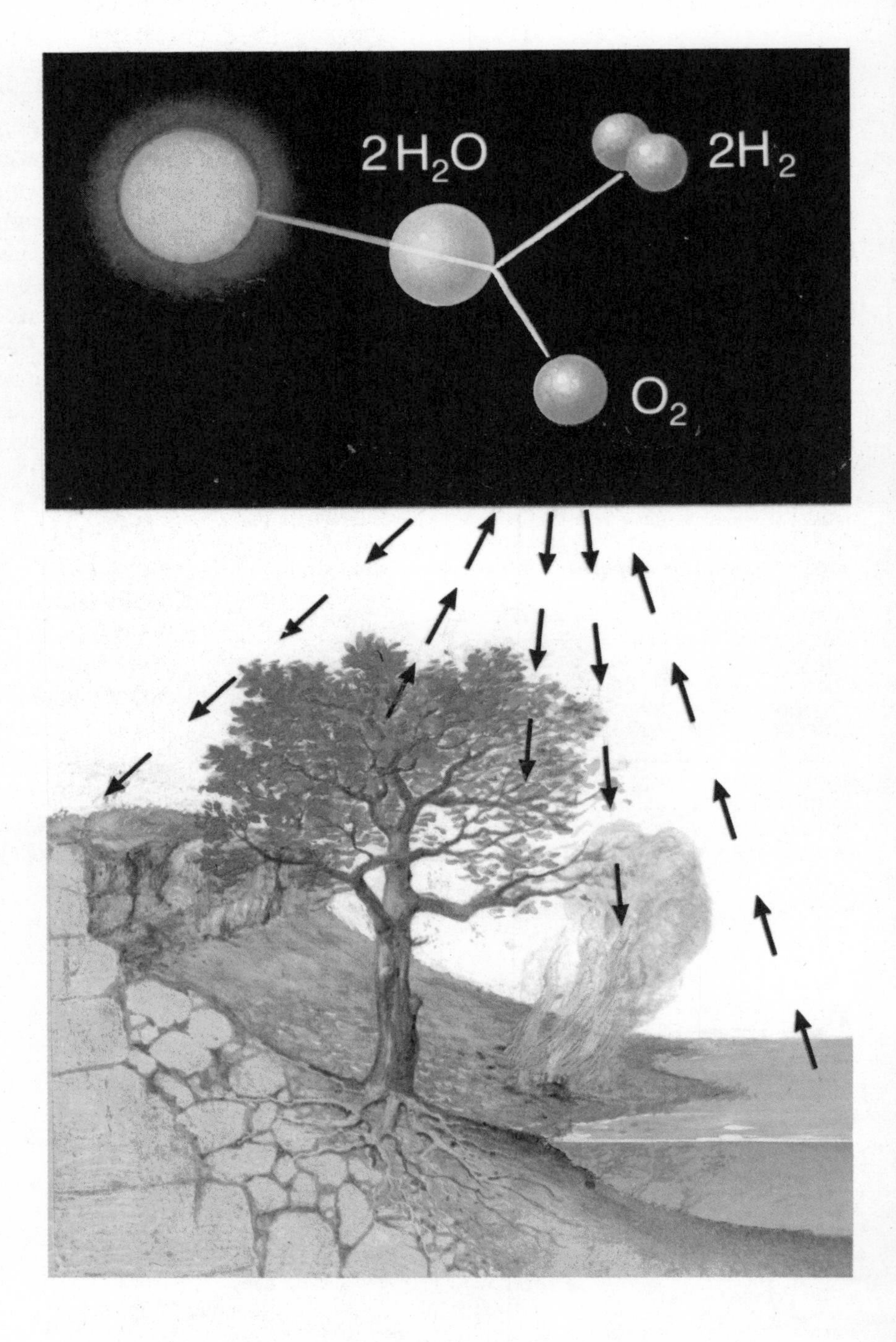

▷
121 The principal source of phosphorus is rocks containing phosphates. The most significant phosphate mineral is apatite. Rock weathering releases phosphorus into animate nature, particularly into the sea and the skeletons of its organisms. Phosphorus is a very effective plant food. For this reason people use it in considerable quantities. It is the only biogenic element which will be short in supply in its natural form in the future. Deposits of raw minerals used in the manufacture of phosphate fertilizers are being used up at a rate similar to that of fossil fuels. However, phosphate fertilizers, used so much in agriculture, are easily washed away; more than 50 per cent of phosphorus is washed into the sea without ever having fulfilled its use as a fertilizer. There are no natural cycles able to take on board the enormous quantities of phosphorus used in agriculture. (The capacity of animals to use phosphorus in the construction of their skeletons is limited.) Therefore, most of the phosphorus is ending up at the bottom of the sea, with only a very small quantity returning to the land, by way of birds' droppings, or 'guano'. For these reasons the passage of phosphorus in nature is down a 'one-way street'. We can hardly speak about its short-term cycle, although it is possible that after hundreds of years it will return to its place in the soil.

and minerals, aluminium remains 'in situ', whereas other components are carried away — or at least that is how it was in the past. The geological present has seen the advent of 'acid rain'. This has the effect of altering the way aluminium, bound in sandstone and other rocks in the form of oxides, behaves compared with its previous lengthy geological history: it becomes soluble through the action of acid rain, and in this form is poisonous to living lungs. Admittedly this is a simplified example, not described in complete detail, and it may prove merely to be a passing phenomenon. Nevertheless, if a river or stream is polluted by aluminium, it does have an effect: the fish die.

There are many such examples of changes brought about by Man. It is no great pleasure to leaf through specialist magazines concerned with chemical elements in the lithosphere, atmosphere and hydrosphere. The amount of lead, for example, moving 'unhindered' through the lithosphere as a result of human activity is eighteen times higher than natural flows. Cadmium is five times higher and zinc three times higher. All these metals are highly toxic.

So far we have dealt with apparently simple processes, such as how one of the simplest compounds, water, behaves on the Earth's surface and how it is involved in geological processes. Understanding the cycle and activities of water, however, can help us to understand the behaviour and movement both of chemical elements and of compounds in which elements of biosphere and lithosphere are recycled, above all by the interaction between animate and inanimate Nature.

The carrying capacity of water and its ability to move massive quantities of material — not only fine mud or sand — is well-known. Water, especially rainwater, is also a very good, and sometimes surprisingly powerful solvent. In addition to its oxygen and two hydrogen molecules, rainwater also contains carbon and nitrogen dioxide, which together with water form 'weak' acids. It must be admitted that Man has helped in the course of the industrial revolution to make these acids so strong that they are having an extremely harmful effect on both inhabited and virgin land. Like atmospheric gases, water, whether pure or acid, does not respect national boundaries. If today's water alters the character of geochemical processes, this should be taken seriously. The changes involved are worldwide, not merely local. The composition of rainwater has changed because we burn fossil fuels which produce large amounts of nitrogen and sulphur dioxide. Because of this, the characters of both natural processes and elemental cycles have also changed, as the illustration on the following pages show.

The existence of saline seawater is made possible by the capacity of ordinary rainwater to act as a solvent. The

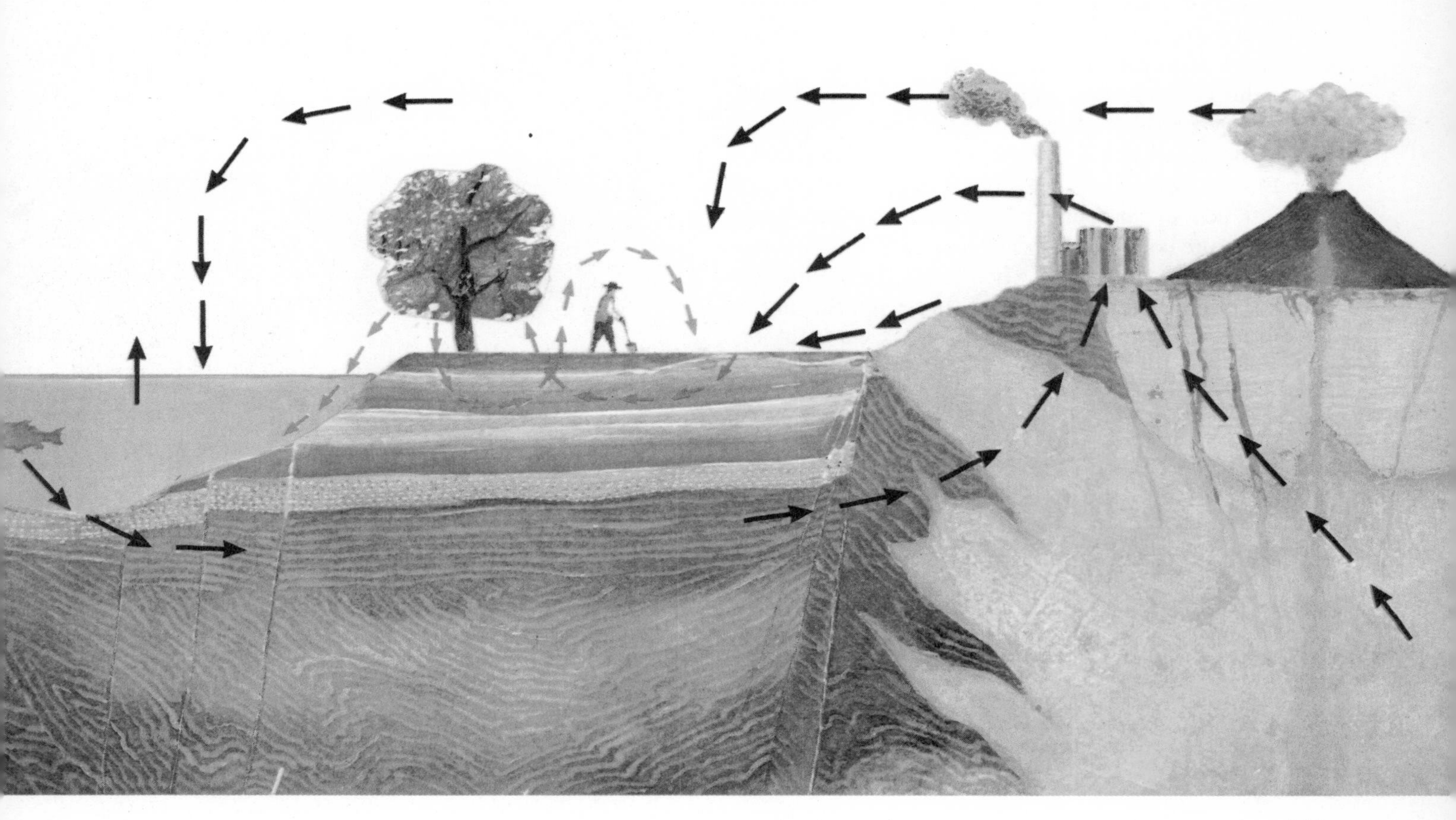

water in streams and rivers, even though it is known as 'freshwater', readily accumulates and dissolves chloride, sodium and many other ions and carries them to the sea. Man affects the composition of river waters by using this natural runoff solvent to carry away industrial waste. Water readily dissolves not only easily soluble and naturally occurring substances such as salt, but also industrial fertilizers, herbicides and pesticides. These are then borne by rivers into the oceans, where they undergo chemical changes, the full implications of which are not yet known.

Even pure rainwater can form magnificent caves in limestone. What it is not able to carry away it then, by a reverse process of crystallization from evaporated solutions, deposits on rock walls in the form of stalactites, stalagmites and other limestone decoration. The solvent properties of water are also apparent in the grocery trade, which retails mineral drinking waters, often carbonated. This water comes from the deeper terrestrial cycle. It once precipitated in the form of rain, infiltrated the crust, where it was heated up and passed through rocks. Since it has such a marked capacity to act as a solvent, it became enriched with mineral or gaseous components such as calcium, chlorine, sodium or carbon dioxide, nitrogen dioxide and sulphur dioxide. Via natural routes the water reaches the surface, where it flows out or is drawn off, either warm or cool. This kind of water is a highly important transporter of chemical elements in the terrestrial crust, forming part of the process of chemical differentiation. Mineralized waters also give rise to veins of metal ore, the majority of which are formed by warm waters (sometimes by hot waters) that are part of the deep cycle. Most mineral waters are not primary waters, i.e. waters escaping from the upper mantle and which have never been part of the hydrosphere. On the contrary, waters occurring in the form of mineral springs have generally already been on the Earth's surface and formed part of both the hydrosphere and hence also of the upper water cycle, therefore being recycled. They reach the deeper parts of the crust, heat up, are enriched by dissolved components – perhaps ore components which may have become deposited in a suitable place. Then, after some time has elapsed, often thousands of years, they reappear on the terrestrial surface. It should be made quite clear in this regard that mineral waters include neither water that has passed through rubbish dumps, nor water polluted by human activity, even though this water does have a high mineral content. There is surely more than enough evidence of the effects of this type of water on the countryside.

The water cycle in Nature is the fastest and most powerful movement of matter on Earth. Not even the formation of the ocean floor or the vast extent of natural volcanic activity can be compared with what occurs during water cycles. Nor is Man himself able to compete with the amount of matter, and energy with it, that is transported by water. The relations between the lithosphere, atmosphere and hydrosphere have achieved a fine balance, within which natural self-regulating mechanisms have formed. We cannot be certain how Nature will respond to these altered chemical conditions, although we know in theory what kind of reaction could occur. The instance of acid rain and the general increase of acids in the environment is both surprising and worrying, and yet similar situations have arisen in the geological past. We know from geological observation, for example, that ice ages were preceded by a marked increase of acids in the environment. The problem is that our knowledge about the cycles of chemical elements and of water itself is limited. It is often very difficult to identify and distinguish natural changes from man-made ones. Although the recording of these changes has not been going on for long, the first

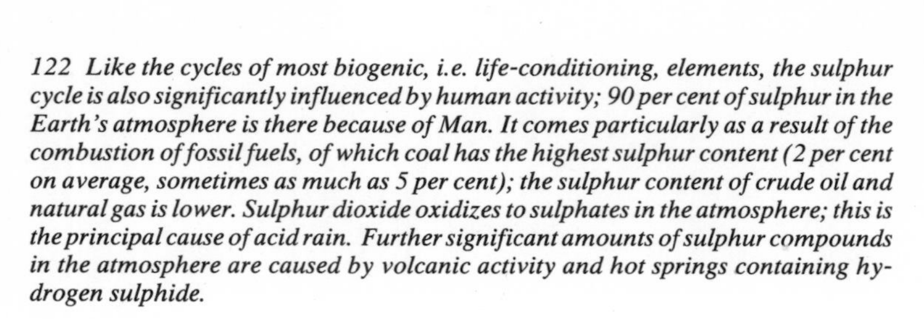

122 Like the cycles of most biogenic, i.e. life-conditioning, elements, the sulphur cycle is also significantly influenced by human activity; 90 per cent of sulphur in the Earth's atmosphere is there because of Man. It comes particularly as a result of the combustion of fossil fuels, of which coal has the highest sulphur content (2 per cent on average, sometimes as much as 5 per cent); the sulphur content of crude oil and natural gas is lower. Sulphur dioxide oxidizes to sulphates in the atmosphere; this is the principal cause of acid rain. Further significant amounts of sulphur compounds in the atmosphere are caused by volcanic activity and hot springs containing hydrogen sulphide.

warning signs are discernible: a rise in the carbon dioxide content in the atmosphere, a nitrogen dioxide content that is several times higher, the incomparably higher levels of heavy metals, e.g. lead, in river and sea waters, and the huge increase in nitrate levels in surface waters. All these things occur as a result of human activity and can be spoken of in terms of global change.

We shall now look at illustrations of the geochemical cycles of some biogenic elements, i.e. elements essential for the existence of the biomass. First, we will try to describe individual events separately, then to classify them and understand them in detail. In doing this it is possible to gain some insight into the way each separate factor works, but, of course, each separate element of this complex network of occurrences is linked to all the others. For this reason it is necessary to understand each isolated component and then see how it works in relation to the whole.

Take, for example, a minute section of the carbon cycle and its link with energy fluctuations on the terrestrial surface: carbon has a most important thermostatic function, being one of the most indispensable cogs in this clockwork machine. The amount of carbon in the atmosphere determines up to a point the amount of heat retained by the Earth. If the amount of carbon, in the form of carbon dioxide, increases, a greenhouse effect or rise in temperature occurs. This brings about an increase in the amount of water that evaporates into the atmosphere, which in turn increases the amount of rainfall. However, raindrops absorb carbon dioxide from the atmosphere, so that the rain is more acid and more frequent. Acid rain increases erosion through the dissolving of rocks containing carbon dioxide and calcium carbonate. This water then ends up in the sea. Calcium carbonate and carbon dioxide become building materials for the shells of marine organisms. When the animals die, their shells then become the basis for marine sediment. Within this process the flow of material cannot be divorced from the flow of energy. The fact that the temperature on the Earth has maintained a steady level throughout long geological eras and that rocks containing calcium carbonate have formed part of the terrestrial crust throughout the Earth's geological history illustrates both the balance and effectiveness of the various processes at work. The spider's web of relationships among these processes has so far proved to be sufficiently flexible, but Man is stretching it to breaking-point. We still have a long way to go before reaching an understanding of the processes of natural recycling and of the basic parts played by the interactions between the atmosphere, hydrosphere and lithosphere. On the whole, Man has not grasped the importance of these until the last decade. In isolated local instances, where reforestation and conservation programmes have been initiated, forests are beginning to grow again, the amount of acid rain is beginning to decline, and plant and animal species threatened with extinction have begun to increase in numbers. Such places, however, are few.

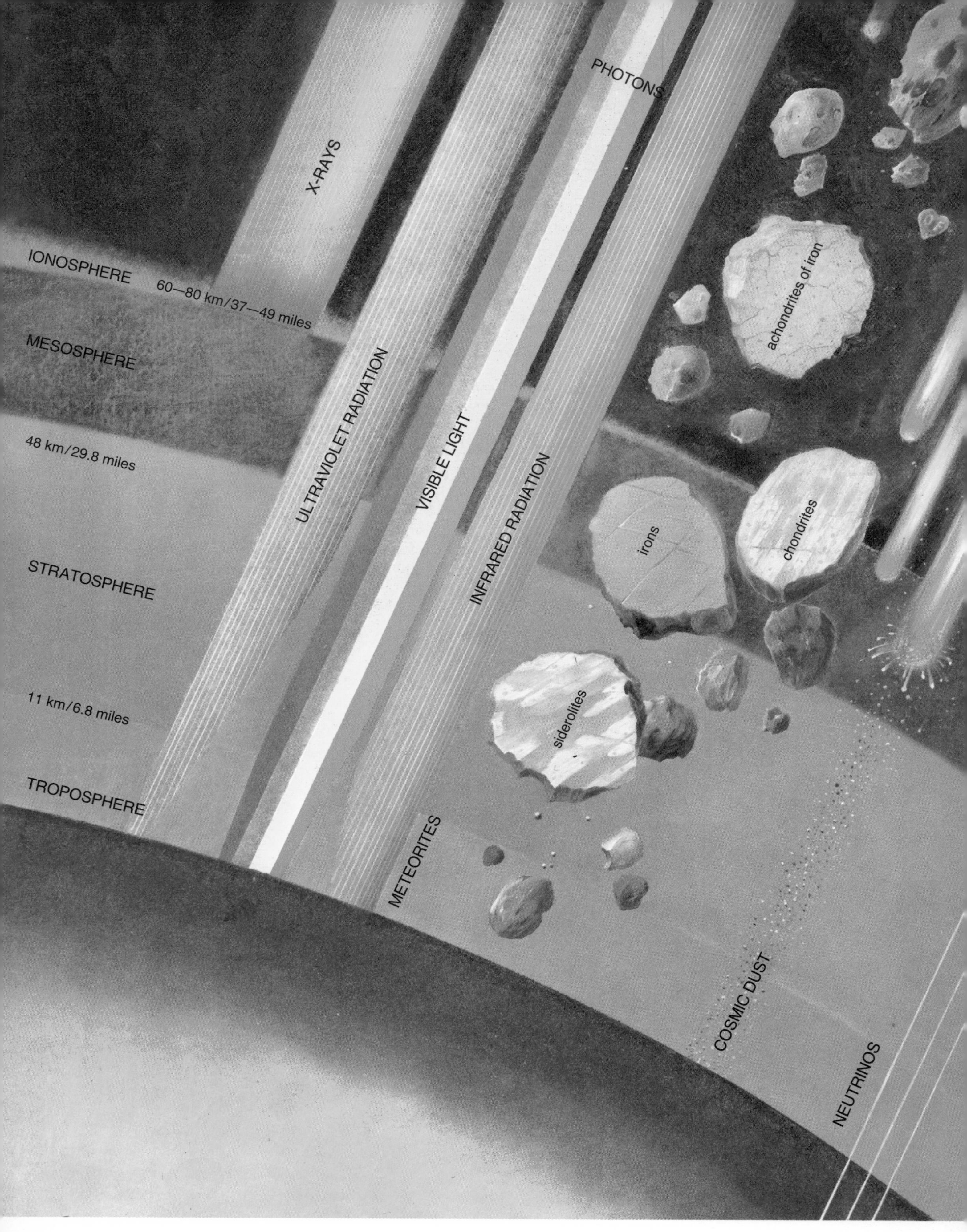

PHOTONS
X-RAYS
IONOSPHERE
60—80 km/37—49 miles
MESOSPHERE
ULTRAVIOLET RADIATION
VISIBLE LIGHT
INFRARED RADIATION
48 km/29.8 miles
STRATOSPHERE
11 km/6.8 miles
TROPOSPHERE
achondrites of iron
irons
chondrites
siderolites
METEORITES
COSMIC DUST
NEUTRINOS

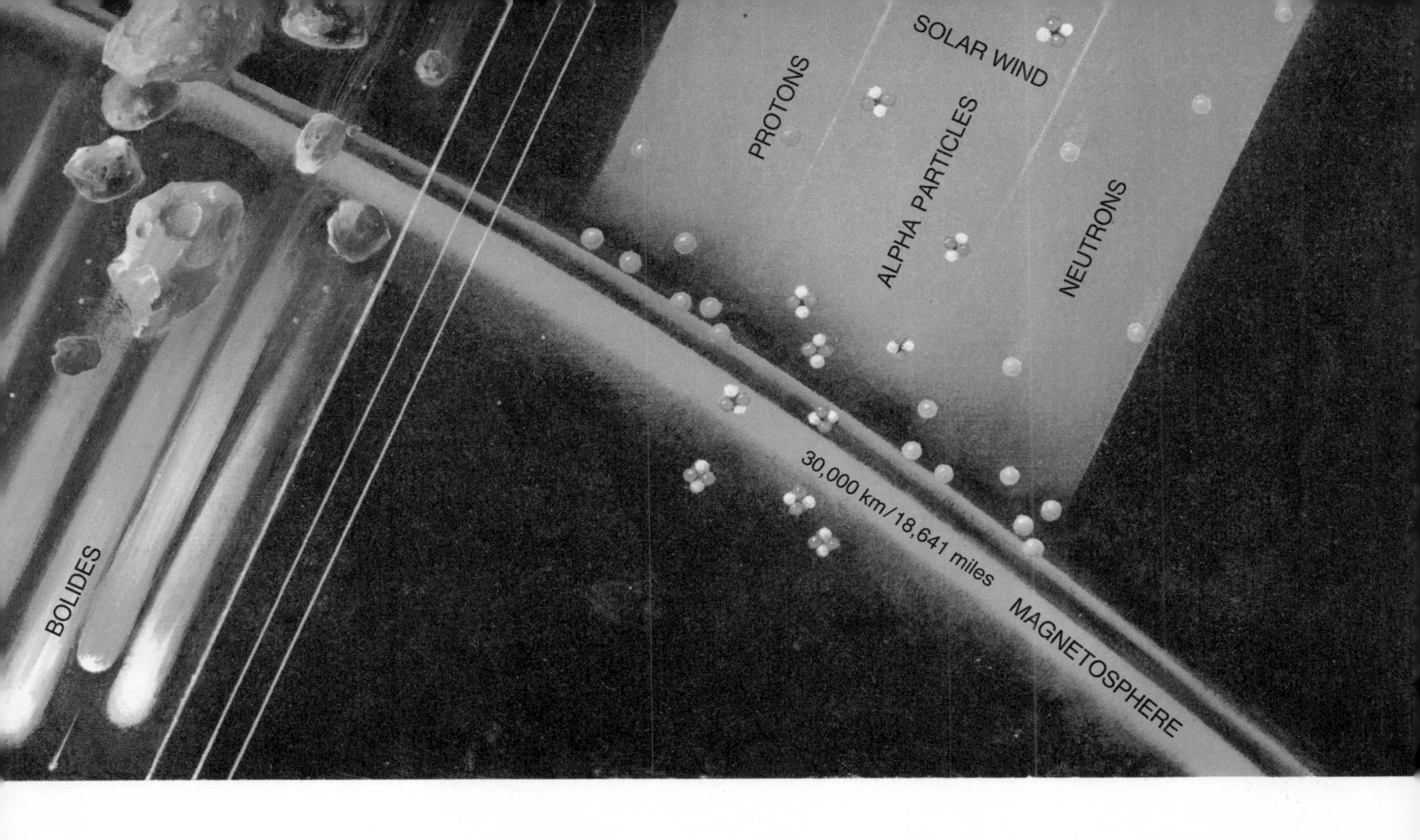

THE EARTH IN SPACE

123 Man is able to travel into outer space because the Earth has a permeable atmosphere. However, it is not equally permeable to individual types of electromagnetic waves. Electromagnetic radiation of several wave lengths are heavily reduced, others disappear completely. This is favourable to life and has been adapted to the spectrum of transmitted radiation. For instance, in the case of ultraviolet radiation less than one-third of the overall quantity in the Earth's proximity actually reaches the surface. Similarly, the quantity of infrared radiation reaching the Earth's surface is reduced by reflection into outer space and by absorption (see the explanation of the solar constant). X-rays are absorbed by the ionosphere. Elementary particles, which form part of the solar wind, do not reach the Earth because of their electric charge they are absorbed by the magnetosphere. There are also numerous solid particles of the mass forming part of our Solar system, which do not penetrate to the Earth's surface. The small ones burn in the atmosphere at altitudes of over 80 km/50 miles, many minor cosmic bodies disintegrate and fall on the Earth in the form of dust. Only some meteors become meteorites, i.e. those pieces of cosmic matter that fall on the Earth's surface (the picture gives their rough classification).

The Roman poet Lucretius (Titus Lucretius Carus) in his poem *On the Nature of the World* asks a question which is still being asked today. Do other worlds or planetary system exist? Is the Earth really so exceptional? The answer given by Lucretius in the first century B.C. is a straightforward one: 'It is highly probable that this world is the only one that was created.' Today's scientists tend to be more divided in their beliefs.

A great deal has been written on this theme, both scientific and unauthoritative. Many people have described their 'encounters with extra-terrestrials' seriously and in science fiction form. Beings from other worlds coming to Earth and our discovery of their worlds are themes which have provided people with so far inexhaustible fuel to fire their imaginations. There are those who believe such thoughts are beyond imagination; it seems possible, if not likely, that solar systems exist which, if not the same, are similar to our own. So far, however, there is no clear proof

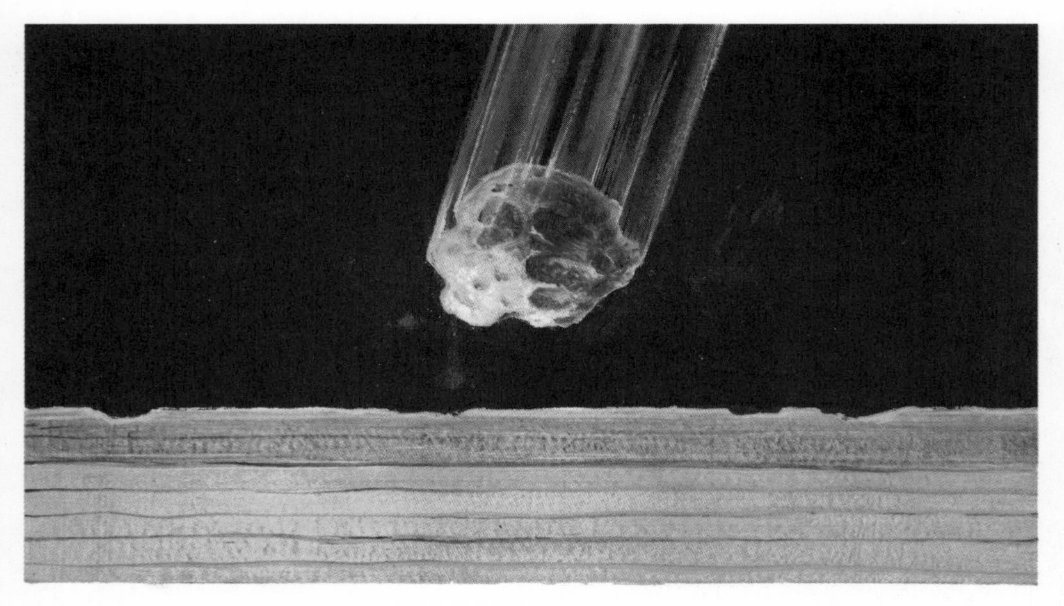

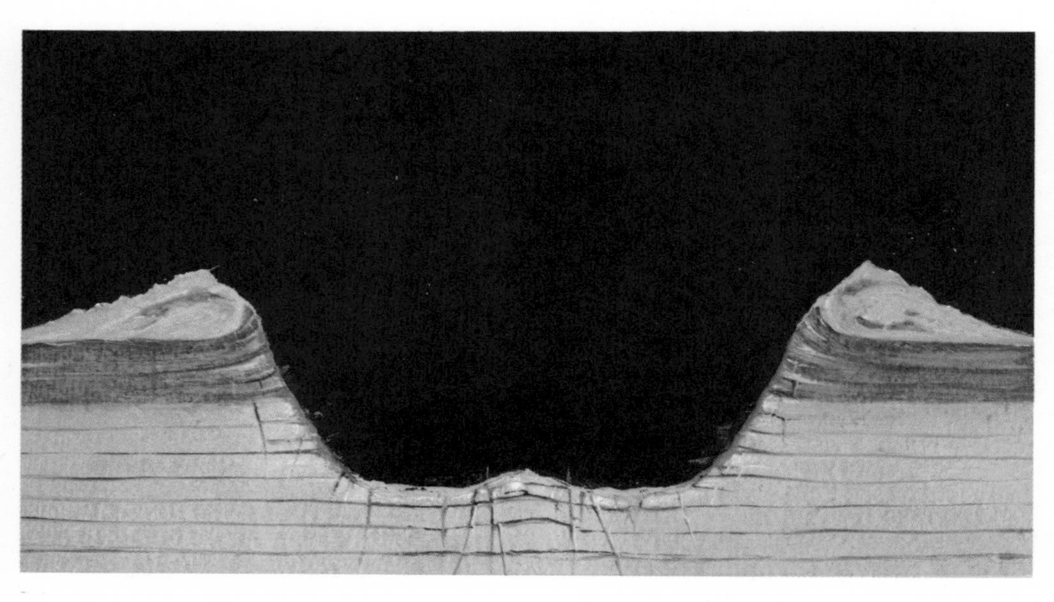

124 A space body, e.g. a big meteorite, an asteroid or a small planetesimal, when colliding with the Earth or any other planet, forms an impact crater. A small meteorite is slowed down by the atmosphere and does not produce a crater, but a big meteorite could form such a big crater that the quantity of material displaced and flung into the atmosphere could cause a major catastrophe. Because of the way in which it is formed, an impact crater has certain characteristic features. Due to the instantaneous conversion of the meteorite's kinetic energy into thermal energy on the site of impact, the ejection of a great quantity of material from the crater and the reaction of the Earth's crust to the impact, the crater walls usually have an inverted sequence of strata, with frequent occurrence of breccia, often cemented with molten mass. The crater is surrounded by material which has been ejected from it. In the centre of the crater there is a central uplift.

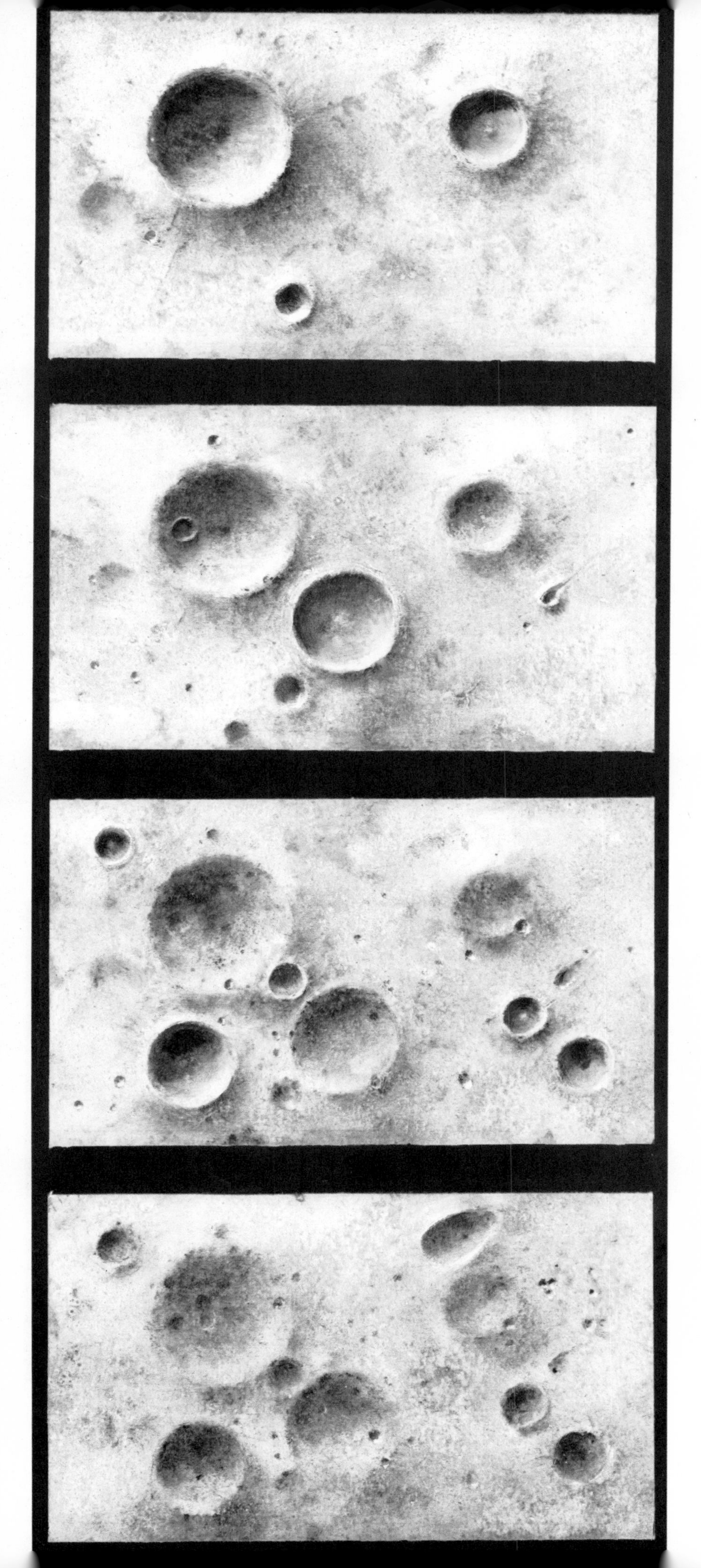

125 A comparison of the Earth with the Moon and Mercury shows the important role played by internal processes in the formation of the planetary surface. Where the planet is stable and has been devoid of any volcanic activity for a long period and has no atmosphere or water, the surface may be covered with craters, the number of which is continuously increasing. The craters of earlier origin may be covered with younger ones, the material released by the more recent impacts filling and covering the old ones. The sequence of surface changes, and the way the surface ages over time, is illustrated by this 'cinegram' showing that the number of craters per unit surface area also determines the age of the planet.

126 To determine the age of a planet (or the Moon) without touching its surface, all that is necessary is to count the number of craters present in one unit area. Fortunately some laboratories have in their possession samples of Moon rocks. It is possible to make an accurate measurement of their age by radiometric methods. This is done by constructing a calibration curve, with the number of craters per unit area on the vertical axis and the age of the rocks on the horizontal axis. From the study of the Moon's surface we know that the number of meteorites decreases in the course of time. The same also applies to the Earth. This fact means a favourable forecast for our existence: throughout the course of geological history the probability of the Earth's colliding with another celestial body has decreased.

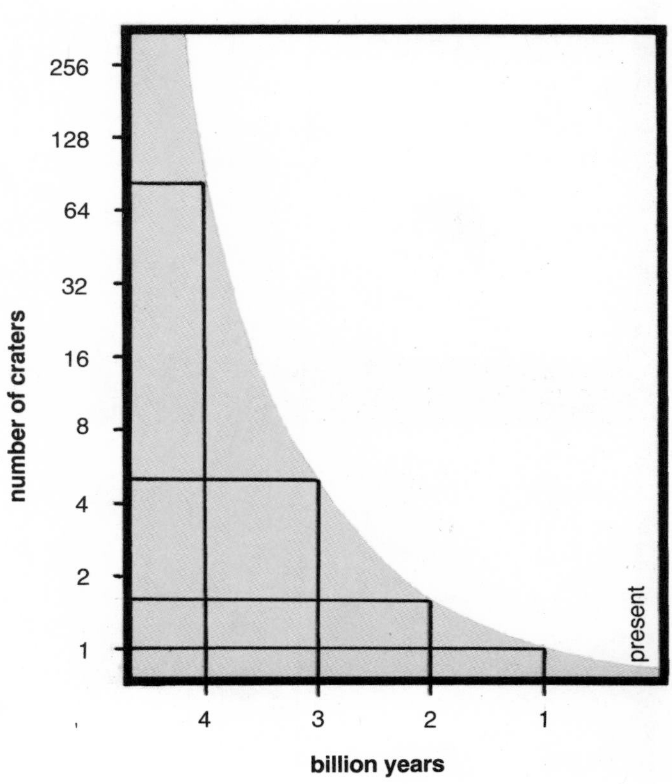

◁

127 One of the best known meteorite craters is in Arizona. It is one of the first craters to have been proven of meteoritic origin. It is called the Devil's Canyon Crater or Barringer Crater. Because it was proved to have originated from a collision with an iron meteorite (pieces of meteoritic iron were found in it), an attempt was made to find the meteorite by drilling, and to extract it in the same way as iron ore. However, the attempt was unsuccessful; the meteorite had not only disintegrated in the impact, but because enormous amounts of kinetic energy were, at the time, converted to heat, it had also evaporated.

128 A number of minor meteoritic craters are situated in the Australian Northern Territory. They occurred quite recently, less than 5,000 years ago, as a result of a 'meteoritic shower'. In a relatively small area there are 12 craters which range in diameter from 2 to 180 m/6 .5 to 590 ft.

that this is so. Astronomers studying and monitoring results from the Infrared Astronomical Satellite (IRAS) assert that this has been one of the most successful and fruitful space expeditions because it has provided possible signs of the existence of another solar system. Telescopes on board the satellite have picked up a strange and unusual heat source, close in astronomical terms to Vega, a star of exceptional size and brightness in the northern sky. This heat could originate from another system.

The existence of a solar system does not necessarily mean the existence of life, but questions continue to be asked. Does this mean that we are not alone? How do we differ from the universe around us? What unites us and

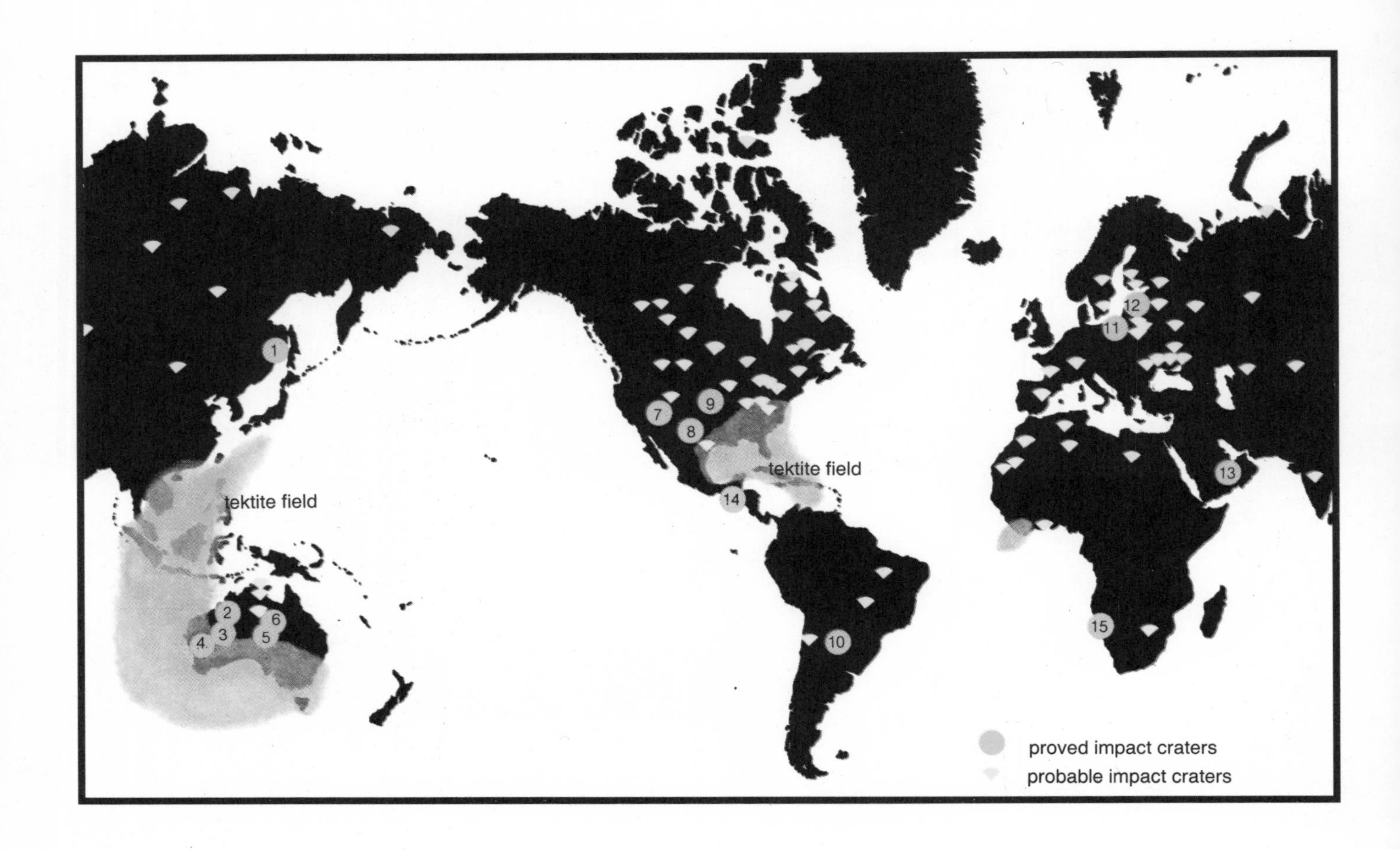

129 The present-day surface of the Earth shows traces of meteorite impacts. The effects of internal and external forces, such as weathering and sedimentation, however, are wiping away these traces very speedily. It is for this reason that there are so few impact craters in existence on the Earth in comparison with the Moon and other planets whose internal volcanic development has already come to an end. The map differentiates between the documented impact craters, i.e. those in which meteoritic material has been reliably proved, and possible or suspected impact craters.

1 – Sikhote Alin (Russia) 0.27 km/0.168 miles, 2 – Wolf Creek 0.85 km/0.5 miles, 3 – Vevers 0.8 km/0.49 miles, 4 – Dalgaranga 0.21 km/0.13 miles, 5 – Henbury 0.15/0.09 miles, 6 – Boxhole 0.185 km/0.114 miles, 7 – Meteor Crater (Arizona, U.S.) 1.2 km/0.75 miles, 8 – Odessa (Texas, U.S.) 0.168 km/0.105 miles, 9 – Haviland (Kansas, U.S.) 0.11 km/0.68 miles, 10 – Campo del Cielo (Argentina) 0.9 km/0.56 miles, 11 – Morasko (Poland) 0.1 km/0.62 miles, 12 – Kaaliyarvi (Russia) 0.11 km/0.068 miles, 13 – Wabar (Saudi Arabia) 0.97 km/0.606 miles, 14 – Cicxulub (Mexico) 170 km/106 miles, 15 – Roter Kamm (Namibia) 1.3 km/0.9 miles.

what divides us? Answers to such questions are general, but unequivocal: for the time being, we will have to go on considering ourselves exceptional. The composition and structure of our planet is, as far as we know, unique. It is a planet rich in water, dynamic and yet in a balanced state. We do pay a high price for this, however — compared with other planets — we have more in the way of earthquakes, volcanic activity and other natural and atmospheric catastrophes; all these are results of the Earth's vitality.

Quite extraordinary conditions had to be created for life to come about on the Earth at all. A mere shift in some of the parameters of the planet's orbit, its distance from the Sun, its mass, or even an unexpected evolutionary event might be enough to trigger a global catastrophe. Just how well do we know the boundaries beyond which the planet must not move, in order that its life and balance may be preserved? Perhaps we do not know our own planet at all. We have become accustomed to judging the entire universe by terrestrial criteria, but our experience so far has shown this to be misleading. We looked with the eyes of an earth geologist at the Moon, assuming it to be no more than a cold, dead planetary body. It took the landing of men on its surface to make us realize that we had made a number of false assumptions based on experience gained from our own planet.

In the past, people imagined Mars to be populated by little green men. Later on an experiment was conducted, whereby instruments were sent to Mars in order to ascertain some form of life. Nothing was found — and yet a mere ten years after this experiment it would be difficult to find anyone who would state categorically that they found the Viking experiment entirely convincing. People are still willing to believe that life exists on Mars. Even within the last ten years our concept of what constitutes a living organism has changed, and the range of conditions within which life is considered possible (even on Earth) has increased. It is also possible that we do not know our own planet as well as we think we do. Many of us live, work and move about on the Earth, blissfully unawere of the damage we are doing.

As has already been shown, evidence of primeval life is looked for through examination of meteorites. It is supposed that these are the remnants of ancient cosmic matter. It is also possible that most of the planets in our solar system were formed from material which originated from a common source. If we follow on from this theory, we

130 Present-day collections probably contain more meteorites from Antarctica than from all other continents put together. The map shows principal locations of meteorites in Antarctica:
1 — Allan Hills
2 — Belgica Mountains
3 — Yamato Mountains
4 — Novolazarov
5 — Neptune Range
6 — Theil Mountains

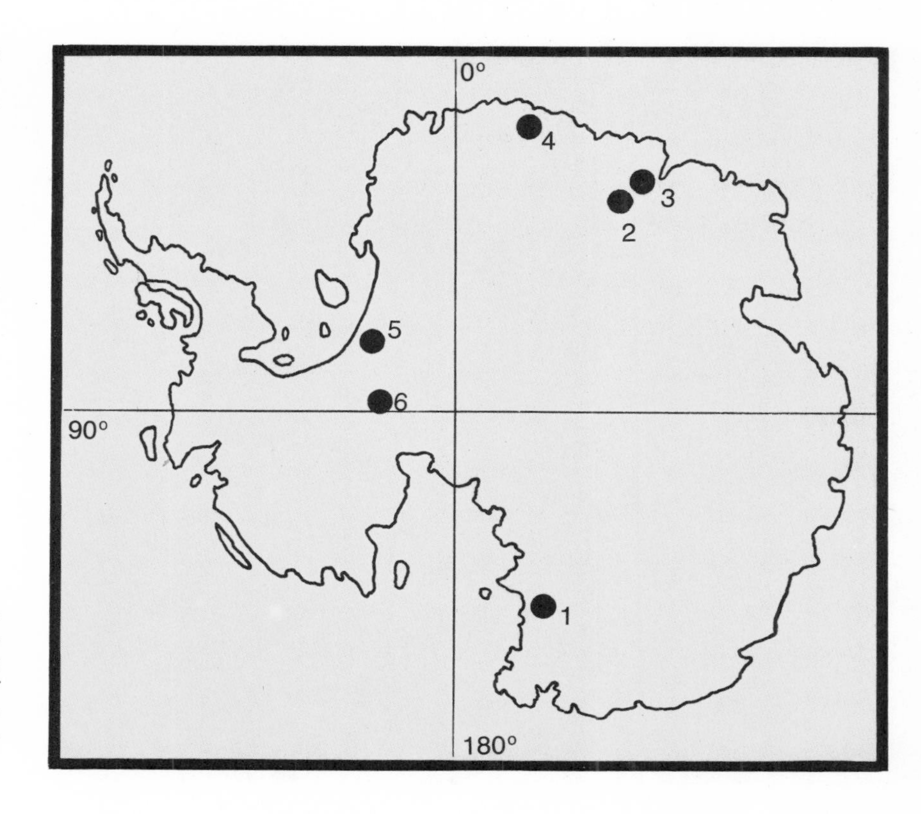

131 The most favourable conditions for the preservation of meteorites can be found in Antarctica. Meteorites landing on a glacier remain preserved in it and move with it. If the glacier hits an obstacle and if there is considerable evaporation due to climatic conditions, the meteorites appear on the surface creating a meteorite 'gold mine'.

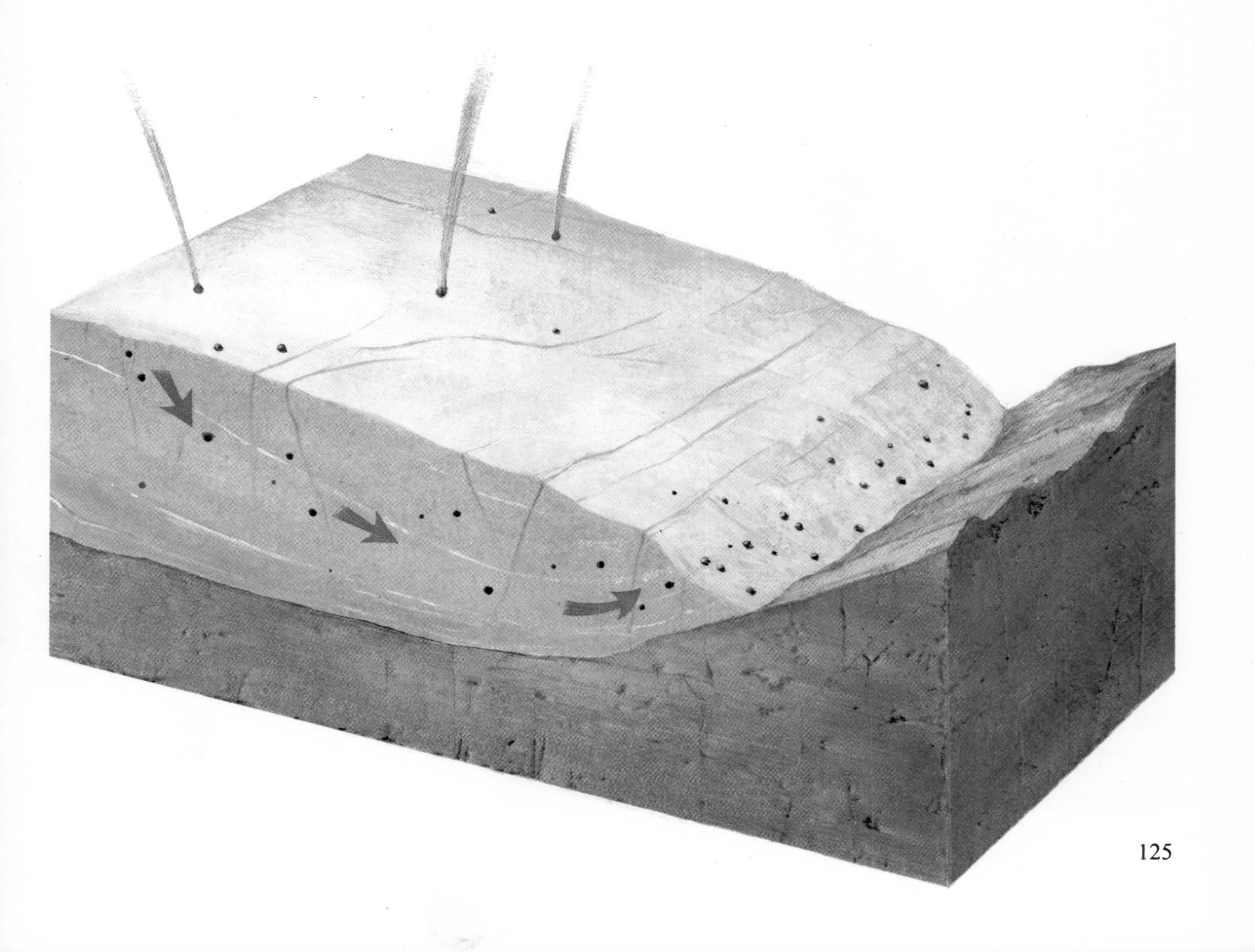

132 It would be wrong to assume that all craters on the Earth's surface originated either from volcanic activity or as a result of a collision with a space body. There are also man-made craters caused either by gun shells or underground nuclear tests! The example seen here is one of 600 existing in the Nevada Desert in the United States.

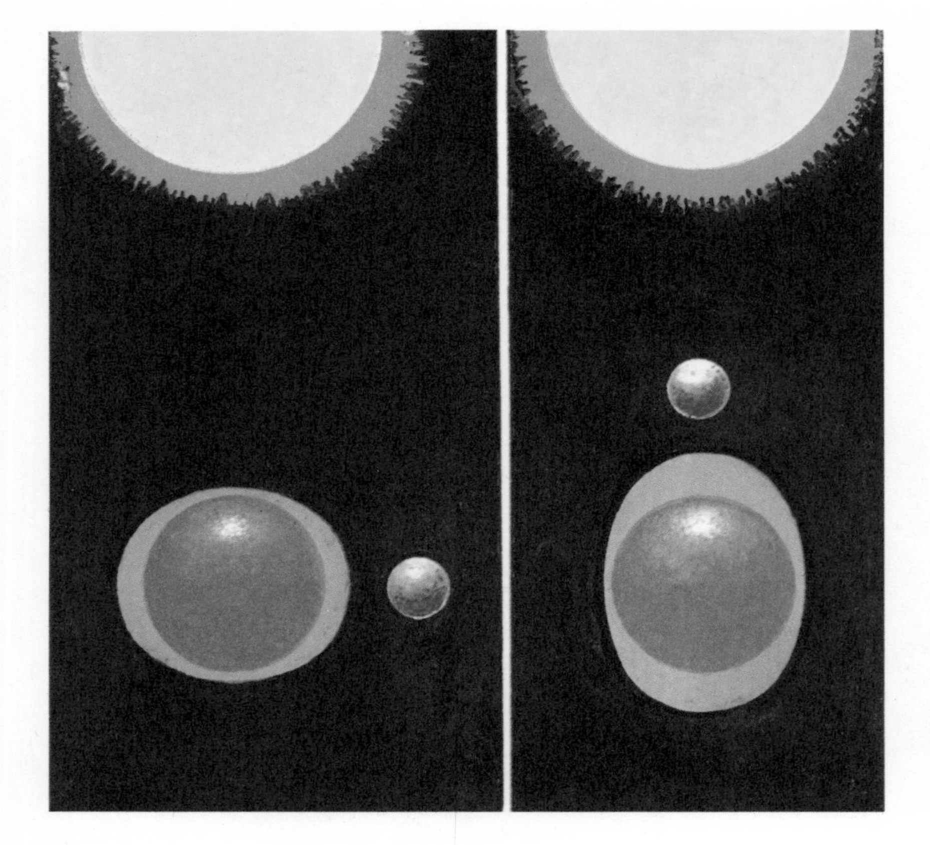

133 The tides — the twice daily rise and fall of sea level — is due to the Moon and the Sun. This was known to people in ancient times, however, the explanation of this phenomenon had to wait until the discovery of Newton's laws. The mutual influence of Moon and Sun can be seen here. The Moon, although it has less mass, has a greater influence over the tides, because it is much closer to the Earth than the Sun. Their combined effect is shown on the right of the picture.

▷
134 Man-made craters used for the cultivation of vine grapes on the Canary Islands. The craters trap natural humidity which improves wine quality.

could also assume that most planets of the inner solar system, i.e. those close enough to the Sun, could support life. At the moment, however, no evidence of life has been found on other planets, and it is, of course, possible that it has, in fact, only occurred on Earth.

If the planets of the solar system did originate from the same source of matter, there would be grounds to assume that their original geological and atmospheric development were also similar. Scientists presume that there was no substantial difference between the original atmospheres on Earth, Mars and Venus: and yet the Earth's present atmosphere differs from its own original one. By the same token the present atmospheres on Earth, Venus and Mars are all different.

The Earth's present atmosphere is known as a secondary atmosphere. Like the terrestrial crust, it has altered and reformed over millions of years. The composition of a secondary atmosphere depends on climatic conditions, which in turn are affected by the composition of the atmosphere: it is a continuous cycle. What, however, are the reasons for the difference between the Earth and the rest of the planetary system? The existence of water in a liquid state on the planetary surface depends on surface temperature, i.e. on its distance from the Sun. Liquid water was obviously a precondition for the emergence of life on Earth, and, thereafter life itself altered the atmosphere. If the Earth were situated closer to the Sun, the surface temperature would be higher and it would not be possible for

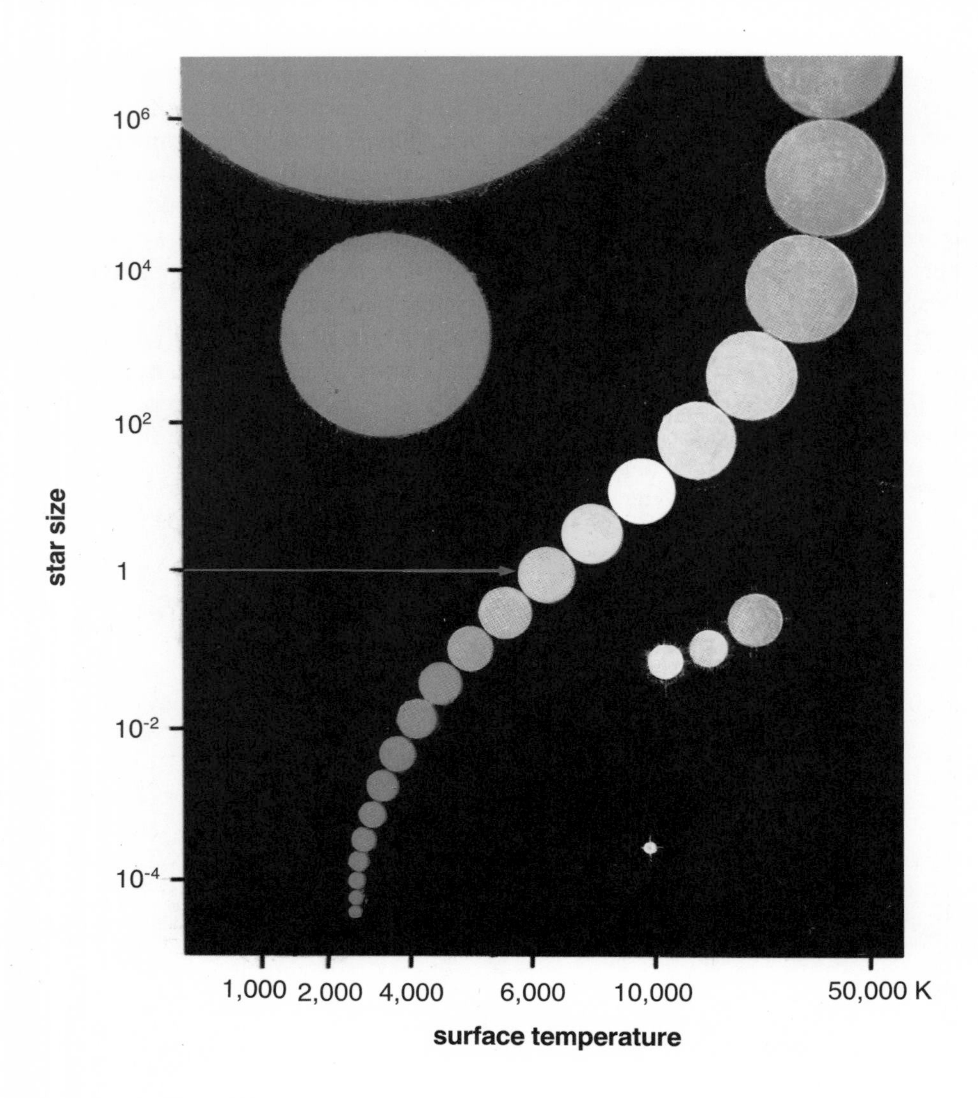

water to exist as a liquid. Life, therefore, would probably not be able to form, because all the materials which one assumes the structural components essential for life must contain, would not be available. To follow this line of thought further, if fluid, liquid water did not exist on Earth, the terrestrial metabolic system would probably also not function in the way it does. It is altogether possible that the lithospheric plates would not move, that they would not slide under one another or collide, and almost certainly the continents would not have the present granitic composition.

Let us look at the physical interaction, in terms of energy and matter, between our Earth and the rest of the universe. We have already noted falling meteors and meteorites, but we have not yet mentioned the protective role of the atmosphere, which in fact prevents most fine cosmic particles from reaching the Earth. A meteor, in fact, is any bright moving body formed by a small mass of matter from outer space, and which is made luminous by the compression of air when it enters the Earth's atmosphere. A meteorite is merely a meteor which manages to land on the Earth. Small meteors weighing fractions of a gram are burned up in the upper layer of the atmosphere, disintegrating as they collide with air molecules, thus causing the 'falling star' effect of an ionized trail in the atmosphere. On the other hand, large meteorites or bodies the size of asteroids decrease in speed as they enter the planet's atmosphere and fall to Earth, although only rarely in the case of massive particles weighing tons.

Other links between the Earth and space appear to be of a non-material character. People find it hard to imagine cosmic radiation, the electro-magnetic wave motion of various lengths, or the flow of elementary particles — perhaps because this type of radiation and these particles are invisible and cannot be seen at a glance outside the small and narrow range of the spectrum that is visible as light to the human eye. The illustration shows the range of electro-magnetic waves that reaches the Earth from space at the same time showing what an effective filter the Earth's atmosphere is. Only a minute proportion of this electro-magnetic spectrum in fact ever reaches the Earth. Other radiation, for example X-rays or ultra-violet rays (electro-magnetic radiation of extremely short wavelengths), is usually caught in the upper layers of the atmosphere by oxygen, nitrogen or ozone. Not even infra-red rays reach the Earth, being absorbed by condensed water and reflected back into space. Electro-magnetic wave motion of longer wavelengths is similarly caught in the ionosphere.

Just as the Earth is protected from the greater proportion of electro-magnetic waves, so it is protected from

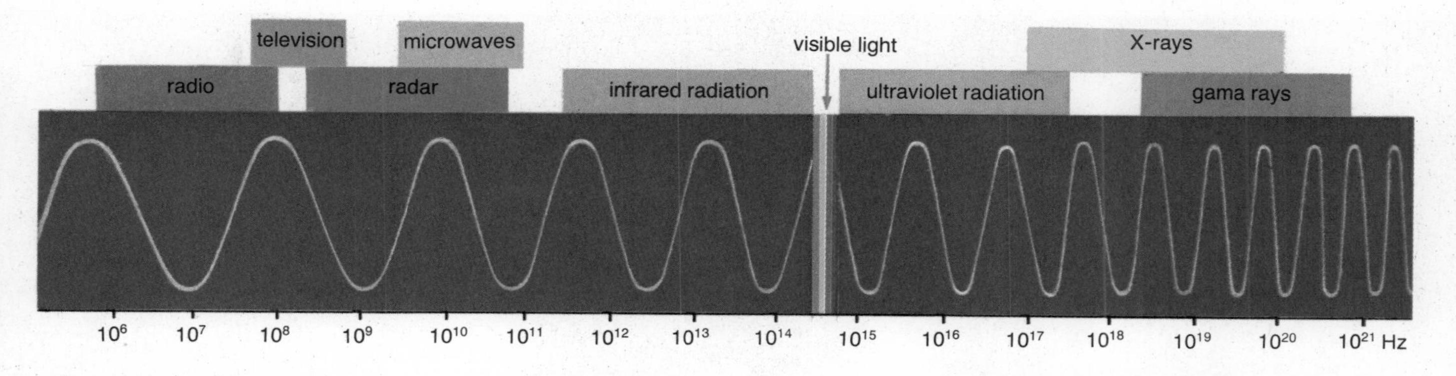

◁

135 One of the most well known astronomical diagrams is the Herzspring-Russel diagram, simultaneously illustrating the history and forecasting the future of the stars including the major star in our solar system, the Sun (red arrow in the picture). This is a simplified version of the diagram. The horizontal axis indicates temperature, which corresponds roughly with the luminosity and age of the star. The vertical axis indicates the star size. The principal sequence of star development is shown by the sinusoidal curve of increasing star size. Generally it holds that the older the star, the greater its luminosity. A star's characteristics, i.e. age, luminosity and the way in which it develops, however, depend on its mass. Outside the principal sequence there are giants and super-giants (upper left) and dwarfs (upper right). The more mass the star has, the quicker it develops.

136 The visible spectrum, i.e. that part of the electromagnetic spectrum able to be seen by the human eye, is only a very small part of the entire spectrum which ranges from microwaves to hard radiation.

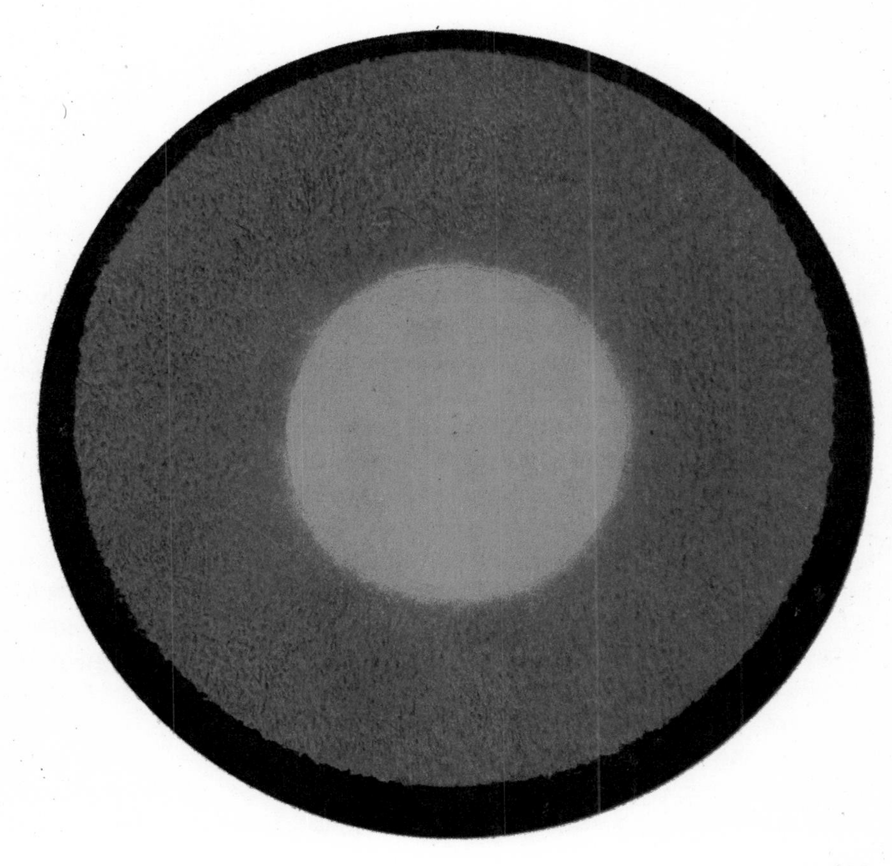

137 A peculiar planetary feature is the marked asymmetry of surface break-up. The Earth has an irregular distribution of land and sea, as do the Moon and Mars. Even the internal structure of perfectly spherical planetary bodies is not symmetrical. The Apollo missions concluded from measurements taken that the crust of the Moon is thinner on its visible side than on its hidden side. Whether the Moon has a core, as suggested here, has remained a point of discussion for the past two decades.

138 Two areas of proof in respect of 'communication' between the Earth and the Sun are the Aurora Borealis and Aurora Australis. Particles of solar wind penetrating to Earth's atmosphere are attracted by the magnetic poles of the Earth. In these areas the molecules present in upper strata of the atmosphere are ionized or charged. The light effects accompanying these processes are Aurora Borealis in the northern hemisphere and Aurora Australis in the southern hemisphere.

electrically-charged cosmic particles such as those ejected by the Sun and known as solar wind. In this case, however, the Earth's protection is not its atmosphere but its magnetosphere — the magnetic field surrounding it. The magnetosphere gives rise to the Van Allen belts, in which most electrically-charged particles passing within the vicinity of our planet are caught. These particles do, nonetheless, make their presence felt, travelling from the Van Allen belts into the Earth's ionosphere in the magnetic polar regions. The Aurora Borealis clearly shows the disturbances in the ionosphere caused by elementary particles entering.

However, not all particles from space are caught by the protective layers of the atmosphere or magnetosphere. Some particles attain such velocities that they are not caught by any of these protective traps. Physicists who want to create an environment where the action of these highly accelerated particles is not evident must place their instruments deep below the Earth's surface. There are also cosmic particles which fall with such energy that they are stopped neither by the atmospheric layer, not even by the solid lithosphere, slowing down only slightly as they pass through the entire planet.

Solar radiation as such, and the transmission of energy from the Sun to the Earth, is determined by the movement of photons. Other components of solar radiation, such as solar wind, a flow of protons, bring little in the way of en-

▷
139 Information contained in rocks is difficult to read, until we know the basic relations between its component parts. Like every solid, liquid or gaseous substance rocks consists of protons, neutrons and electrons which, combined, form atoms. The atoms of one or several elements form molecules from which the mass of a crystal is constructed. Molecules of one type, organized into crystalline matter, form a mineral, and an aggregate of mineral forms rock. The particular arrangement of minerals in rock and the distribution of elements within individual minerals makes it possible to read information contained in rocks.

ergy to the Earth itself. This is not only because they are far fewer in number than photons, but also because electrically-charged particles, protons, are lost in the Earth's protective magnetic trap.

Examination of the surfaces of planets without atmospheres, e.g. Mercury and the Moon, and which may be defined as geologically non-dynamic, reveals interesting evidence of another kind of communication between planets and space of which the Earth appears to have been deprived. On these planets, falling material leaves its mark in the form of craters, in this way helping to shape their surfaces. There are few such craters on Earth: researchers who have made an intensive search for them have reliably documented no more than ten, some two hundred more having been recorded which may have arisen in a similar manner. We have no reason to assume that meteorites avoid our planet, but the Earth is a dynamic body, and traces of this kind are probably wiped out by its vitality and the rapid and powerful geological processes at work on the boundaries between its lithosphere, hydrosphere and atmosphere.

Looking at the Moon, formations can be found there which are 'young' in lunar terms, having come into existence three billion years ago. These are its most recent lava flows (rocks as old as this are a great rarity on the Earth's surface). However, there are substantially older formations on the Moon. Comparing older formations with more recent ones, one can see that the older ones are studded with a much greater number of impact craters (i.e. caused by the fall of meteorite fragments). Since the age of lunar igneous rocks in lava flows has been calculated using radiometric methods, it is possible to calibrate the amount of cosmic material that falls on to the planetary surface within a certain unit of time in the course of a geological age. It is clear from such studies that the amount of large meteorites falling on the Moon has declined over time. It may be possible to draw an analogy here: it is likely that in the case of the Earth, also, the number of sizeable falling meteorites in particular is fewer. This is a potentially helpful piece of information for us as inhabitants of such a planet, i.e. that the number of major collisions, and hence the possibility of a collision of the Earth with a cosmic body, declines with the passage of time. It would, therefore, seem possible to state that, in the long period of planetary existence in our solar system, freely moving material has already largely been 'caught', and that there is currently much less of this material in the vicinity of the Earth than there was at the beginning of its existence, in its first thousand million years.

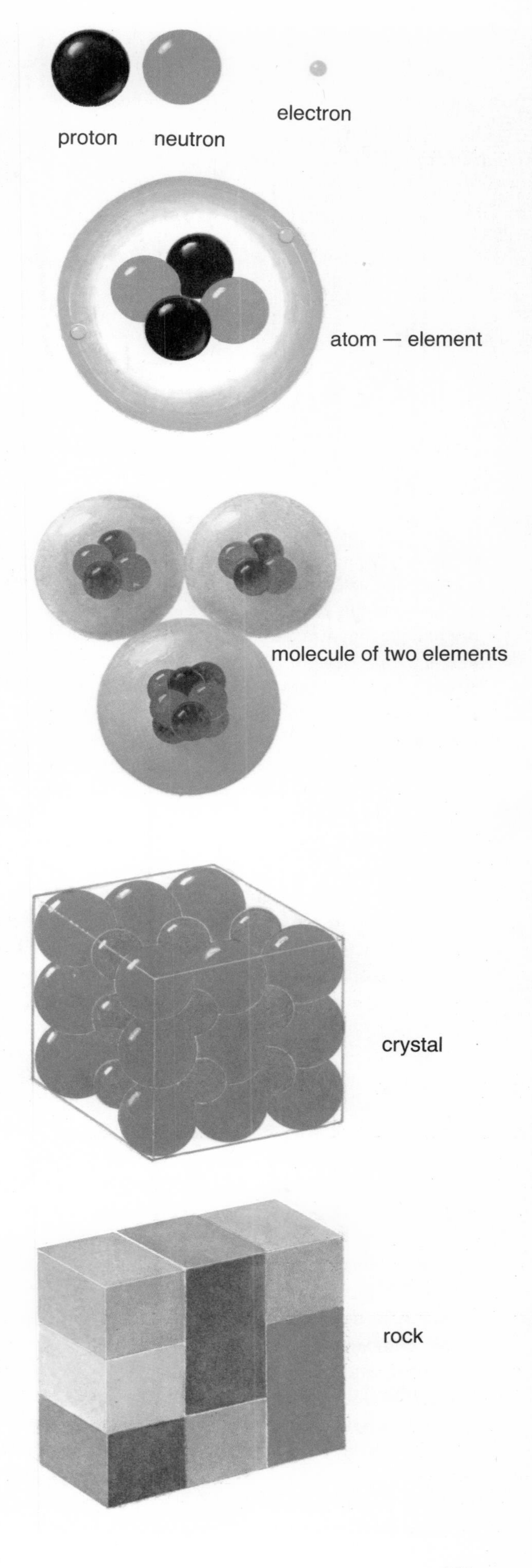

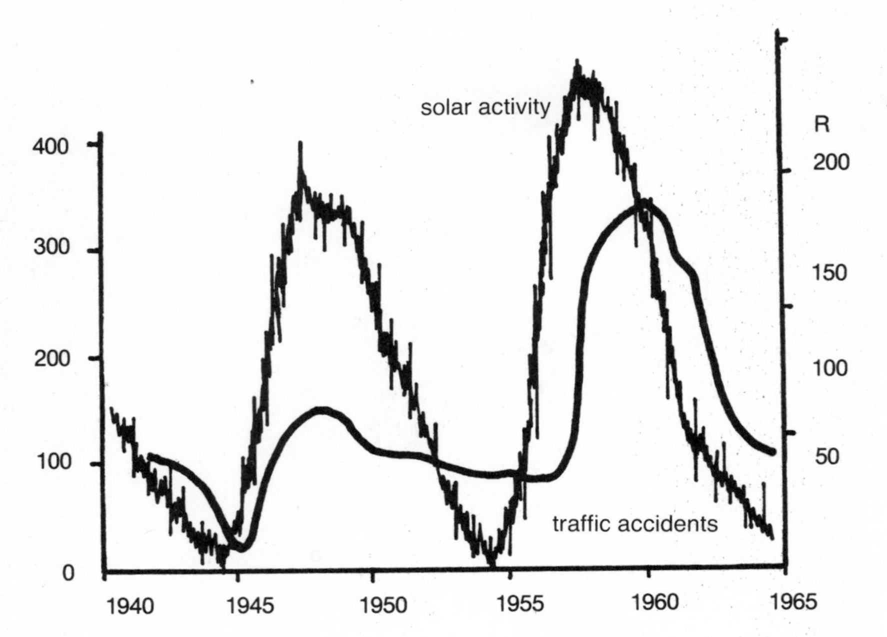

140 This diagram illustrates the relationship between solar activity and human behaviour. Solar activity is expressed by the jagged line, the number of traffic accidents in Japan by the smooth line.

Among those studying the Earth and who are genuinely concerned with ecological issues, there are many who do not believe that the cosmos has any effect on the behaviour and activities of Man. To them, this would be pure speculation within an area which is little known or understood. Let us take, for example, the links between the Moon and the Earth. Among the most curious of these links, for instance, is the average duration of human pregnancy, which is 266 days — unbelievably close to the elapse of nine planetary months (265.8 days). The average human menstrual cycle is 29.5 days, which is comparable with the average length of the planetary month — 29.5 days. In the past even people's psychological disturbances have been linked with lunar activity — although this is a matter for debate. Connections have long been made between human health and solar activity, the state of the magnetic field, the character of sun spots and the weather on Earth.

Geologists and geophysicists, however, generally prefer more straightforward and immediately evident links. These include the ebb and flow of the ocean tides. Despite its relatively modest mass, the Moon plays a far more important role in the ocean tides than the much more massive and remote Sun. The Moon in a similar way acts on the terrestrial crust which, like the oceans, also has its fluxes. The connections between this ebb and flow and geological activity lie in the part they play in the erosion, deposition and transporting of both living and inanimate material. They also affect certain life-cycles, as well as bringing about particular astronomical consequences. These come about through a decrease in the speed of the Earth's rotation, which in turn is a result of the ebb of the ocean tide. The tides, as we have said before, are caused by the mutual gravitation effects of the Earth and Moon. In this way the days become longer and, therefore, decline in number over long geological eras. These changes, however, are barely discernible within a single human lifetime, or even within the entire period of human habitation of this planet, as they can be registered only on a scale of millions of years.

Ever since time began Man has been drawn to the stars. Before he had any way of reaching them, he assigned to them mystery and power, and even made gods of the Sun, Moon and planets. Perhaps they were gods to an extent: they held for him the power of life and death. Drought, cold, flood and fire kill, just as warmth, rain and settled weather provide food and comfort. Nowadays these 'gods' still carry great power (although they do not affect our food sources quite so directly). Space, however, perhaps because of its vast and seemingly boundless nature, still possesses a deep and glorious mystery.

Throughout the period of the Apollo lunar missions, when pieces of the lunar surface were brought to Earth, dozens of research teams eagerly set about examining them. Scientists analyzed this material using all the techniques then available. They strove to disentangle the proportion of lunar material traceable to meteorites, which elements had been brought by the solar wind and which elements were present in unusually small amounts. Since this material was being studied by many teams, each tried to outdo the other in the quality of its work. Progress was unexpectedly swift, and results came surprisingly quickly. The results were cross-checked between a number of laboratories involved in analyzing and processing this rare material and these methods are now applied to terrestrial rocks and the processes at work with them. Many instruments were in fact first developed out of an enthusiasm and love for space research, later to be used in more routine work here on Earth. The objection might be raised that science and research ought to be rational matters, and that the instrument technology that was developed for space research would have been developed anyway. Some results would indeed have been produced, but ask a chef whether he cooks only to feed people, or for the enjoyment of cooking, or a reader whether he reads to learn

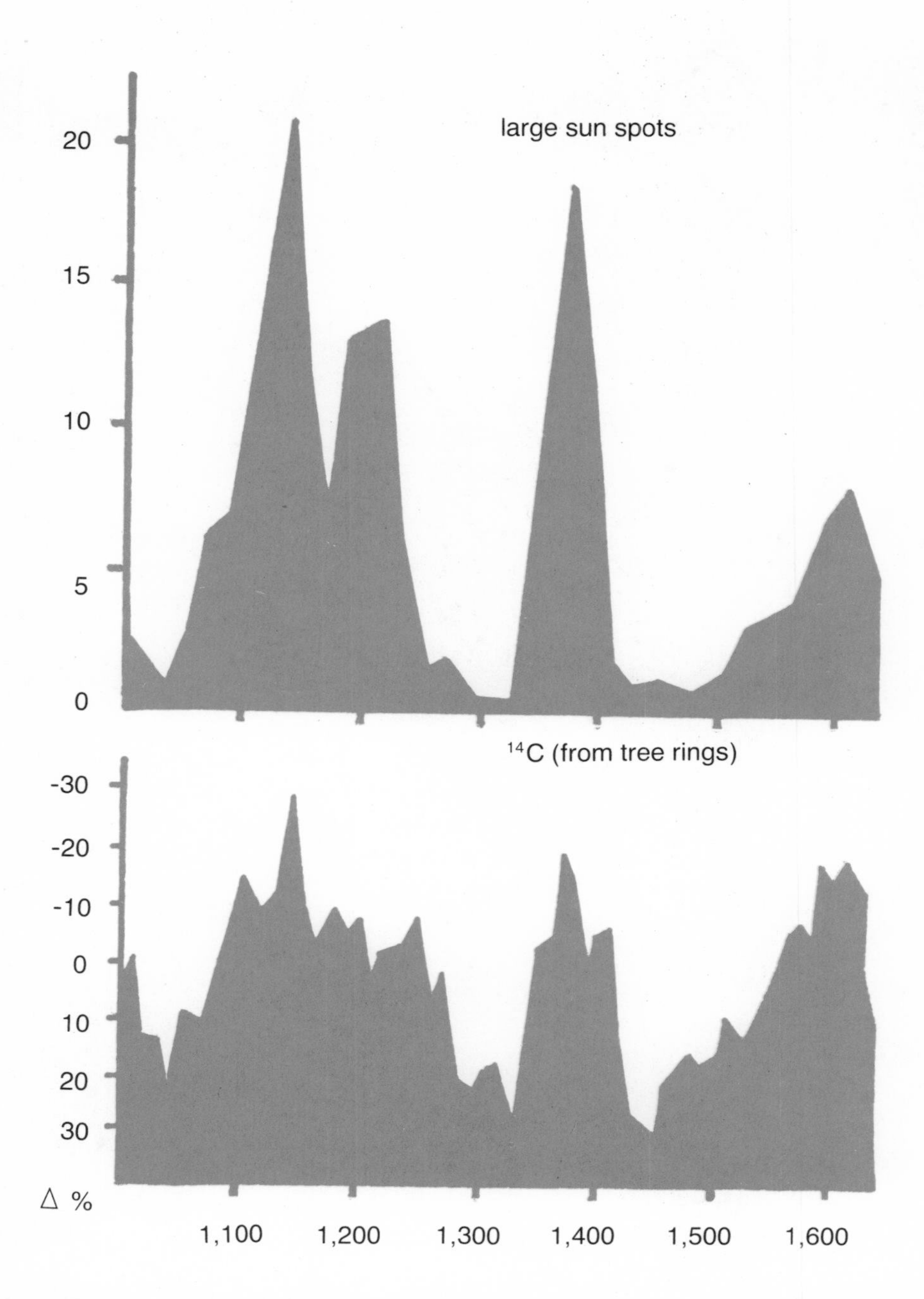

141 The relation between solar activity (derived from historical records) and the content of radioactive carbon occurring as a result of increased intensity of cosmic rays on the Earth. In the upper part of the picture the cumulative number of sun spots is shown on the vertical axis, in the lower part the vertical axis shows the ratio of the radioactive and stable carbon isotopes. The horizontal axis shows the age in both cases (the dates were arrived at by counting the annual rings of trees).

something or for the enjoyment of reading; there are likewise many people who work because they enjoy working. For most of those involved in space research, this sense of enjoyment is their central *raison d'être.*

Many futurologists and dreamers predict that we will one day exploit space and the planets for their mineral resources. Although this is an attractive idea, it does have its drawbacks. The issue of mineral resources and the natural resources of which they form part is not a matter of immediate necessity. Their potential exploitation, however, is an energy and a geological issue. Space resources will then become important for cosmic travel and colonization, but secondary in terms of life on Earth. We know from comparing material brought back from space with similar material from Earth, that Earth's geological and geochemical processes have progressed further than any among all the planets in terms of the concentrations of specific components. In other words, it seems unlikely that mineral deposits superior to those on Earth will be found on other planets. It is more likely that more primitive, less differentiated substances will be found, and that any exploitable components in this material will be present in dispersed form. As will be seen in the following chapter, a mineral deposit constitutes a strange anomaly in inanimate Nature. Only the Earth, with its 'digestive system' in which water, surface weathering and sufficient heat, both internal and external, play a central role, has achieved an all but perfect mastery of the concentration of those substances necessary to Man.

It was not the original purpose of this book to write about cosmic matter or problems in respect of Earth and its relationship with the rest of the universe. It is difficult to avoid doing so, however, since the links between the Earth and the universe are so close. When speaking of the Earth's atmosphere it cannot be done without reference to the whole universe, nor is it possible to consider its composition without knowledge of physical processes occurring in surrounding space.

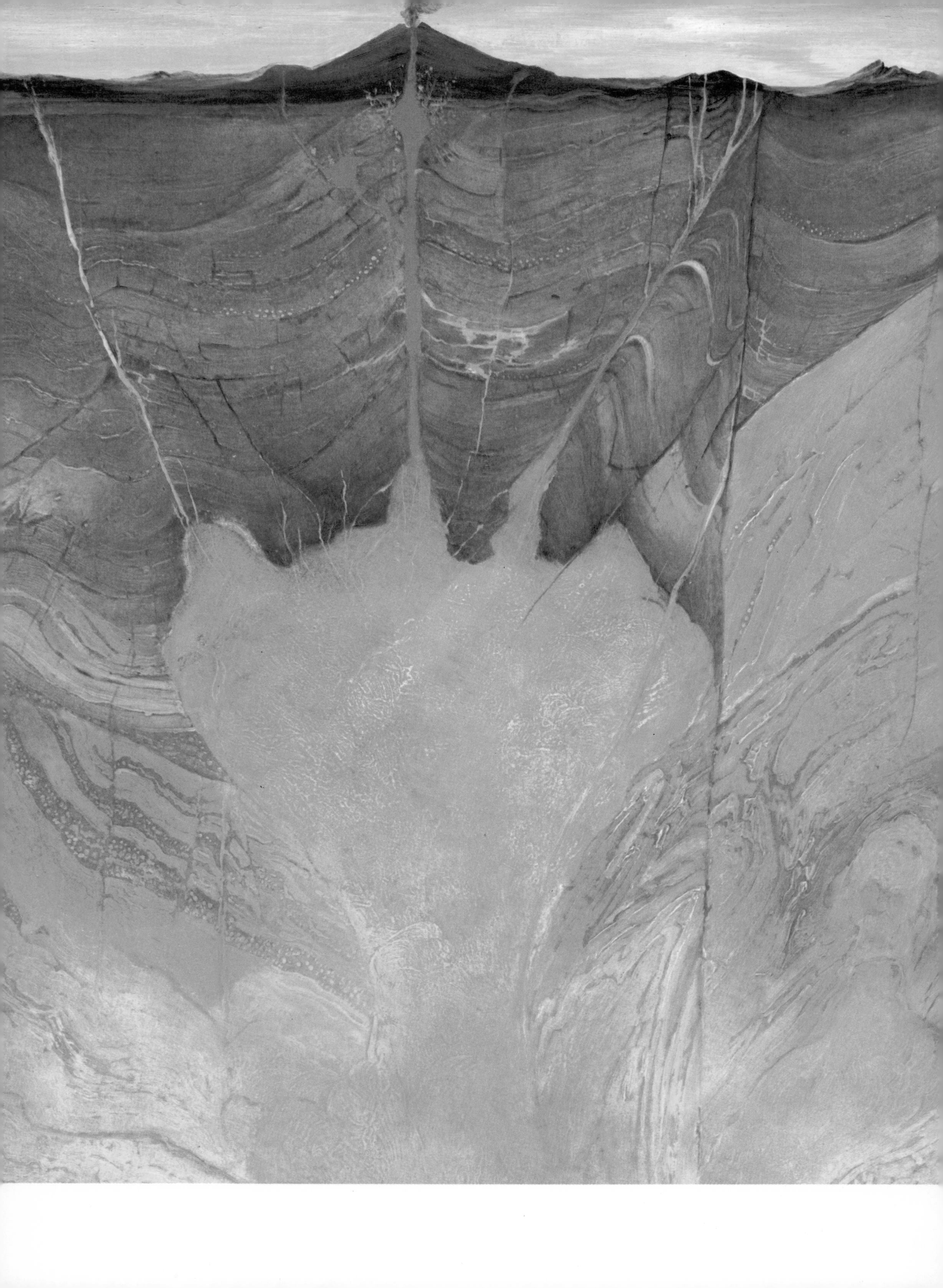

RAW MATERIALS AND RESOURCES

142 The principal geological processes involved in the formation and development of the Earth's crust are magmatic activity, weathering, sedimentation and metamorphosis. The magmatic activity is evidenced by an enormous plutonic body, i.e. magma which has solidified below the surface, from which fissures and vents branch off to supply the volcano on the surface. The occurrence of hot, molten magma is the principal cause of different elements in the crust and is often responsible for the formation of deposits of raw minerals. This also happens in the course of the metamorphosis, which changes the mineral composition of the rocks. In the latter case considerable quantities of substances are released from which raw mineral deposits originate. For example, in the upper parts of magmatic granite masses significant concentrations of tin ores originate; in metamorphic rocks copper or iron ores may occur. The formation of raw mineral deposits requires not only the favourable chemical composition of the source and the presence of favourable traps, such as faults and folds, but also chemically active rocks. In sedimentary rocks, represented on the right, raw materials of another type accumulate, i.e. those caused by weathering and the activity of various organisms. They include not only raw fuels such as crude oil, natural gas and coal, but also clays and phosphates used in agriculture. However, in sedimentary rocks, too, extremely favourable traps are necessary for deposits to form. Raw mineral deposits in sedimentary rocks are usually quite large and are the preferred source. Apart from this sedimentary rock basins are usually the best source of drinkable ground water.

The greater part of this book strives to avoid classification of natural phenomena into black and white categories, and strives, rather, for a holistic approach. However, it is necessary at this point, for reference purposes only, to be reminded of one essential fact. Resources are divided into two different categories: renewable and non-renewable. Even though these terms should be self-explanatory, let us take a look at some examples illustrating the differences.

Renewable resources include, for instance, wood, which is part of the biomass that is exploited, mostly for paper manufacture. New forest stands will grow, and although it may take some time, the landscape will, under favourable conditions, recover after felling. Another example of a renewable resource is wind energy. Non-renewable resources, on the other hand, include such things as minerals or fossil fuels, i.e. coal, oil and natural gas. These resources leave an empty space after extraction which cannot be expected to fill up again. Even so, there is no precise dividing line between renewable and non-re-

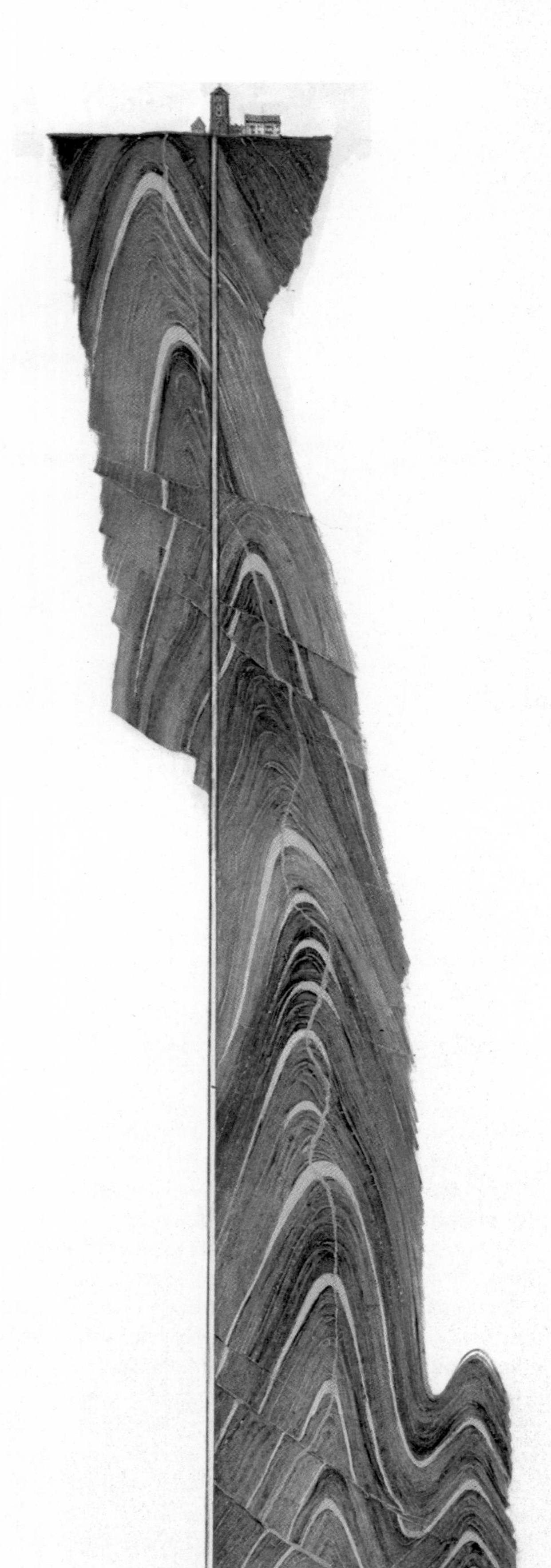

▷
144 Hard and weather-resistant rock appears on the Earth's surface as a resistant formation similar to a knot in a tree. Here, the resistant formation is a quartz vein which may contain, for example, gold. However, useful minerals do not occur only in resistant rocks. If less resistant rocks bear precious stones such as diamonds or resistant metals such as gold or platinum, placer forms where the rocks disintegrate (right). Placer, a deposit of sand, gravel, etc., may contain useful substances in concentrations several times higher than the mother rocks.

143 Raw mineral deposits require an adequate trap, which may occur in vents, open cracks and places of stress relief in the Earth's crust. One such place is the fold saddle. The fact that free spaces in folds form can be demonstrated by bending the pages of a book. The example of the concentration of a useful mineral occurring in fold saddles comes from Bendigo in Australia: the concentration of gold-bearing quartz. This type of deposit is called 'Bendigo' in technical literature.

newable resources. Let us take, for example, a source of ground water. It has already been acknowledged that water is the single most characteristic and valuable feature of our 'blue' planet. Since we know that ground water forms from rainwater, we might be tempted to take the renewal of water sources for granted. However, after intensive drawing-off of water, say for irrigation, it can sometimes take thousands of years for such a reservoir to replenish itself. Sometimes, in places where fossil water reserves have been drawn off, i.e. waters which have been underground for many geological eras, it is highly unlikely that these subterranean reservoirs will ever replenish themselves. Although the amount of water on Earth might seem to be virtually inexhaustible, scientists have in fact calculated that this quantity is only sufficient for 20 billion people.

In the case of non-renewable resources, the situation is quite different: here there is not even a remote prospect of renewal. After the extraction of a coal seam, only empty space remains. This, of course, should be filled up to prevent subsidence, but a new coal seam will never form there. This applies not only to coal or crude oil, which are non-renewable sources of energy, but also to other raw materials, e.g. copper, zinc and iron ores, raw materials for ceramic manufacture, clays and fillers used in the manufacture of paper and artificial fertilizers.

Man has always used raw minerals, and in modern times we have even named historical eras after the manner in which these resources have been used. Knowledge of how to use mineral resources may be regarded as a measure of the degree of advancement of a human society. In the course of time, men have come to use a greater variety of minerals. In the past there were the Stone, Bronze and Iron Ages; the modern age has been referred to as the Steel or Atomic Age. Perhaps in the future we will look back on a Silicon Age. In the past Man required different things from mineral resources. He looked for very rich ores that did not require a great deal of processing. Similarly he did not need the vast quantities of minerals that are required today. Imagine how many iron axes or arrow heads could be made from a single iron bridge, such as those which used to be constructed until the middle years of the 19th century.

A glance back into history shows that rich ore deposits did once exist on Earth. Archaeologists, for example, have recorded how North American Indians in the Lake Superior region obtained pure copper. The processing of pure copper into utensils requires nothing more than thorough forging. In this way impurities are removed and the copper can then be made into utensils. There is documentary evidence of the discovery of pure meteorite iron, and utensils made by Eskimos from this iron have also been found. Finds of pure silver or gold were similarly once not uncommon, although today they are somewhat

145 The complex structure of fluorite veins in the Santa Clara mine in the German Schwarzwald is due to a dense network of cracks in metamorphic rocks along which hot, fluorine-enriched water rose. Here we can see the main crushed zone and groups of lateral torsional cracks. Economic exploitation of such a deposit is not easy.

rare. Most metals do not occur in Nature in pure form, but usually in the form of chemical compounds — in other words, minerals. The pure metal is then obtained from these minerals through various means such as reduction, smelting, chemical or electro-chemical processing. This, of course, requires a powerful energy source.

We often encounter, through the media, statements that the supply of one or other raw material will be exhausted in ten or twenty years. Serious economists and geologists usually take this kind of sensational declaration with a pinch of salt. It should be explained, however, that they are not merely inaccurate, but also unproven. They do not allow, for example, for any future discoveries of mineral resources. Although it is unlikely that these will occur close to the surface of the Earth in already geologically charted regions. They will probably occur in geologically less well-known regions, or in the industrialized world at greater depths. This is one objection that can be raised to announcements that the supply of resources will run out. They fail to mention that in these statements they are referring to the exhaustion of known reserves of natural resources.

In the case of soil, which as we have already noted defies all classification, not even this much applies. The amount of cultivable soil is limited to the dimensions of the terrestrial surface and destroyed land horizon carried away by erosion signifies a permanent loss for a thousand years or more. In the case of ore or other mineral deposits, there is still some hope of these being found in the deeper parts of the Earth.

Geologists further divide raw material supplies according to whether they are verified or calculated, meaning either that the quantity and quality of the raw material has already been verified by means of borehole work or other exploration, or that a presumed supply has not yet been verified according to quality and quantity, but that its existence has already been confirmed and, further, that it is probably exploitable.

Another objection which could be made against categorical statements regarding the exhaustion or exhaustibility of mineral resources concerns their quality. Such statements generally involve the types of ores and raw materials which are extracted at present, i.e. relatively rich ores.

However, raw materials whose content of useful constituents is quite low or hard to extract do occur in Nature — frequently in the vicinity of extracted mineral raw materials. It must be decided whether the cost of extracting these useful constituents is worthwhile — i.e. whether it will outweigh their current market value. On the other

146 The ore vein is a plate-like body, usually highly complex in shape. The veins tail out, join and branch.

148 Metasomatism is a process which takes place during the formation of an ore deposit. The original, chemically easily reacting rock is pushed away by the mineral.

147 In the vicinity of hydrothermal veins adjacent rocks undergo 'hydrothermal alteration'. Such locations may be rich in mineral ores.

149 A stockwork forms in a densely cracked zone.

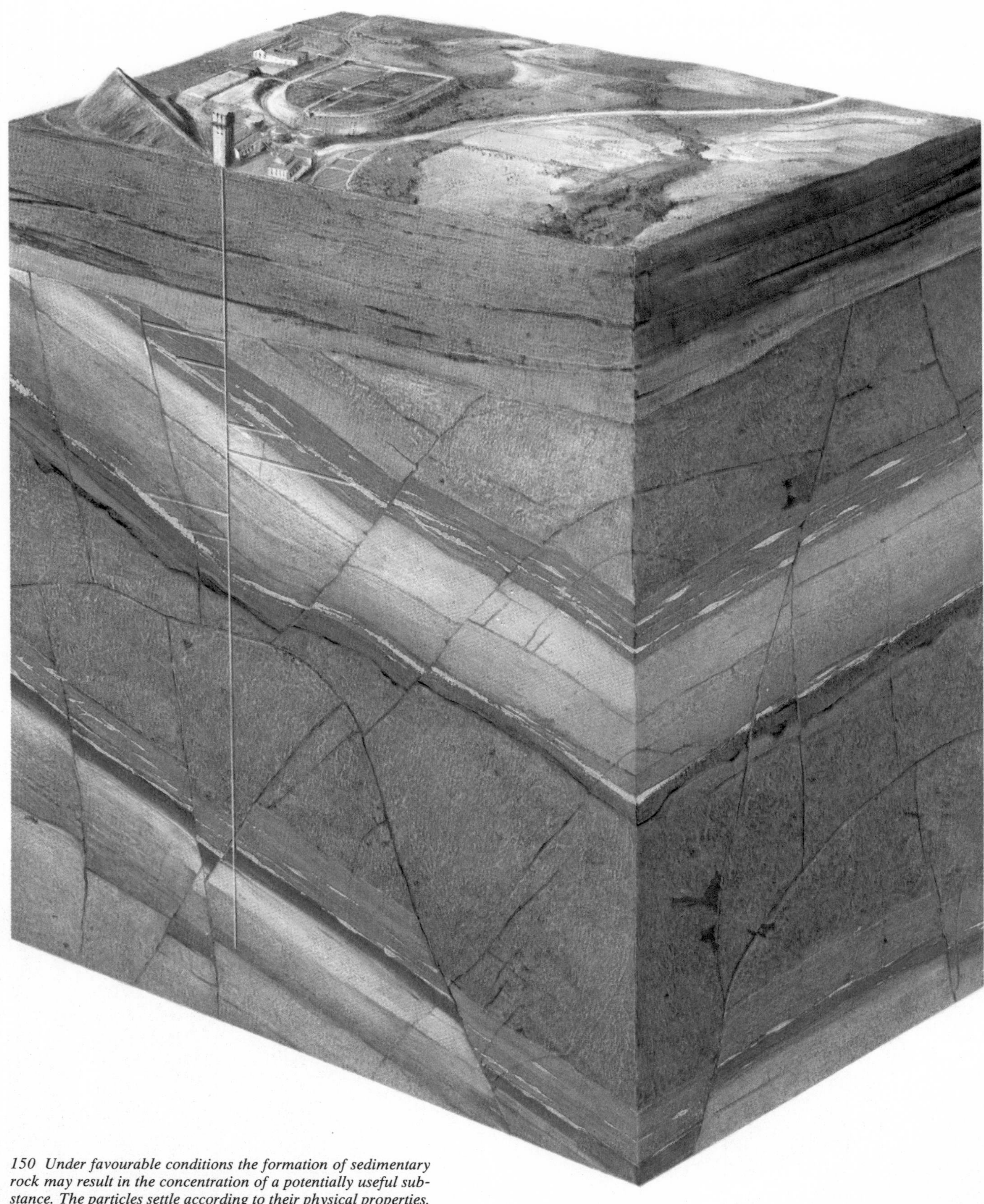

150 Under favourable conditions the formation of sedimentary rock may result in the concentration of a potentially useful substance. The particles settle according to their physical properties. In a still section of a river, clay or other fine particles settle, in a fast-running current only heavier substances such as coarse gravel will fall to the bottom. In this way minerals accumulate in high concentrations. Chemical separation of rock components plays a part. Here we see one of the biggest gold deposits in the world, Witwatersrand in the South African Republic. This is a coarse gravel deposit in a two billion years old river bed. The economically interesting parts are shown in yellow.

hand, if the price of a given ore were to rise as a result of increased demand, scarcity, or for political or speculative reasons, a relatively poor or a less readily processed raw material would then be worth obtaining. This fine, and sometimes movable boundary often results in only the better parts of mineral raw materials being extracted. Therefore, any statements made about the exhaustibility of raw materials also needs to include a statement about which grade of raw materials is exhaustible. Lower grades of the same mineral may be plentiful. There are, of course, cases of the reverse: in some branches of human activity an exploited raw or other material is successfully replaced with something else, with the result that the price of the material drops, and again only the best deposits are extracted. This occurred, for example, when satellite links were launched on their orbits around the Earth: the price of copper fell, because there was no further need to lay ocean cables. In recent times it has occurred a number of

151 The complex route of diamonds to alluvial deposits in valleys, which takes millions of years, is illustrated here by the Panna diamond deposit in Central India. Diamonds usually occur in rocks which form at great depth and travel to the surface, pushing through the Earth's crust in the form of stocks or necks. The diamonds occurred in these rock formations through the process of weathering, and by subsequent weathering they were released into rivers. Here they formed alluvial deposits from which they are mined today.

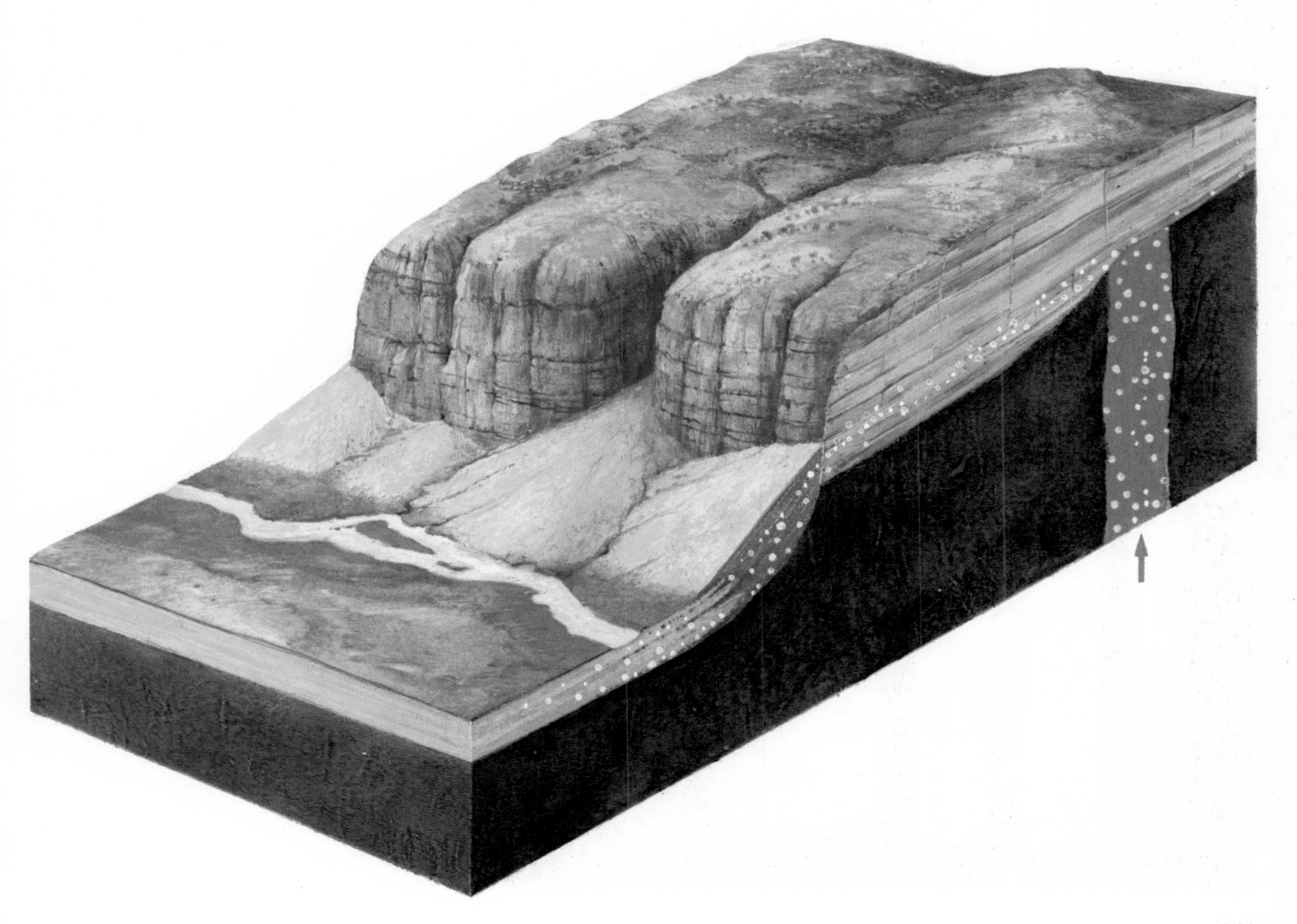

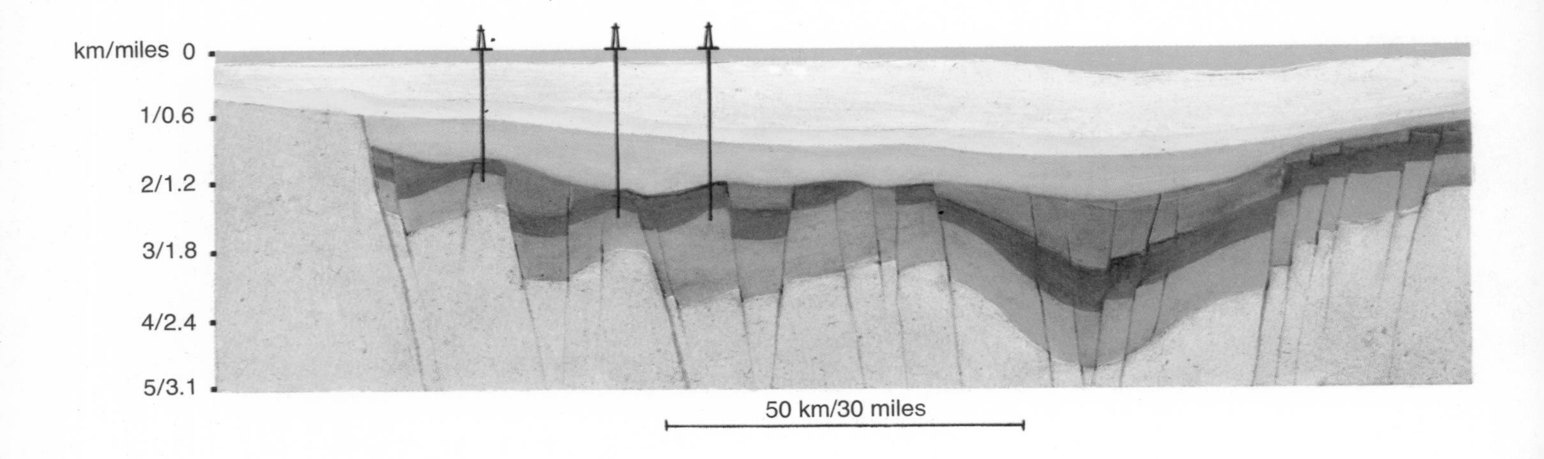

152 Crude oil pools can be found in sedimentary strata. In order to retain the oil (the same applying also to natural gas) the rocks must be strong and porous. They must also be overlaid by other rocks which hold the oil in. Here is an oil site in the North Sea, between Shetland and Norway, where oil is located in the rocks of the Triassic period. More recent rocks form the upper lid.

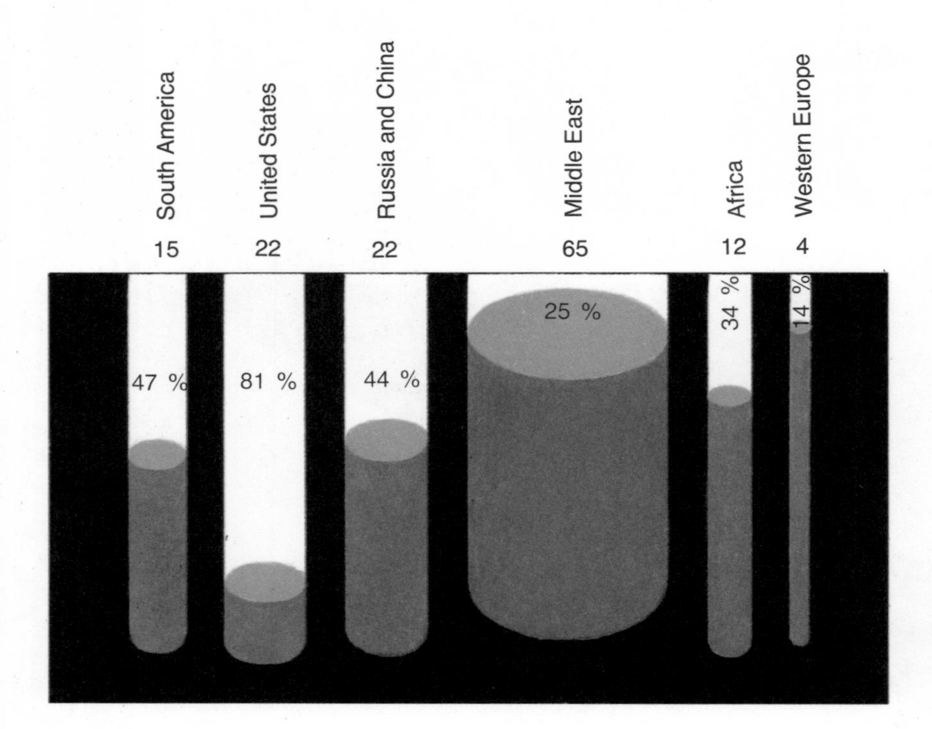

153 At this point in history, oil is one of the world's most important energy sources. The barrels in the picture represent the volume of verified oil reserves. The figures above the individual barrels show the volumes of explored reserves in billions of tonnes. The figures in the white panels show the percentage of exploited known reserves in the given area.

times that the price of a mineral and interest in it has dropped purely because of the ecological drawbacks of its use. This is the case with mercury, an exotic element like thallium. It can also happen, however, that a number of advanced industrial countries stockpile a mineral resource of strategic importance, thereby artificially pushing the price up. The reverse case, where strategic stocks are disposed of or released, similarly affects the price of these resources on the world market.

Geologists concerned with finding mineral deposits have found that there are few good quality deposits and many poor ones. As the concentration of useful constituents in a deposit declines and the ore deteriorates, the number of deposits increases, as does their size. To take this idea ad absurdum, it could be asserted that every rock on the terrestrial surface is a potential mineral resource of ore, since it certainly contains concentrations of metals. Basalt, for example, contains 10 per cent iron, 0.1 per cent manganese, 0.005 per cent nickel and 0.004 per cent chrome — so that even common basalt could theoretically be used to obtain these metals. Of course a chemist or technician would maintain, quite rightly, that although technically feasible it is economically unsound and would cost far too much money, effort and energy to be worthwhile.

Let us take uranium as an example: this is an element which has not been used in large quantities for long (a certain amount was formerly used for colouring glass), its main uses being in defence and in nuclear reactors. As long as the best uranium ores were available, i.e. rich veins of uranite, monazite from placers (sand or gravel deposits), phosphates or lignites with uranium content, it cost roughly $20—35 to obtain 1 kg/2.2 lb of uranium oxide. As demand was great, it became necessary to ob-

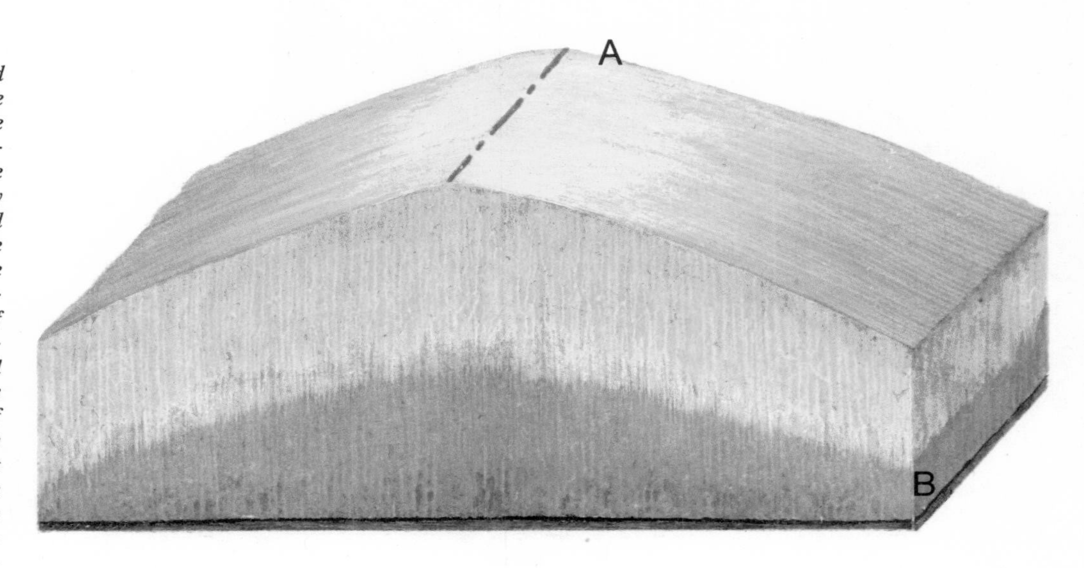

▷
154 If the properties of ground water are understood, it can be protected and its resources can be exploited effectively without destroying them. The upper picture shows the case of a hydrologically uniform environment. Ground water regularly soaks into the pores and cracks in the rock. The ground water level roughly follows the surface morphology of the landscape. In a uniform environment the ground watershed (B) corresponds to the surface watershed (A). The properties of water in a hydrogeologically diverse environment are difficult for geologists to ascertain. One inclined impervious stratum is enough to create a mismatch between the hydrogeological watershed (B) and the surface watershed (A). The lower picture illustrates a diverse environment, the different properties of water in pervious rocks and the presence of water in flaws only in impervious rocks.

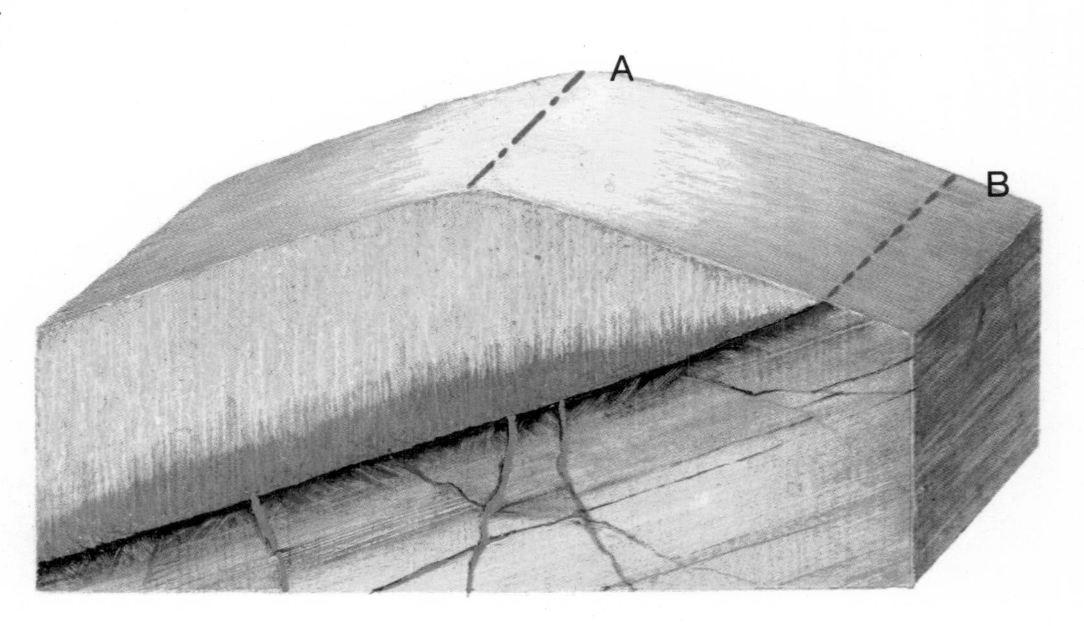

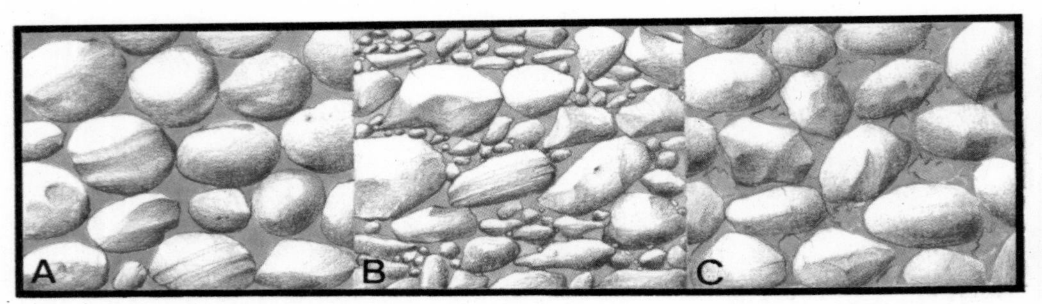

155 The biggest ground water reserves occur in sedimentary rocks, which are substantially more porous than metamorphic or igneous rocks. The degree of porosity also determines the volume of water which the rock can absorb as well as the pore permeability of the rocks. In the rocks, where the porosity is high, the pore permeability is also high. The velocity of ground water flow may range from millimetres to centimetres per second (A). Where the sediment is composed mainly of fine particles, the flow velocity, and consequently the pore permeability is lower (B). In cemented rocks the pore permeability is very low (C).

156 In geological terrains with a small proportion of sedimentary rocks, and igneous and metamorphic rocks in the base, reserves of drinkable water are low. In such a landscape drinkable water occurs only in faults, i.e. open cracks caused by tension or compression. These water reserves are not usually very rich, and cannot be relied on.

157 In sedimentary rocks, such as limestone, cavities and cracks occur which trap water. However, the cracks are often so open that any water that has soaked through to them is not filtered by the rock and the cavities merely let through (and do not retain much) rain water.

158 In Germany each person uses an average of 3 litres/5 pints of water per day for food preparation and drinking, and 150 litres/33 gallons per day for other purposes such as household requirements and bathing. If these figures seem high, it should be noted that in some countries industry and agriculture use 1,500 litres/328 gallons per person per day.

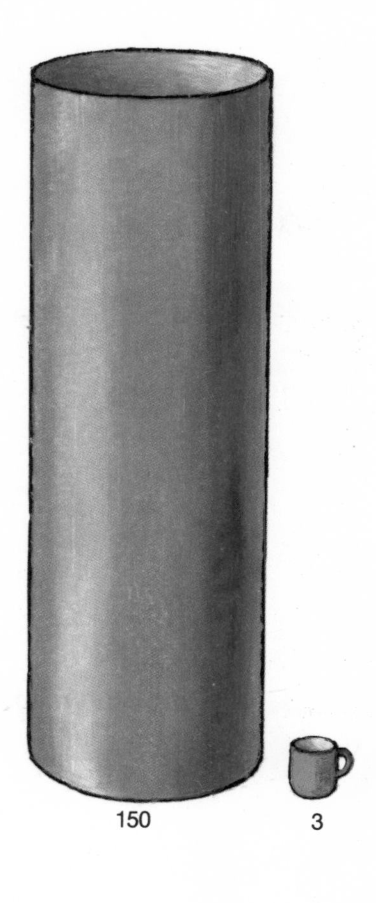

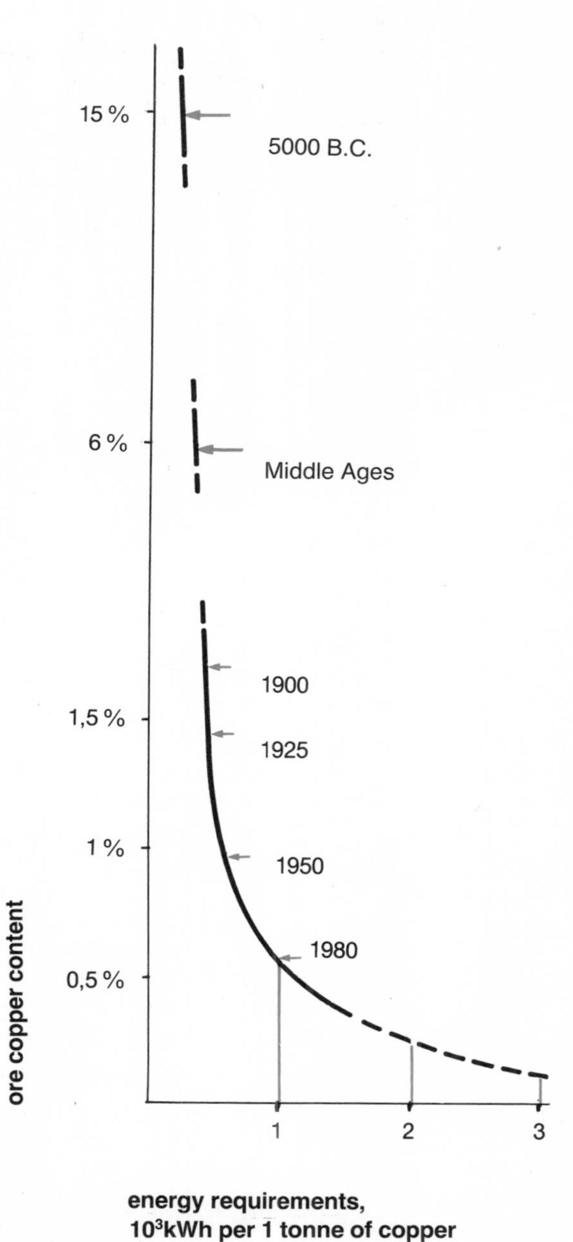

159 Throughout history the use of common metals has increased considerably. As consumption has increased, the richer ores have decreased and poorer ores have to be extracted. This means that the conversion of ores into metals requires a greater investment of energy. The chart shows the increased rate of copper consumption over several thousand years. The vertical axis gives the metal content of the ore and the horizontal axis shows energy output. The curve illustrates the energy requirements of ore processing. The figures along the curve indicate metal content of ore considered still economically feasible at present. The diagram also shows the decrease in ore richness and the increase in energy requirements.

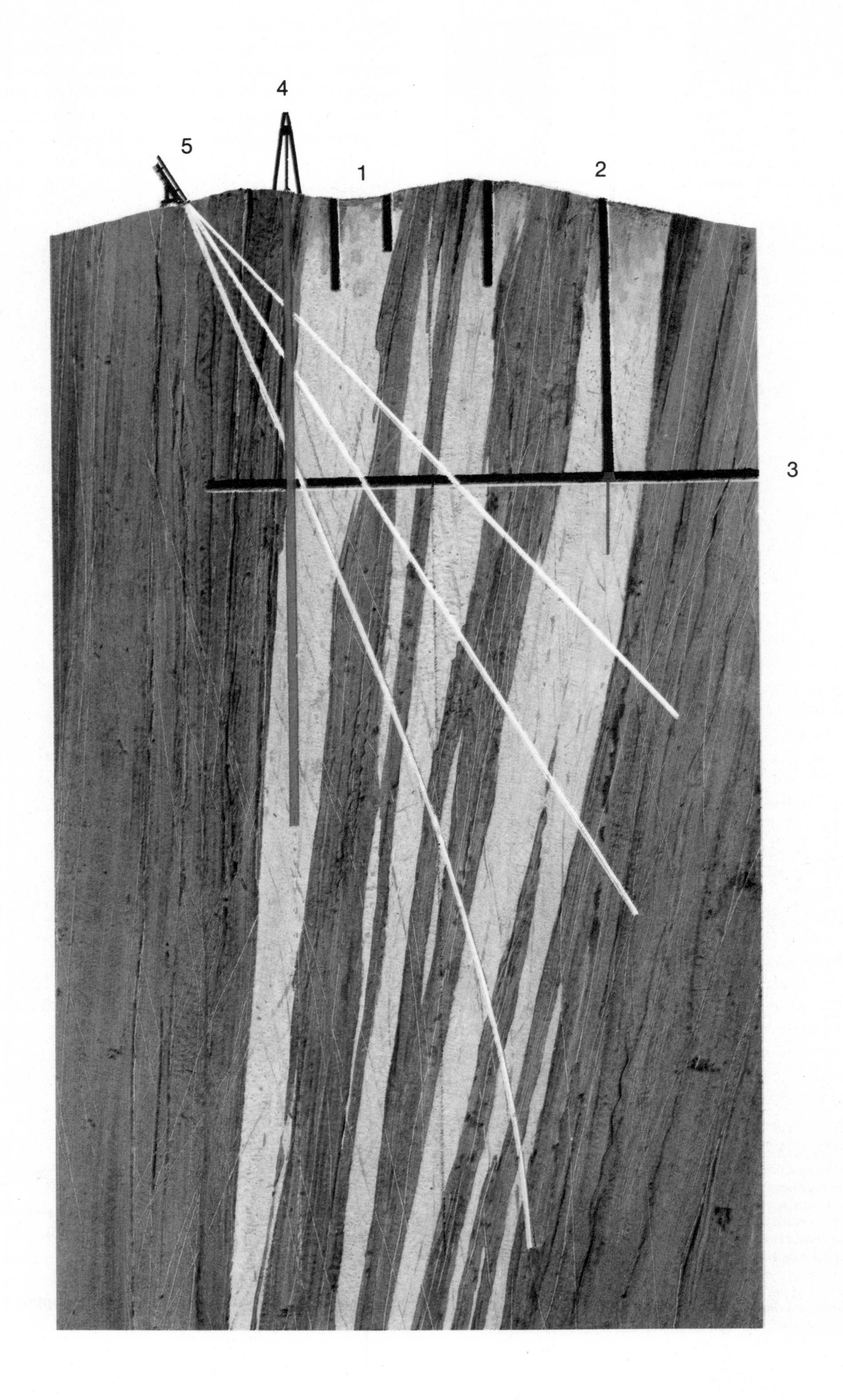
4
5
1
2
3

◁
160 Costs of geological prospecting for raw minerals are often very high, because the extent of the deposit both in area and in depth must be established. For this purpose surface pits (1), shafts (2), galleries (3), vertical core drill holes (4) or inclined drill holes (5) are used.

tain it from poorer quality ores, such as carbonaceous slate: in this case the same amount of uranium required an investment of $35–70. To obtain uranium from seawater would cost $200 per kilogram of oxide, and if using common granite, which contains 4–5 g per ton, the price of obtaining 1 kg/2.2 lb would be around $1,000.

Comparing the average content of a metal in the terrestrial crust with that in an ore deposit, we can see what an enormous leap in concentration is necessary for a mineral deposit to form from such a normal rock formation. The copper content in normal rock, for example, is 0.0055 per cent, but at least 0.6 per cent should be in a deposit. With chrome the gap is even greater, being about 0.005 per cent in normal rock, whereas a deposit calls for around 30 per cent. Any ore deposit worth extracting, even at high cost, therefore, must contain an exceptional concentration of the given metal.

In order to be able to find these metal concentrations in the crust, it is first necessary to understand how they form. Understanding how and why the occurrence of elements is increased makes ores easier to detect. A slightly higher metal content in rock can also be an indication that ore is present. The technological and analytical methods of detecting such minute amounts of metals have improved greatly in the last twenty years. Such methods are also used for monitoring and detecting geochemical conditions in the study of the environment. The ability to ascertain certain environmental situations and to detect the presence of 'artificially' created abnormal conditions such as heavy metals, is a task of paramount importance.

Since the Middle Ages, the sign of high-quality ore has been a rich vein or 'lode'. This was one of the commonest types of deposit sought out in the past. Silver, gold, copper, mercury, lead, antimony, tin and iron were all obtained from such lodes. Extraction from a lode deposit was an advantage, among other things, because the ore could be separated from the waste rock during extraction itself. However, a great many natural preconditions must be fulfilled even for this simplest of ore lodes to form. There must be an open fissure in the terrestrial crust, an enormous source of energy and heating-up of water (usually from a heat source deep within the Earth), as well as rocks from which metals can be leached or by which they can be transported. Only in the case of such a combination of favourable factors can a lode form. Whether it is of good quality is a matter for the prospector, geologist, miner, and finally the economist to decide.

There has recently been a move away from ore lodes in favour of other types of ore, known as massif ores, not only because they are easier to find, but also because they can be extracted more easily by using heavy machinery. Processing is also easier, being done in bulk in large factories. While it is definitely not more sound ecologically to remove huge quantities of ore from large open quarries, transporting it away in massive lorries, to process it in order to obtain the metal from it, this is nevertheless how it is done. Even though this type of mining is done largely out of convenience it involves a huge energy outlay. This sets a great cycle in motion, in which poor quality ore calls for huge energy expenditure in terms of the extraction of the ore itself and of the raw energy resources required, e.g. coal or other fuels.

The most frequently extracted and consumed non-renewable energy resources are fossil fuels, i.e. solar energy conserved in the form of coal, lignite, peat, crude oil, gas and tar sands. Energy is generally obtained from these resources through combustion, and the end product of this process is the release of carbon dioxide and other gases into the atmosphere. Although fossil fuels clearly account for most energy consumption, they are obviously not the most suitable means of producing energy. These are the exhaustible resources of the planet. There is no real prospect nowadays either of detecting them more easily, or of using them in better ways through increasing our knowledge of them and their origin. Since these resources, by virtue of their origin, are concentrated in the uppermost and most thoroughly surveyed parts of the Earth, we can scarcely expect some revolutionary new discovery to transform the fuel and energy economy of the world. Interest in these resources will indeed most probably decline in the near future, chiefly as a result of increasing concentrations of 'greenhouse' gases in the atmosphere.

Uranium and thorium resources are also non-renewable, so that which has been mentioned about ore resources applies equally to raw materials for nuclear reactors. Although nuclear energy does harbour certain dangers (of which Chernobyl was an example) these dangers are on an essentially local scale compared with the increasing worldwide problems caused by the greenhouse effect. However, the kind of blinkered optimism that sees in nuclear energy an ideal solution to the world energy crisis is equally inappropriate. The problems of reducing and disposing of nuclear waste, which are both ecological and economic, are linked with other areas of world research. It is becoming increasingly apparent that without a perfect understanding of the relationships between the various parts of the Earth, its water and other fluid cycles, it is not possible to dispose of nuclear waste safely so as not to jeopardize our own and future generations. In any case, in view of the exhaustibility of resources, the nuclear energy alternative with its so far unsafe disposal methods and finite amount of space on Earth for such potentially dangerous waste management can be no more than a transitional one.

Renewable energy sources come about mainly through the existence of solar radiation, either through its direct use or through its conversion into electricity. Solar energy manifests itself not only in the form of the sun's rays but also through the movement of air masses, winds and water cycles (hydro-energy), and through its part in maintaining

161 Opencast mining is usually cheaper than deep mining. However, it must meet certain requirements according to the dimensions of the mineral deposit, the overburden volume (i.e. rock which must be removed in order to expose the deposit) and, consequently, the volume of dumps, and the volume of annual extraction. It must also meet certain ecological requirements. The picture shows one of the biggest gold deposits in the world, the 'Carlin' deposit in Nevada, in the United States. Hot springs create ore deposits with a high gold content of 10 g per ton / $\frac{1}{3}$ oz per ton in a sedimentary formation. These days a gold content of 2 g per tonne/ $\frac{1}{15}$ oz per ton is considered exploitable.

organic life. Although the exploitation of such resources as geothermal energy or tidal energy may be of local significance, it represents only a fraction of overall global energy consumption.

The exploitation of renewable sources is likewise not without its problems. One should be aware that the disadvantage of 'clean' methods of obtaining energy is that they involve 'low-density' energy, which calls for the construction of extensive structures for concentrating the energy obtained. Take, for example, the large and extensive solar energy panels necessary to obtain relatively small amounts of energy, and requiring not only investment but in many cases conversion of the landscape.

Despite these problems, however, when considering the energy resources of the future, it seems most sensible to opt for renewable ones, as these environmentally friendly sources are drawn directly from nature and do not impinge on its natural cycles nor do they create pollution in the process.

Looking at modern history and comparing the number of natural materials and resources we exploit now shows the massive qualitative leap marked by the industrial revolution of the 19th century, and the proliferation of crafts which took place in the centuries leading up to it. Up to that time, people had used only small quantities of raw materials and resources. Every increase in the range of exploited raw materials in fact signified a new epoch in scientific history, be it the manufacture of ceramics, sulphuric acid, artificial fertilizers, germanium transistors, or the use of rare soils in superconductive materials. Naturally, the exploitation of a new material frequently changes the whole way of life of a society, producing a chain of new innovations. For example, when heat energy is produced from burning wood, not much material is used. A couple of stones around a fireplace, or a stove made of clay or bricks, is all that is needed. To produce heat by burning coal, however, calls for a more sophisticated fireplace or boiler, usually a steel or cast iron stove lined wiht heatresistant bricks, with a sturdy grate and a suitable flue or chimney to carry away waste gases. It is an even more complicated process to heat a house using electricity. First it is necessary to produce the electrical energy itself (which requires considerable amounts of material for producing turbines or generators and dynamos), not to mention the boiler itself, which is no longer merely a boiler, but one with auxiliary technical equipment, a great deal of iron, steel, copper and numerous other materials. The range of materials used increases even more when energy is obtained from nuclear fuels. This involves not only the nuclear fuel itself – radioactive uranium or plutonium – but a reactor container constructed from a sturdy material such as steel, with additional elements such as nickel, chrome, molybdenum or titanium, considerable amounts of shielding and damping materials (e.g. boron compounds), as well as the means for transmitting the energy produced. Even the production of energy from solar radiation, however clean and practical it may seem in addition to being an ecologically sound method, still needs

162 Known world ore reserves are decreasing at an astonishing rate. Shown here are ore reserves of the most common non-ferrous metals in millions of tonnes as they were in 1983 (above). It extraction of ore left by the year 2000 would be very low (below). Every cube represents 1 million tonnes of ore.

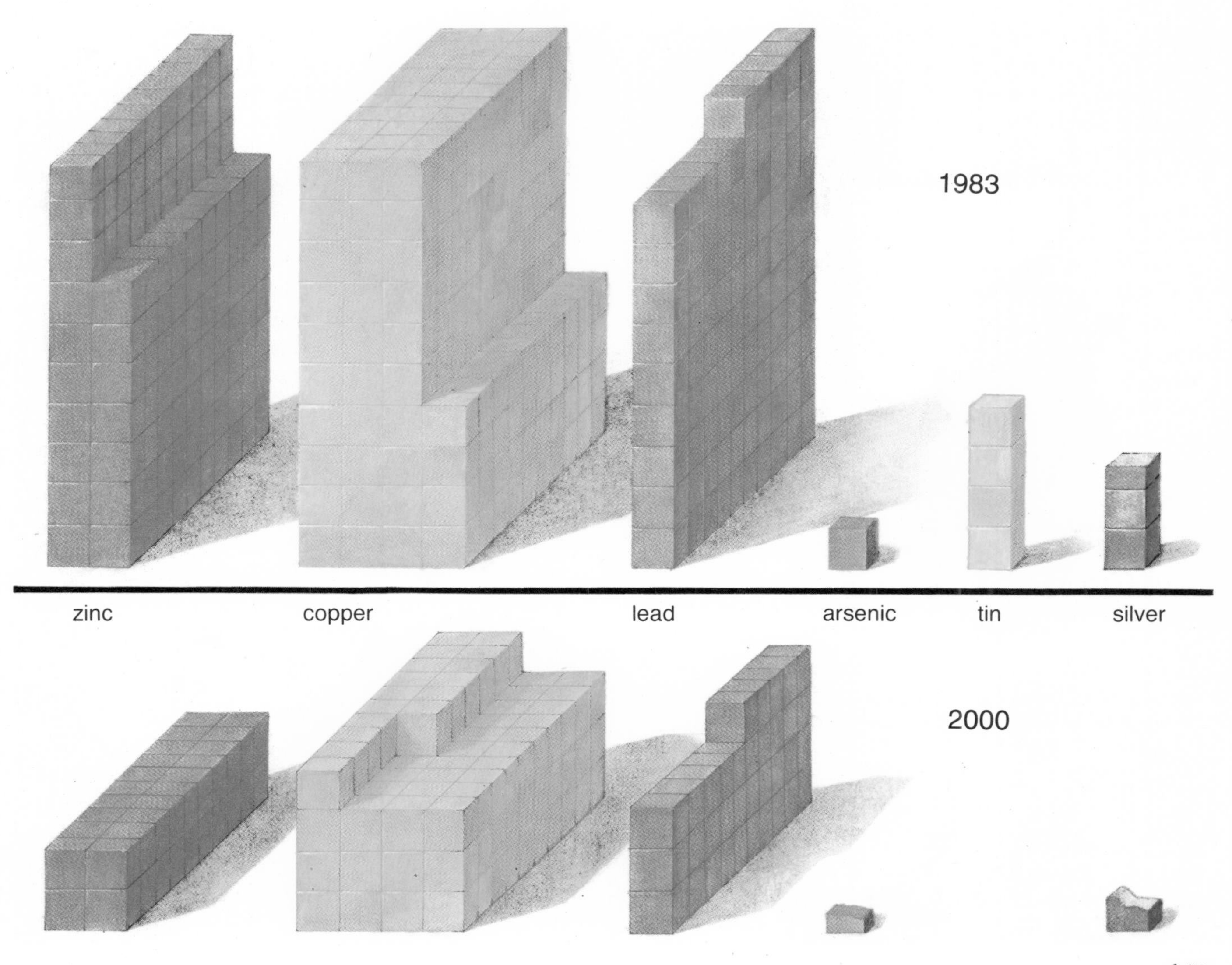

various materials to produce the equipment needed to extract and store it.

The key to our society's lifestyle lies in the way energy is produced and how accessible it is. We have to ask ourselves whether the Earth will be able to maintain us, or whether we will have to find ways to restrict our use of energy in the future. We use it to carry goods and people, store food, cultivate the ground, clean our houses, and generally make life easier for ourselves. We also use vast amounts of natural resources to obtain other natural resources.

In a number of areas these energy slaves have been mishandled. Let us take a look at farming. Heavy machinery is damaging soil structure: the ease with which extensive tracts of land are irrigated leads to a reduction in the productivity of farming land, as well as to increased salt content and deterioration.

So far we have only spoken about 'obtaining' the essential constituents from mineral resources, and about the input of energy required to this end. This seems, in general, to be the way human beings view things: in terms of immediate benefits and high returns. There has been little thought spared for the disposal of waste or the effects of many years of large scale exploitation of raw materials, most of which is used to keep modern man happy and comfortable. This brings us to yet another problem arising from and involving energy consumption: disposal of the waste produced by the mining of raw materials. Energy is used to dispose of waste produced from the extraction of minerals which are used in energy production. It is a vicious circle.

As has already been mentioned, the degree of development of human society depends on which mineral resources Man uses. Human society evolves with the use of each new resource or raw material. The situation prevailing in the present-day world, however, indicates the reverse. Instead of furthering Man's progress, the exploitation of mineral resources is beginning to impede social development. It is all having a negative effect on the landscape, and the atmosphere, causing vast areas of erosion and air pollution. If we were to reduce these effects, it would call for the sacrifice of a great proportion of these resources themselves.

The detection of mineral sources is no easy matter. Geologists must first look to the landscape for clues which usually signify the occurrence of ores. These may be variations in the elements contained either in the soil or plants, or physical evidence of deposits, such as variations in the conductivity of rocks, magnetic properties, or gravity variations. Usually anomalies are discovered, indicating a direct source of ore or an immediately extractable raw material.

Out of every thousand such 'signs' discovered, however, only a hundred merit further examination. The latter usually involves, for example, carrying out an exploratory bore or drillhole, which calls for a certain investment of energy, human effort, time, and therefore also money. The verification of anomalies often reveals them to be misleading, or may show them at first glance to be the result of a low concentration or insignificant amount of the raw material. Of these hundred cases, the number offering any promise falls to only ten. In these successful cases, drilling equipment, excavators and geologists are called on to obtain samples which are then sent to the laboratory for detailed analysis. Investigations are made as to how the ore can best be processed and dressed. There is also an initial assessment made as to how much ore there is likely to be in the given locality, its quality, and how much metal will be obtained per tonne. Finding ore, therefore, does not necessarily always mean the ore can be extracted: this depends on how much ore the deposit contains. Transporting the ore to the processing plant, crushing, dressing and concentrating it, then transporting the concentrate yet again to be processed a second time and have impurities removed, all this has to be taken into account. These processes call for a great deal of time, energy and effort.

This is why, as recent statistics show, only one in ten verified ore finds usually proves promising enough to make it worthwhile obtaining and extracting the metal from it. The term 'worthwhile' usually refers to how much energy needs to be invested in extraction, transportation and processing in order to obtain the metal. To this should also be added another, all too important aspect — the ecological one. Some consideration is necessary if ore occurs on farmland, recreation or conservation areas, or if its extraction will affect ground water conditions. It even has to be taken into account if its processing is likely to pollute the environment. The geologist, therefore, who stumbles across indications of ore has far from won the battle.

The example of ore is neither an isolated nor an extreme one. Modern society not only looks for ores, but also consumes massive amounts of resources in terms of raw energy and construction materials. Look at the illustration showing raw materials, both according to the scale on which they are consumed and according to the financial resources that these amounts represent. This reveals the politico-economical links.

It would be appropriate at this juncture to re-emphasize the marked imbalance in the industrial world in terms of mineral resources. It is obvious that most mineral resources are consumed in the advanced industrial world. The same applies to artificial fertilizers and energy. If the developing countries were to attain the current consumption levels of the advanced industrial world within the next fifty years, their economic and industrial output would have to increase five times over compared with present levels. The

▷
163 We usually hear about the raw materials market only from the daily press or the London commodity exchange. This picture gives a different idea. On the left the raw minerals are arranged according to volume extracted. Apart from water, the need for which far exceeds that for all other resources. Most materials extracted from the Earth are used in building and road construction. After this comes crude oil and other raw materials used in energy production. If we look at the raw minerals market from a financial viewpoint (right), oil is predominant and other more bulky raw materials follow.

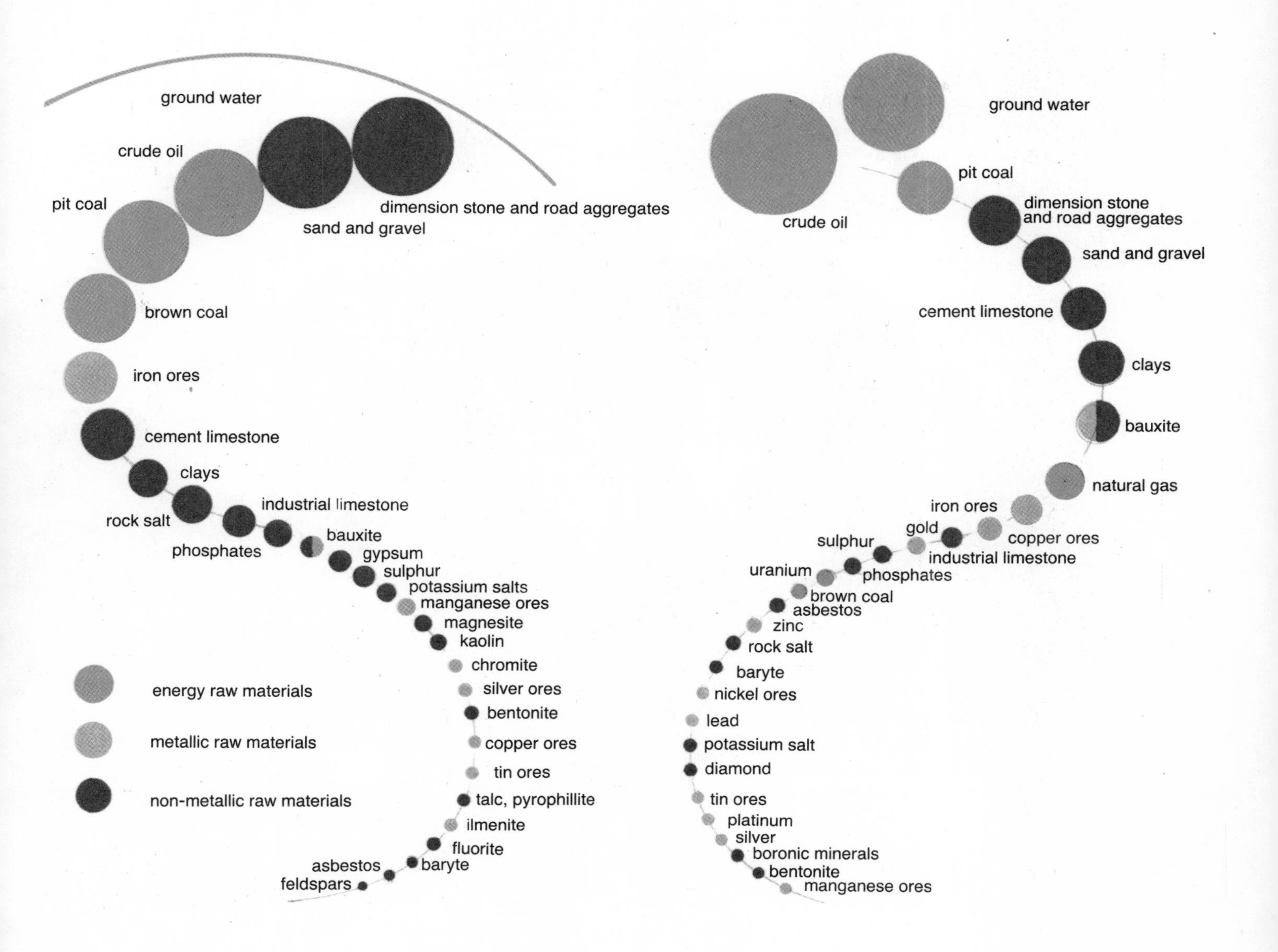

significance of this in terms of consumption statistics of basic mineral, and above all energy resources, is almost beyond our present capacity to envisage.

No country in the world today is entirely self-sufficient in the manufacture of the whole range of materials and mineral resources: every country is dependent on some imports from other parts of the world. Some countries are entirely dependent on them. Japan, for example, imports all its primary raw materials, while other countries are more self-sufficient, importing hardly any — for example Russia and the United States. The fact is, however, that high-quality mineral deposits are few. It is no wonder that a number of territorial conflicts in the past were conducted primarily to gain control of mineral wealth. Today's easy communications and relatively low transportation costs facilitate exploitation of only the best deposits. This is not the case, however, with raw materials used in cement manufacture, or those which are used in massive quantities.

Since there are relatively few of these high-quality deposits, the manufacture of some resources and raw materials is controlled by monopolies. Natural diamonds, for example, are mined almost exclusively by the Republic of South Africa and the former Soviet Union, other producers being of negligible importance. This is also true in the case of platinum and other similar metals, such as iridium, palladium and osmium. South Africa and the former Soviet Union cover around 98 per cent of world demand. There are likewise not many producers involved in the extraction of molybdenum ore, the United States and Zimbabwe extracting more than three-quarters of worldwide demand. The major proportion of wolfram produced is extracted in China, Canada and the former Soviet Union, while worldwide tin production centres largely around South-east Asia and Bolivia, other deposits being of minimal importance. Since, furthermore, every raw mineral resource pertains to a particular rock type, or terrain with a certain geological composition, geological boundaries are just as significant for trade in these commodities as political ones.

IMBALANCES AND CATASTROPHES

164 It can be difficult to prevent catastrophes caused by people. Nevertheless, it is possible. To foresee natural catastrophes and prevent them, however, presumes a perfect knowledge of all laws of nature. One of the most complex fields of forecasting is that concerned with volcanic activity. This example from South America shows a volcano of the Mont Pelée type, with a very complex history. The outer caldera — the circular wall around the outside of the volcano — is of a subsident character. This means that it is formed when the volcano ejects rocks in small batches. This makes space into which the rocks near the surface subside. The inner caldera, situated in the uppermost parts of the volcano, however, may be of an explosive type. In that case the enormous crater, or caldera, is formed by the volcano's eruption. Its dimensions make it possible to estimate the quantity of material thus ejected into the atmosphere. In the vent is a small plug. When observing an inactive volcano, it is always difficult to foretell when and how the volcano will become active. However, an analysis of the deposits of previous eruptions makes it possible to forecast whether or not the eruption will be of the Pelée type.

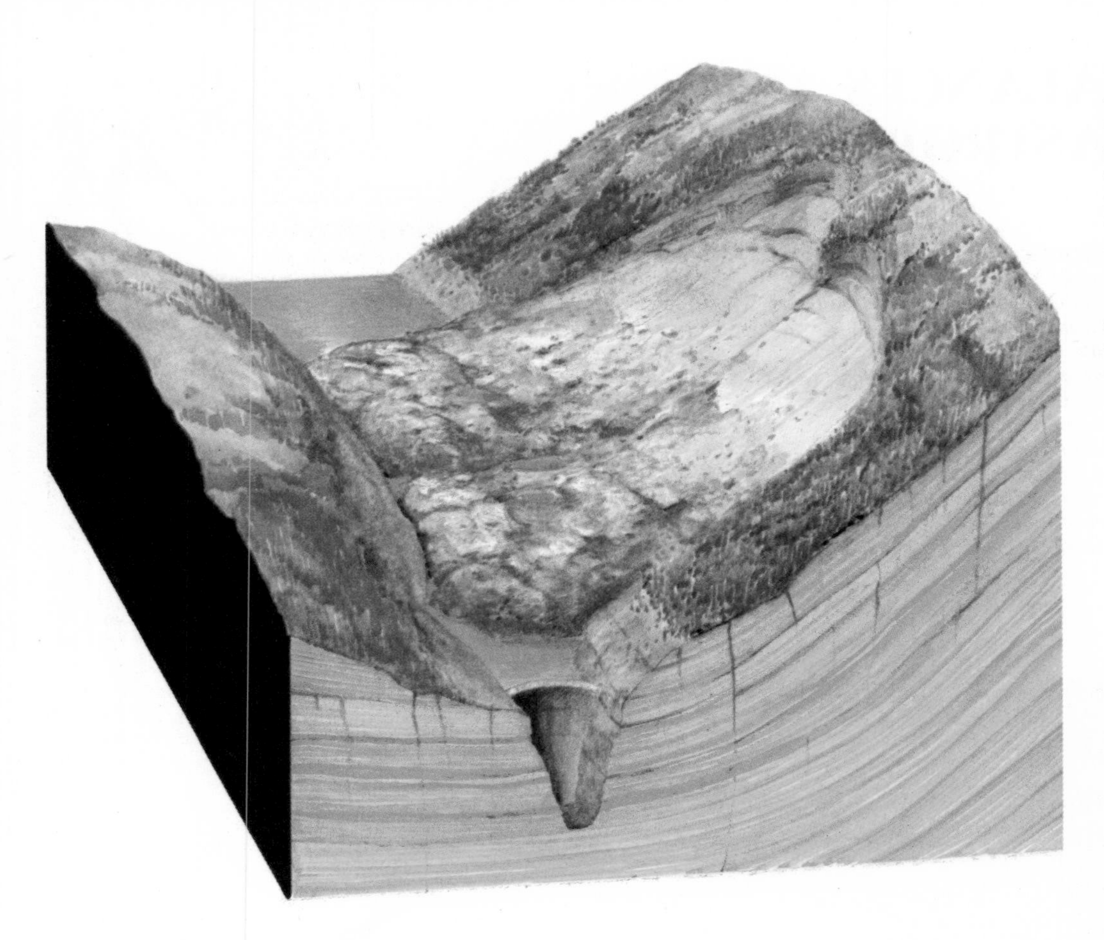

165 A landslide may be considered a catastrophe. Looked at another way, it could be thought of as a useful act of nature. A landslide solves a state of imbalance initiated by human activity. The construction of the Vaillont dam in Italy is one such example. When the dam reservoir had filled with water, the surrounding rock strata became waterlogged and uplifted. Suddenly loosened in this way they crashed into the reservoir.

As in the previous chapter, we may begin here by assessing disasters and classifying them according to origin or cause – firstly natural ones, unaffected by Man, and secondly those caused by unconsidered human activity.

We are familiar with the saying that we are all wise after the event, which applies to all people including scientists. Often we do not fully grasp the implications of a situation until it has already been resolved. We do not have enough knowledge of the Earth, its internal processes and ecosystems, or its possible responses to our actions, to enable us to make allowances for all possible consequences of our intervention into the landscape. When drawing up plans for a dam, no architect does it with the idea that this could cause a catastrophe. Nor does he begin with the assumption that his vision may eventually cause an earthquake in areas which are not known for their seismic instability.

Yet there are cases of just such occurrences. At Boulder Dam in the United States, Hsinchuang in China, Akheloos in Greece and the Kariba Dam, in Zimbabwe, earthquakes occurred after the water sluices had been closed to fill the dams.

The disaster which occurred at the Vaillont dam in Italy offers a different example, in which a 165 m high wave suddenly spilled over the dam, submerging the homes below it and killing over 2,000 people. It was caused by the saturation of material left by an earlier landslide. This large mass of soil and rocks formed the shore above the reservoir; when it became saturated, it dislodged and it slid into the lake. The water level rose and spilled over the dam. These are not natural catastrophes in the real sense of the word, being the result of human activity, a lack of knowledge and planning. In these cases the response of 'inanimate Nature' to the activity was immediate. However, in the case of many imbalances which are potential catastrophes, the results are not immediate, occurring, in some cases, decades later. There are quite probably catastrophes on the way, which we, because of our inability to account for all contingencies, know nothing about.

There has been much written about catastrophes, both in fiction and specialist scientific literature. It is often used by fiction writers to illustrate how different people react in extreme circumstances. On the other hand, information can be found in specialist scientific journals giving facts, figures and accounts by geologists and biologists, of the effects of these unnatural disasters upon our environment. Unfortunately, it does not seem that enough of the right people, i.e. those in positions of power, read this kind of literature. Of those that do, only a small number seem convinced that our harsh treatment of the environment will have any detrimental effect.

Before speculating on the causes of past ecological dis-

▷
168 Landslides along rock strata, like that at Vaillont, are quite rare. Landslides occur most frequently in clay deposits, if a slope's equilibrium is disturbed, for example, by heavy rainfall. The masses slide along a rounded surface (similar to the way in which blancmange slides off the spoon) and the process may last for hours or even days.

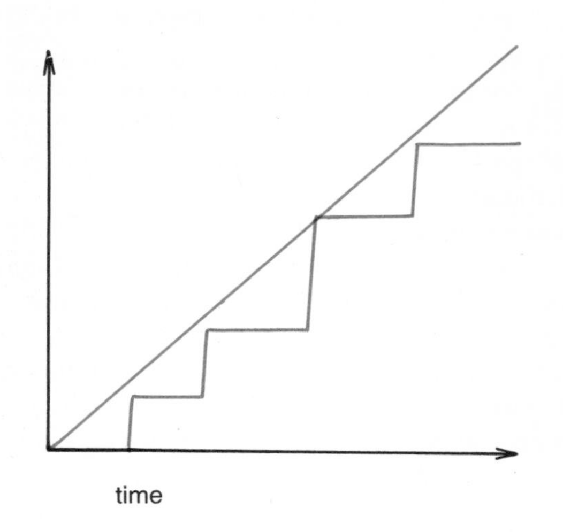

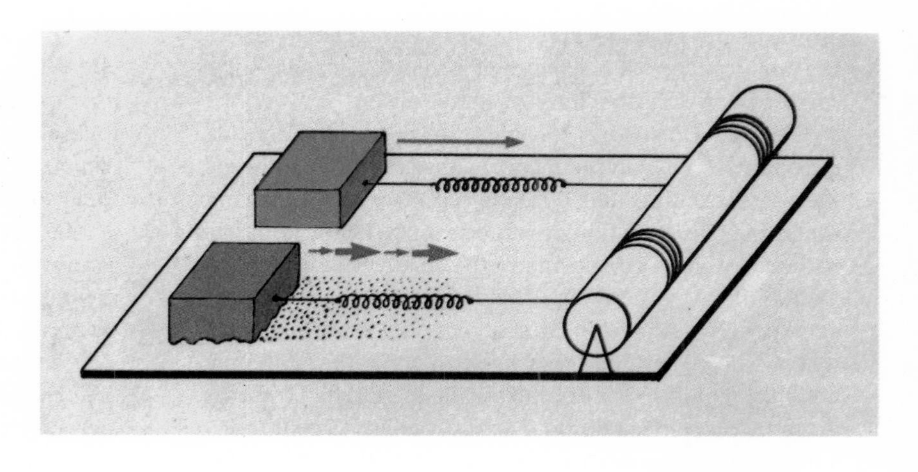

166 The preceding example can also be illustrated by a simple diagram. The red straight line represents the continuous slide of the plate, the blue stepped curve showing the sudden stress release. In both cases the same displacement has occurred in the same period of time. The very principle of gradual stress release form the basis of the possibility of major earthquake prevention. If a place is found in the seismic area, in which stresses are generated and where they are likely to be released, it is possible to release them artificially by a number of minor shocks.

167 Earthquake catastrophes, however incomprehensible they may seem, often have very simple causes. The picture illustrates the example described in the text, in which a smooth plate (red) slides evenly along a smooth, oiled surface, while another, uneven plate (blue) 'jumps' along a bumpy surface. In the case of the rope pulling the blue plate, stresses occur which are released suddenly when the plate 'jumps', while in the case of the red plate, they are released gradually. When stress is released suddenly, an earthquake occurs.

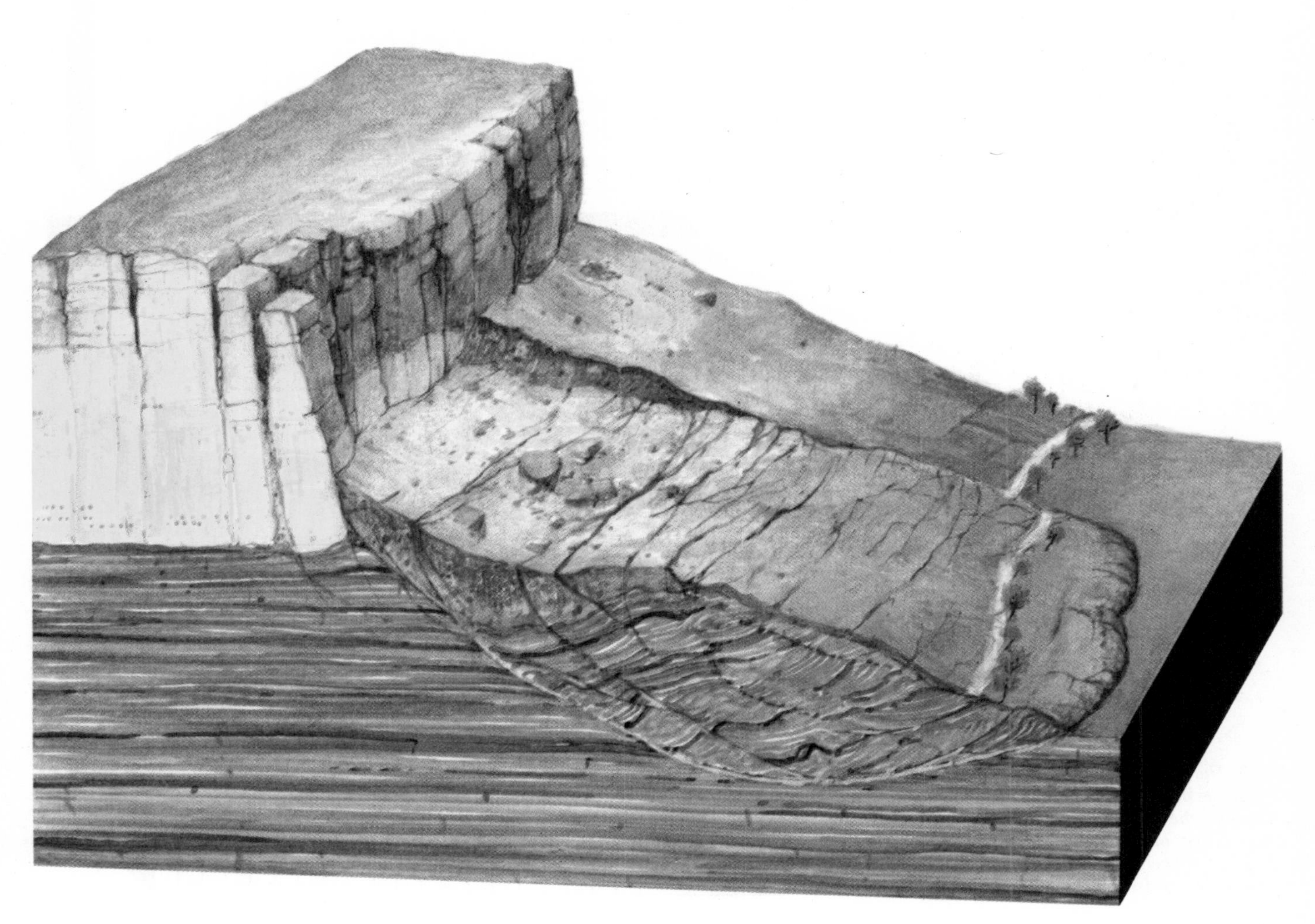

asters, however, let us take a look at disasters in general. Let us look first at the kind of geological catastrophes caused by the Earth's interior metabolism.

Disasters caused by volcanic activity are obviously the most impressive and the most exciting to watch, although the word exciting hardly seems appropriate. In former times, the Christian faith assumed Hell to be located deep within the Earth. This seemed to be an effective idea which would make sinners think twice about their immoral activities. Nowadays, of course, there are few people who would believe that, had they lived an altogether unseemly life, they would spend eternity inside the Earth. However, volcanic eruptions still hold sensationalist appeal today. The sheer magnitude of their activity with its exploding mountain tops, red-hot fields of ash and whole villages swept away in a matter of minutes by gigantic lava flows still bring reporters from far and wide. Volcanic eruptions and their effects have changed little since ancient times. Voclanic ash forms an extremely fertile substrate, the soil above it being able to provide food for many. A volcano's life can be millions of years long, a great many times longer than a human life. Specific episodes of volcanic activity can be so far apart in time that human memory is unable to chronicle them.

The human approach to natural catastrophe is anything but rational. Like the tendency for people to recall the pleasant aspects of their lives, in the main they are optimistic about the future.

Predicting volcanic disasters is not easy. The locations are obvious, since volcanic belts are well-known and quite clearly situated. Cases of new volcanoes becoming active are very rare, although not entirely unknown (e.g. Paricutín in Mexico, 1943). The important question in the prediction of volcanic activity is not where, but when and how the volcano will erupt. Just as a person's behaviour is difficult to predict, so it is with volcanoes. Whether a vol-

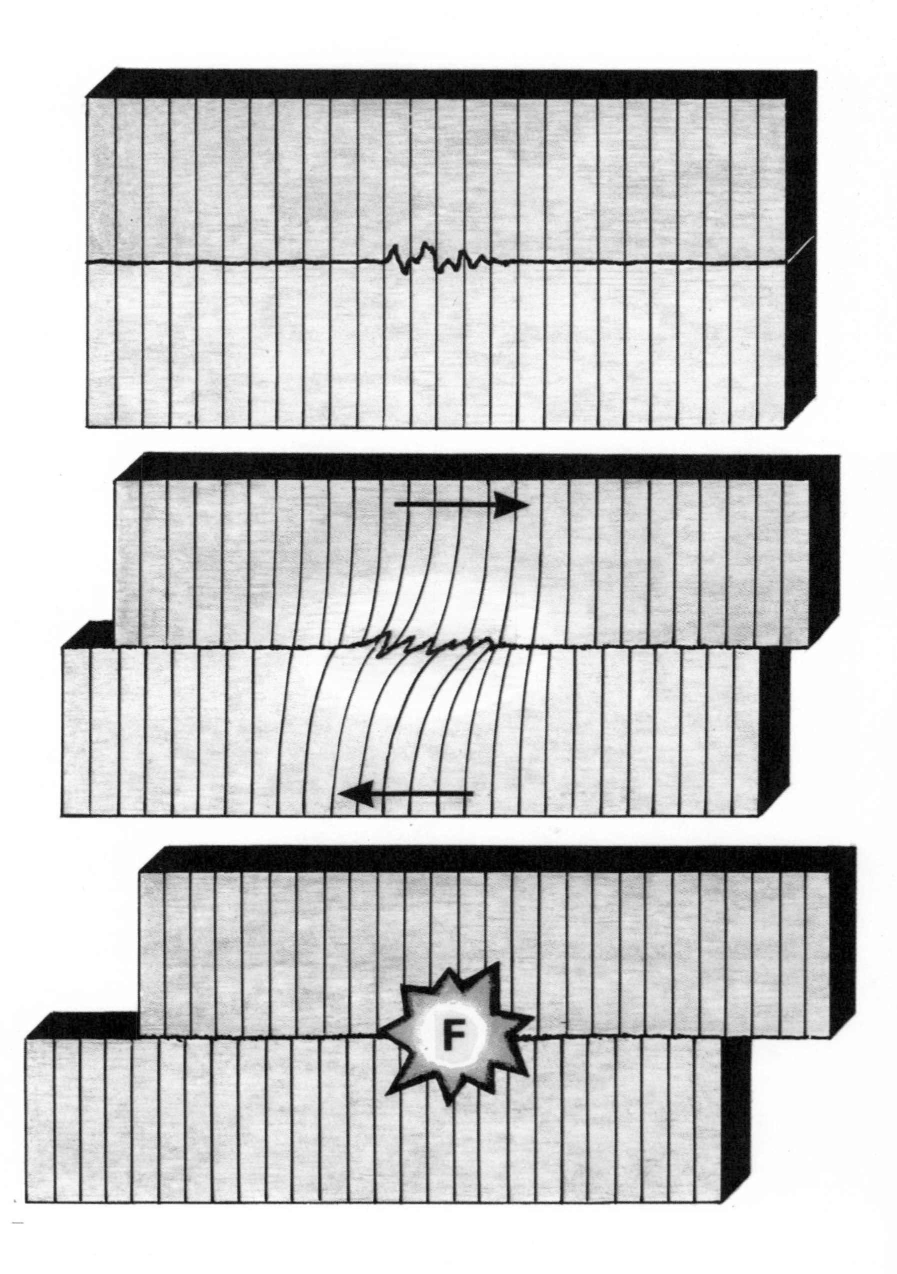

169 The place where an earthquake will probably originate during the horizontal movement of crustal blocks is the very place where the coarse parts of two juxtaposed blocks are situated, in which elastic stresses concentrate. The sudden release of these stresses gives rise to the earthquake focus (F).

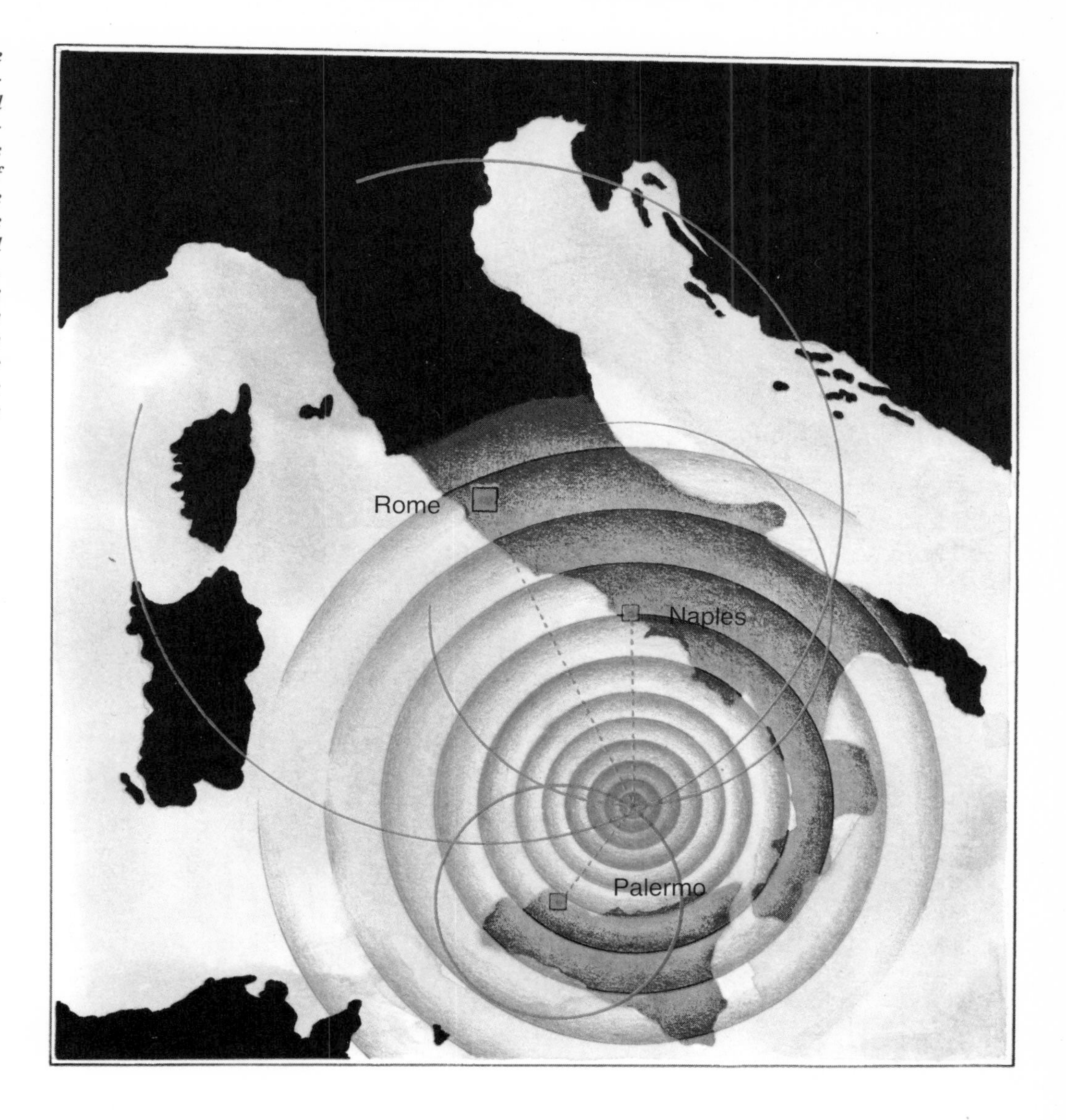

170 Locating the earthquake focus is a simple geometric problem. If the exact time is known and we have several seismicity monitoring stations at our disposal, it is sufficient to know the velocity of seismic wave propagation in the Earth crust. The position of the earthquake focus is determined on the basis of time differences. The epicentre, which is the place on the Earth's surface directly above the earthquake focus, is located at the same time. The geometric determination of the epicentre of an earthquake in the Mediterranean is shown here.

cano will turn out to be active or inactive can be worked out from its products. The character and activity of volcanoes does not usually alter much in the course of their lives. When it will erupt, however, is not really possible to predict with any accuracy. Nevertheless people do try; they monitor volcanoes and earth tremors, day and night, recording gas emissions and spending thousands of hours simulating the conditions prevailing at depth, where magma forms. The results are encouraging, but so far not positive. The depth at which magma forms, the character of the rocks in which it forms, the way it reaches the surface, the surrounding rocks with which it becomes amalgamated, and the way in which, and depth at which, magma crystallizes, all have a bearing upon the way a volcano erupts. Another determining feature in volcanic behaviour is the amount of water present. Magma contains not only water deriving from the time of its formation, but also water that it has drawn upon on its way to the surface. The way water separates from magma and is released, however, makes a difference. There are Plinian, Strombolian and Pelean eruptions, each characterized by the length of its plume and the quantity of products expelled, as is shown in the illustration.

It is necessary to collate information on a great many factors in order to be able to predict volcanic danger. In addition to the measurement of potentially imminently active volcanoes and the changing nature of their slopes, using laser apparatus, the temperature, composition of gases and water and, probably most importantly, frequency and strength of earth are all painstakingly monitored. These factors accompany the intrusion of magma from its sources to the magma chamber, a container within the volcano, and from there up to the surface. Only then is it possible to make any kind of prediction. Even so, accuracy as to the scale and timing of an eruption cannot be guaranteed. On a number of occasions, however, for example in the case of Mount St. Helens in the United States, or Tolbachik in Kamchatka, predictions proved successful.

The prediction of volcanic activity, particularly in

171 Sudden stress release in seabed rocks or the release of enormous stresses during the eruption of a volcano can cause a catastrophe of a different nature: a giant sea wave called a 'tsunami'. The picture shows the formation of the tsunami during the eruption of the volcano Krakatoa. The parts of the sea coast, which were flooded and almost completely destroyed by the tsunami, are shown in red.

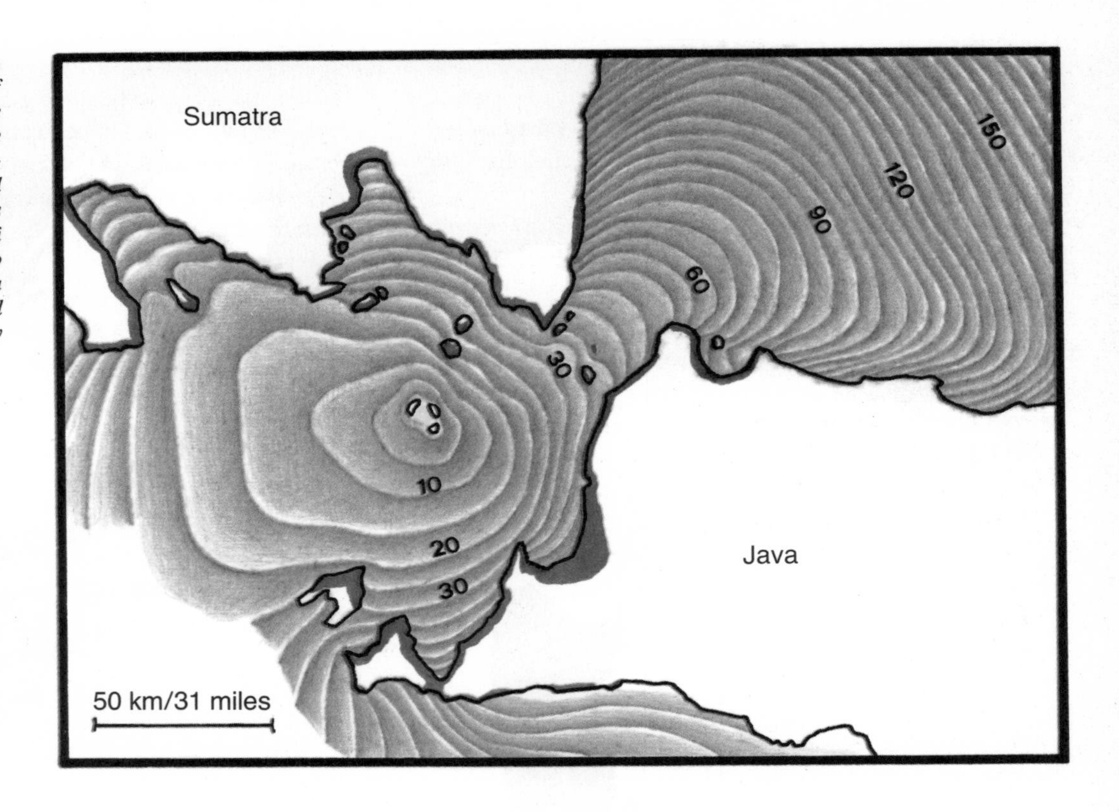

172 A number of earthquake foci beneath a volcano do not necessarily mean there is danger of a large and destructive earthquake. Minor earthquakes accompany the activity of the magmatic hearth just beneath a volcano. Seismic harmonic vibrations, accompanying the rise of the magma, may even assist in forecasting an eruption and estimating the dimensions of the magmatic hearth. It can be assumed, however, that it will not cause a major destructive earthquake.

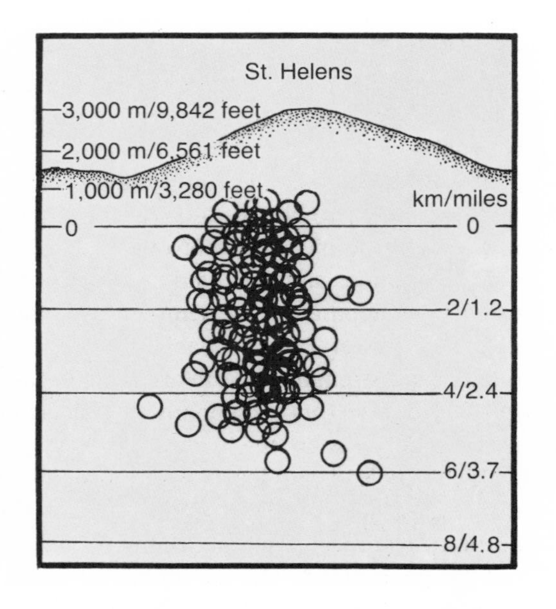

densely populated areas, can in a sense carry more of a risk than the eruption itself. Imagine a situation in which a major eruption is predicted, so that it becomes necessary to evacuate a town of several thousand people within a few hours. Not only can this lead to great confusion through the interruption of business and family relations, but there are always some people who will exploit a panic situation for criminal purposes. In such cases a natural disaster gives rise to a human one.

The history of volcanic disasters offers countless examples. The island of Thera (Santorini) in the Aegean, known for its volcanic eruptions, is the site of an ancient disaster, as is the eruption of Vesuvius described so memorably by Pliny the Younger. We may thus proceed to the modern era — for example the eruption of the Krakatoa volcano in Indonesia, or of Mount St. Helens in North America. Nevertheless, the eruption of a volcano brings not only death and the destruction of homes and fields. In many cases the following years bring with them a deterioration in the ctimate, bad harvests, fogs, acid rain, and even bad wine quality and poor forest growth.

A volcanic eruption, throwing fine dust particles into the upper parts of the atmosphere, and which as a result of stratospheric circulation are distributed over the whole planet, is capable of having a long-term effect on the climate of the planet as a whole. This provides further insight into how the internal workings of the Earth, which in terms of cosmic energy is a relatively small and apparently insubstantial entity, can with a great expenditure of energy affect a source such as solar energy, which is many times greater and more powerful. It is this knowledge of the effects of volcanic eruptions, combined with those of major meteorite collisions with the Earth, which has led scientists to their warning hypothesis of the 'nuclear winter'.

Another type of geological disaster over which people so far have little control is earthquakes. These have a great deal in common with volcanoes, occurring in those regions on Earth which were described in the first chapters as geologically active, i.e. showing evidence of current or recent activity – the junctions of lithospheric plates. It is therefore relatively easy to predict where earthquakes will occur, but almost impossible to determine when, or how strong they will be. The classification of earthquakes is given in the table, which evaluates them according to their potential ability to harm Man.

It would not be appropriate to give examples of destructive earthquakes numbering the dead and the value of destroyed property: such generally known facts can be found in any book about disasters. In any case, statistics change. Other earthquakes may occur, or with any luck we may soon see a vast improvement in our ability to predict them, and as a result, how to prepare for them successfully.

Since earthquakes have been with mankind as far back as the beginning of history and further, there have always been attempts made to explain their origins. These have included animal myths, where earthquakes are caused variously by the presence of catfish or elephants, which either reside underground or support the Earth itself, by subterranean fires and winds, or, and this is the view that has become established in our own century, the movement of sections of the Earth's crust. It was shown in the late 1960s that the focuses of earthquakes, which are concentrated within well-defined belts, mark the junctions of lithospheric plates. Even here, though, there are exceptions: earthquakes which have their focuses deep inside plates, in places which are not otherwise active, bring unpleasant surprises. To clarify the idea of earthquakes constituting a release of tectonic tension, let us try to imagine the following. We place two plates on top of two more. The first two are made of metal, being polished and smeared with oil, the second two are coarse, unfinished, rough with uneven surfaces. We attach the upper two plates to a winch, towards which we draw them using a strong rope; the lower plates are fixed to a support plate. In the former case, where the surface of the two plates is smooth, the upper plate will move along quietly and evenly, while in the latter case the movements of the upper plate will be irregular and interrupted, sometimes being at rest with the rope taut and not loosening until the plate jumps along a little again. This jumping and releasing of the taut rope may be compared with what happens during

173 Estimating the quantity of material ejected from a volcano, particularly during eruption, is very difficult. It can be determined most easily after the volcanic activity has ceased, by measuring the thickness of fallout. The picture shows fallout quantities of various eruptions documented throughout history: Mount Vesuvio in A.D.79 (described by Pliny), Tambora (the biggest eruption ever recorded), Krakatoa (which claimed many thousands of lives) and Mt. St. Helens (one of the most recent eruptions). The small figures near the panels give their dimensions in kilometres and miles; the numbers in cubic kilometres give the approximate volumes of solids ejected from respective eruptions.

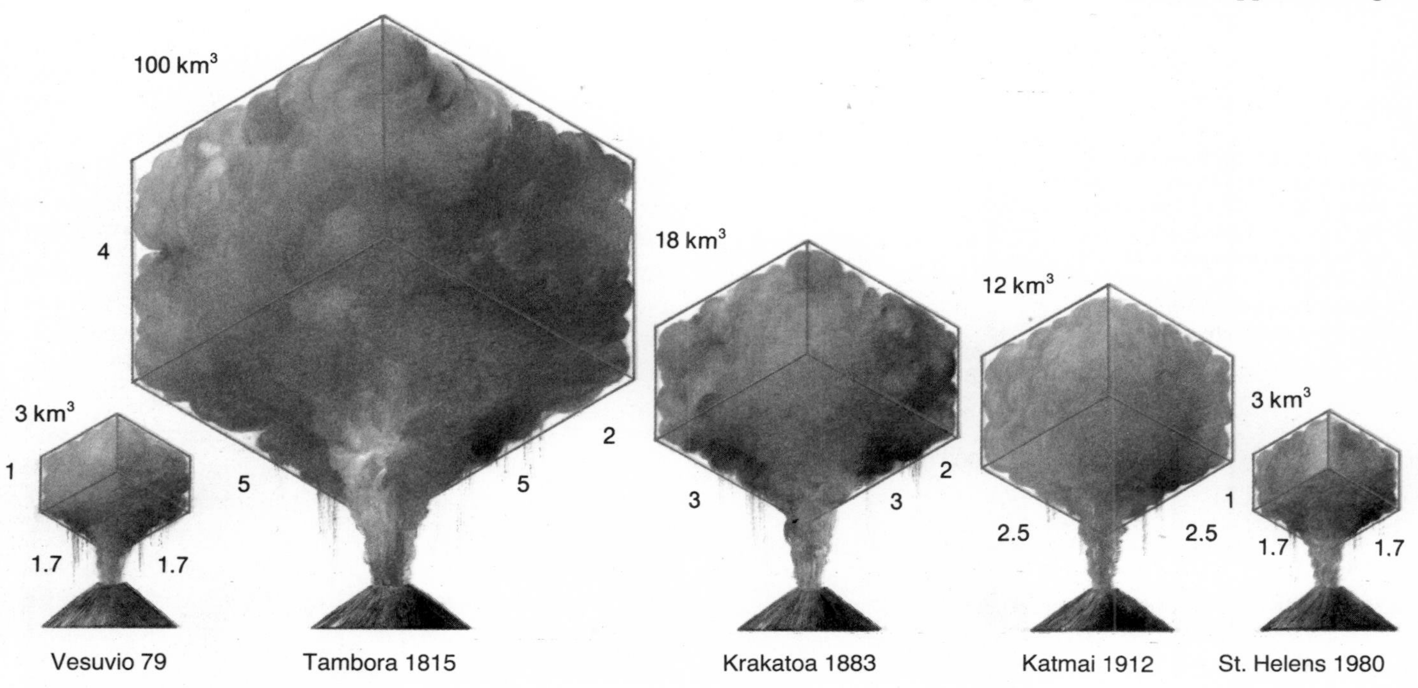

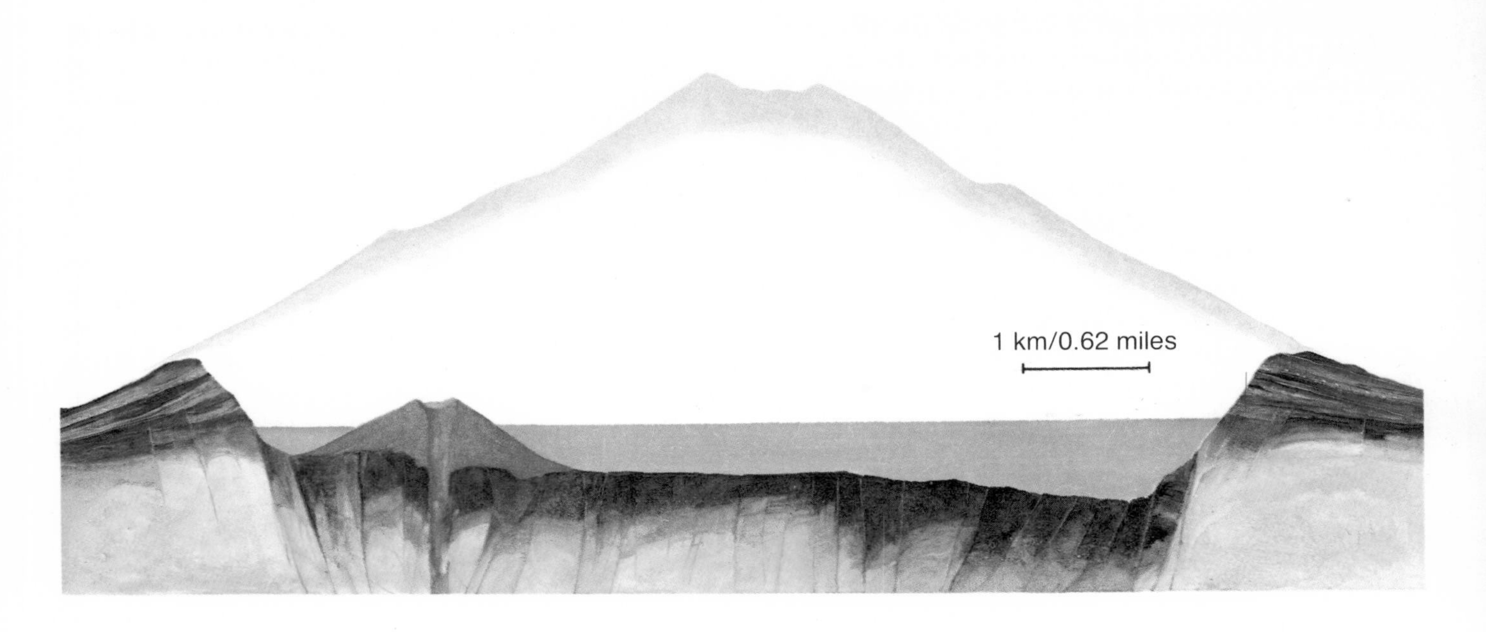

174 Another example is the volcano Mazama, the remains of which form the present Crater Lake in Oregon, in the United States. In this case, also, the whole top of an enormous mountain was 'shot off'. It is assumed, however, that not all of the missing top (some 80 cu km) was ejected into the atmosphere. A considerable part of the material sank into the crust, giving rise to a subsidence caldera.

an earthquake. There is an enormous release of stress which has been accumulating in the rock massifs. The terrestrial crust responds to such a release of tension, during which a fault or tectonic disturbance, or movement along an existing fault occurs: it makes waves similar to those on the surface of water. This is the earthquake itself, the tremors and undulation — a reaction to movement of matter within the terrestrial crust or mantle.

Most earthquakes arise in the solid, rigid part of the Earth, the lithosphere. Earthquakes in the asthenosphere

▷
176 The occurrence of hot lava, gases and an avalanche of stones on the slopes of volcanoes of the Pelée type are among the most dangerous manifestations of volcanic eruptions. Avalanches of this type rush at a great speed, which is several times higher than the speed of a motor vehicle. The temperature of the hot cloud exceeds 200°C/392°F and destroys all living things in its path.

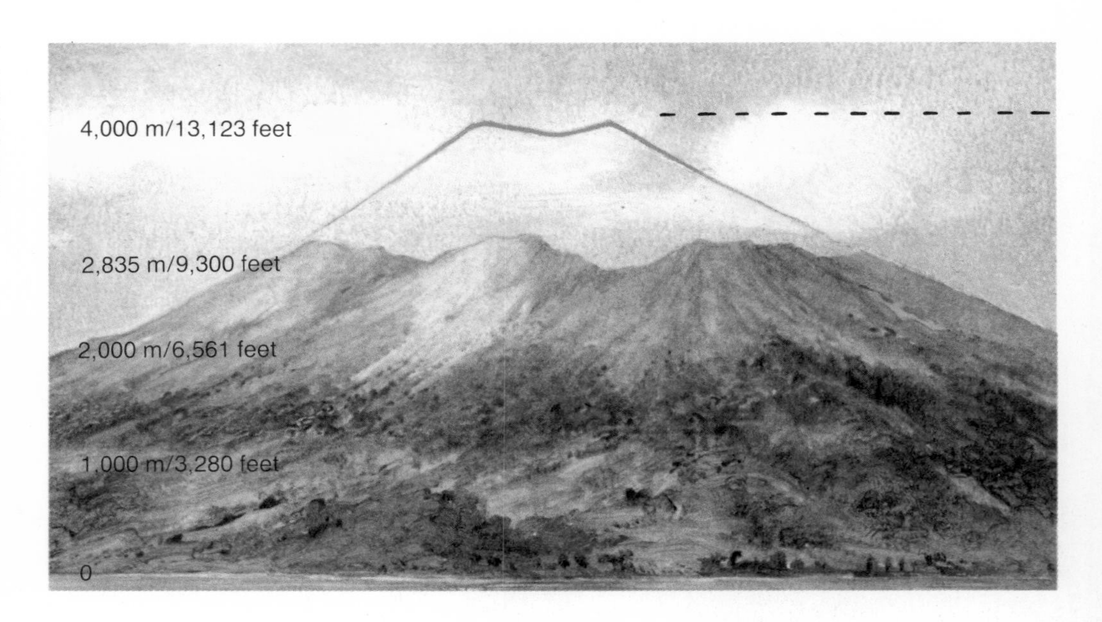

175 In 1815 the Tambora volcano attained the elevation of almost 4,000 m/13,123 feet above sea level. The volume of the 'shot off' top can be estimated at 18,000 cu m/23,543 cu yd. According to records some 100 cu km/130,795 cu yd of solids were ejected.

are rarer, being restricted either to regions where magma intrudes, or to regions where the solid lithosphere is in contact with the ductile asthenosphere, perhaps in a region of subduction.

People try to predict, monitor or even plan for earthquakes, as they do with volcanic eruptions. This type of work is equally painstaking, exhausting and lacking in results. Man is at the mercy of the whims of Nature.

The tectonic plate hypothesis has nonetheless contributed greatly to an understanding of earthquakes and the mechanism by which they come about. In turn, this has helped to pinpoint places where earthquakes are likely to occur. These places are then studied, monitored and, in some cases, structurally altered, in order to prevent the consequences of earthquakes, or even an earthquake itself. Let us return to our example of the two metal plates. If the zone of contact can be successfully and accurately determined within which the plates, in this case rock masses, move, boreholes can be drilled there and water forced in under pressure. This serves the function of oil between the metal plates. The tension should then be released in small, comparatively bearable doses, i.e. in the form of minor earthquakes. This gives rise to the hope that along fault lines of this kind major earthquakes will no longer occur, if the tension can be dissipated in this way.

The idea of people being able to gain control of thousands of kilometres of earthquake zones is an appealing one, but it should be borne in mind that drilling boreholes is a highly expensive matter, and even these are of no use in controlling earthquakes whose focuses are situated at depths of tens or even hundreds of kilometres. There is no other recourse, therefore, than to continue to reckon with earthquakes, to construct and build with good sense and to be prepared for the fact that they generally strike when least expected.

Another purely geological phenomenon, associated with earthquakes and difficult to control, is the *tsunami*, or seismic sea wave. Here again we can use our example of the plates: through the release of tension in rock masses on the ocean floor, a massive wave arises which spreads at a speed of several hundred km per hour across the whole ocean. There are well-known cases of *tsunamis* arising on the South American coast which hit the shores of Kamchatka at a speed of 700 km per hour. The Pacific is not the only place where *tsunamis* arise: the eastern Mediterranean or the Atlantic coast of Spain and Portugal are also at risk from this danger.

Like earthquakes, *tsunamis* are classified by their various degrees of severity. Since the two usually go together, it is frequently impossible to work out which proportion of the damage was caused by the earthquake itself and which by the *tsunami*. The causes of *tsunamis* are various; most often they result from earthquakes, submarine deposit slides, or volcanic eruptions.

The modern world has a wonderfully sophisticated communications system, making it easy to provide almost instantaneous information about earthquakes in cases where *tsunamis* are forming. It is more difficult, however, to respond to such warnings, since many of them turn out to be false alarms. The problem closely resembles warn-

177 One of the greatest dangers of a volcanic eruption is a plugged vent. Gases accumulate below the plug, which consists of solidified lava which was initially highly viscous. The pointed rocks in the vent are called Pelée needles after the volcano in which they were first recorded. Although the eruption of such a volcano is very difficult to forecast, some success has been attained in this field. Forecasts are based on measurements of the bulging of the volcano slope and the activity and composition of gases. Successful, for instance, was the forecast of the eruption of the Mount St. Helens volcano in the western part of the United States. The imminently threatened valley was evacuated in time and loss of human life thus prevented.

178 The type of eruption also influences its consequences. Eruption of gases and fine solid particles and their ejection into higher atmospheric strata means their speedy dispersal over a large territory and, consequently, this influences world weather (the right hand peak in the picture – Bezymyanny). Lateral eruption, as in the case of Mount St. Helens (the left hand peak) has disastrous consequences in the immediate vicinity of the volcano. However, unless its products reach the stratosphere, it is improbable that it will influence solar radiation on a world scale.

ings prior to volcanic eruptions, where economic, political and human characteristics play a crucial role in decision making.

The effect of geological disasters – earthquakes, volcanic activity or *tsunami* – is generally local: there have been few disasters which significantly affected the evolution of the planet in one fell swoop. There have been, however, many which affected evolution locally, little by little. In highly exceptional circumstances (once or twice in a thousand years) volcanic eruptions affect global climatic conditions for some years. This leads to significant changes in the biosphere. The more dramatic the changes or effects, the less frequently they occur.

The same applies to another catastrophic event, so far outside of Man's influence – the collision of the Earth with meteorites. The Earth has experienced many minor meteorite showers: some one or two dozen substantial meteorites weighing several kilograms fall on the Earth every year. The chance of the Earth colliding in the course of a human lifetime with meteorites weighing, say, several tons, is infinitesimal. However, the collision of cosmic bodies has played a significant role in geological history and most catastrophes of this kind have become what are nowadays regarded as landmarks in the evolution of the planet and its organic life. It is possible that whole species and genera of animal life were wiped out at the time of such disasters, and were replaced by new, more evolved or adaptable species. Since encounters with planetary bodies, for example asteroids or large meteorites, have always had a disastrous effect on the history of the world, usually of an ecological, global and apparently unsurvivable nature, the geological history of the world is divided up according to them. The most striking of these was the extinction of the dinosaur which occurred at the time of transition between the Mesozoic and the Tertiary Eras. There are many theories put forward to account for this. Some researchers in the last century adhered to a movement known as Lamarckism, and asserted that the dinosaurs died out slowly. Others suppose them to have died out rapidly, the cause of their extinction being the fall of a giant meteorite and the ecological disaster that followed it. This is known as the Cuvierian theory. A meteorite collision was possible since, as we have seen, the history of the Earth, especially in its initial stages, was a history of collisions. Evidence of a meteorite fall taking place at the end of the Mesozoic Era has been found by re-

◁
179 Volcanologists differentiate between three basic types of eruptions: Pelée, Pliny and Stromboli types. The picture shows a quiet ash eruption of Stromboli type, forming a symmetrial cone of loose material. This is disastrous to any people living in the surrounding area, if sudden rain washes down the volcanic ash.

searchers in almost all places on Earth where the layer marking the boundary between the Mesozoic and the Tertiary eras is exposed and visible. This thin layer, only a few millimetres thick, is enriched with traces of elements from the platinum group, particularly iridium. These elements are known to occur in several times greater concentrations in meteorites than on the Earth's surface. These increased proportions of specific elements are, therefore, presumed to have originated from a meteorite collision.

What happened after the meteorite landed is also the object of much theorizing on the part of experts and laymen alike. It is assumed by one movement that climatic changes occurred, leading to the dying out of green plants, so that dinosaurs and other animals starved to death. Other researchers claim that after the meteorite hit, a massive global fire ensued wiping out everything in its path. Of course all life on Earth could not have ceased to exist, as there would have been no 'jumping off point' for other, more advanced and robust species to develop. The emergence of mammals in particular marked a great leap forward in evolution.

It is a mistake to assume that ecological disasters present problems to everybody. They have occurred frequently throughout the history of the world, and what may have signalled the end of existence for one class of animals may have been a downright advantage for another. Take, for example, one of the first of these catastrophes — the formation of an oxygen atmosphere on Earth. This began as an emission of gases from the Earth's interior. Probably as a result of bacterial activity, a chain reaction was set in motion, leading to the formation of free oxygen from some form of gas, presumably carbon dioxide. This is sometimes referred to as an oxygen explosion, and it is highly likely that in the beginning there was an even greater amount of oxygen on Earth than there is now. Geologists studying Archaean and Proterozoic rocks are easily able to identify the rock horizons which formed during this period of abundant oxygen. They stress that this was a global event — today we would call it a disaster, if looked at in terms of the survival of the primitive organisms living at that time. As disasters are usually looked upon in terms of their effects on human life (and, as we know, there was no human life on Earth at the time) they are viewed from the standpoint of their effect on the whole planet, and are termed 'bio-events'. This is merely a way of describing sudden events in the biological evolution of the Earth.

Geologists who tried in the past to classify the course of events according to the order of deposit layers nowadays speak of 'eventostratigraphy' as a way of referring to major events in the history of Earth. These include collisions with meteorites, major volcanic eruptions or groups of eruptions, the over-reproduction of certain species, or other unforeseen events.

We should not forget that the Earth is part of the whole solar system. Nor should we forget to look to surrounding space to realize the erratic nature of evolution, the importance of ordered states, and above all the final nature of the consequences of irreversible events which occur within evolution. Let us look, for example, to the planet Mars. Modern research has shown that the surface of this planet has a striking natural landscape. Some of its formations can be explained by wind activity, others attributed to the existence of polar ice-caps consisting of carbon dioxide in a solid state. There are other formations, however, which can only be explained as a result of the activity of great riv-

180 In 1919 the Kelut volcano erupted on Java. The crater was full of water (some 60 million m^3/2,118 ft^3). The consequences were terrible: 104 villages were buried and 5,110 people killed. The Dutch colonial government decided to drain the lake which reformed in the crater after the eruption. By means of 7 tunnels on levels differing by 10 m/32 feet the water level in the lake was reduced by 55 m/180 feet. The following eruption, which took place in 1951, was almost without harmful consequence. Only the tunnels were destroyed and the lake formed again. A further eruption which took place in 1966 was again catastrophic.

ers. The amount of water currently to be found on Mars is infinitesimally small – only a slight amount in the atmosphere and a certain quantity in the permafrost (the permanently frozen ground). This brings us to the obvious question: what happened to all the water that formed the canyons and valleys on Mars – areas of erosion so huge that they make Grand Canyon look like a narrow stream. Where did this water go? Did it evaporate? If so, why did it not fall back to the planet's surface as rain? Did Mars undergo an ecological disaster so great that it destroyed all water on the planet? Could it be that there was once life on Mars and that it died out once the water was no longer available, or even that water and life were destroyed simultaneously? What caused this loss of water? Was it the interior heat of Mars, or something to do with its magnetic poles? There are more questions than answers.

Similar questions may be asked in connection with Venus. The planet known as the sister of our Earth is characterized by heat, a scorched surface and an unbreathable, heavy, toxic and corrosive atmosphere. It is of similar dimensions to Earth, with a similar surface rock composition, but its conditions are not favourable to life. Whereas it may be said that conditions for life may once have existed on Mars, the same cannot be said for Venus. Although our knowledge of its surface is only slight, we cannot rule out the possibility of an ecological disaster there either. Presumably the atmosphere acts like a greenhouse, warming the planet. This may have led to overheating. An overheated Venus and an overcooled Mars represent two extremes. What will happen to our Earth? The future does not look altogether hopeful. The hydrosphere that makes the Earth what it is – an exceptional planet capable of regulating its own heat and metabolism – is being jeopardized by the development of human society.

The formation and evolution of the Earth, life, and ultimately of Man himself on this planet are the result of a long evolutionary process, of which catastrophic events have formed an inseparable part. Disasters accelerate evolution: the Earth has so far been able to handle them, and evolution has continued. Man, however, is currently

◁
181 Water on top of an active volcano, either in the form of an ice or snow cap or that of a crater lake, is of enormous potential danger if another subsequent eruption occurs. The picture shows the disrupted crater with the remainder of the crater lake in the Alter volcano in Ecuador.

the single greatest geological agent, his activity far exceeding the natural flow of materials. It is Man who has cleared and then destroyed millions of hectares of arable land, Man who is wiping out the tropical rainforests, causing the Asian lakes to dry out and become deserts. In order to satisfy his own comfort, he is seriously polluting the atmosphere with many different toxic substances.

The current state of the terrestrial surface, including the atmosphere, is critical, and we are responsible. The Earth is sick and needs treatment at an ecological intensive care unit. So far the damage seems to be on the surface. The interior of the Earth, the part that provides it with energy, and the disposal unit for its unhealthy waste, is so far in good order. This may only be an illusion, however, since we do not have the means to record any changes to the interior of the planet.

We should deal separately with one particular disaster that is without doubt the result of human activity. What we are talking about, of course, is the depletion and possible eventual exhaustion of the Earth's natural resources. For the most part, this disaster is proceeding unobserved. Not only does it include the obvious mineral resources, but the soil itself. The way in which Man has treated the soil throughout human history is unprecedented. An increasing number of problems have arisen in connection with the soil and the soil horizon. The layer of deep soil containing a high level of humus and the essential components necessary to support plant life is extremely limited. Certainly there is not enough to support many more people than it already does, at the same time preserving its natural systems, such as the tropical rainforests.

Let us look to Africa for an example. Until 1970 Africa was more or less self-sufficient in terms of food production. A mere fifteen years later, however, every fifth person in Africa needed food imported from outside Africa. This should make us all stop and think. One certainly cannot discount the part Man has played in the drying out of this continent. At first the primeval forest was cleared for farmland. This, in itself, eventually led to massive droughts and consequent famine in a number of regions. An equally perilous process is currently taking place in the tropical rainforests of South America.

In other parts of the world, food production has increased far more rapidly: ratios of population growth and food production are given in the illustration. The data indicate that within the global economy, food production is increasing faster than population growth. Theoretically, this means that fewer people should starve each year. It should be borne in mind, however, that the richest 15 per cent of the world population use more than a third of all artificial fertilizers produced, and that a quarter of the world population is starving, at least for part of the year.

The devastation of natural ecosystems is proceeding even faster than the decrease of land able to be cultivated in Africa. The acidification of soil in Central Europe is, if anything, proceeding even more rapidly. Although we do not know the exact connection between these changes, we can at the very least see the cause as being due to some form of human activity.

A table in the first chapter illustrates the flows of vari-

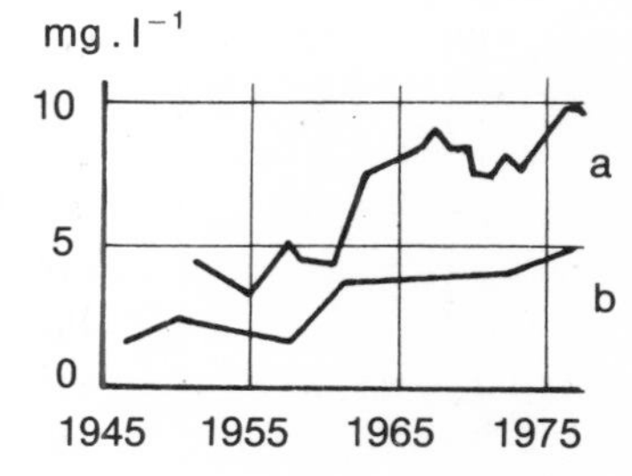

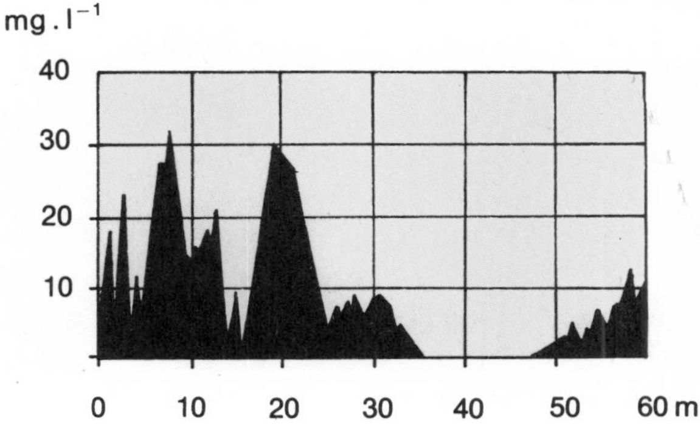

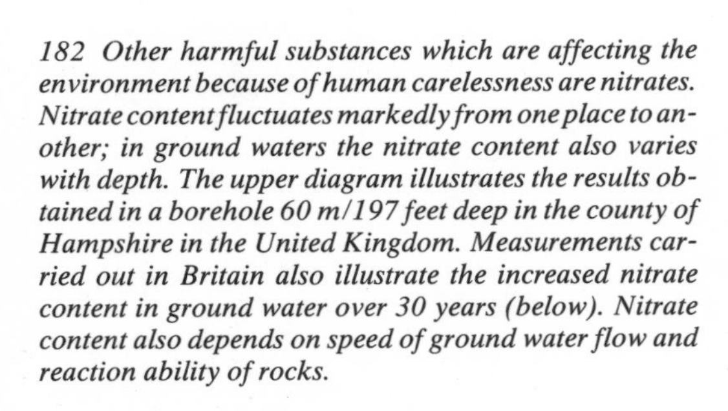
182 Other harmful substances which are affecting the environment because of human carelessness are nitrates. Nitrate content fluctuates markedly from one place to another; in ground waters the nitrate content also varies with depth. The upper diagram illustrates the results obtained in a borehole 60 m/197 feet deep in the county of Hampshire in the United Kingdom. Measurements carried out in Britain also illustrate the increased nitrate content in ground water over 30 years (below). Nitrate content also depends on speed of ground water flow and reaction ability of rocks.

a — waters in Triassic sandstones (Worcestershire)
b — waters in Cretaceous strata (Surrey)

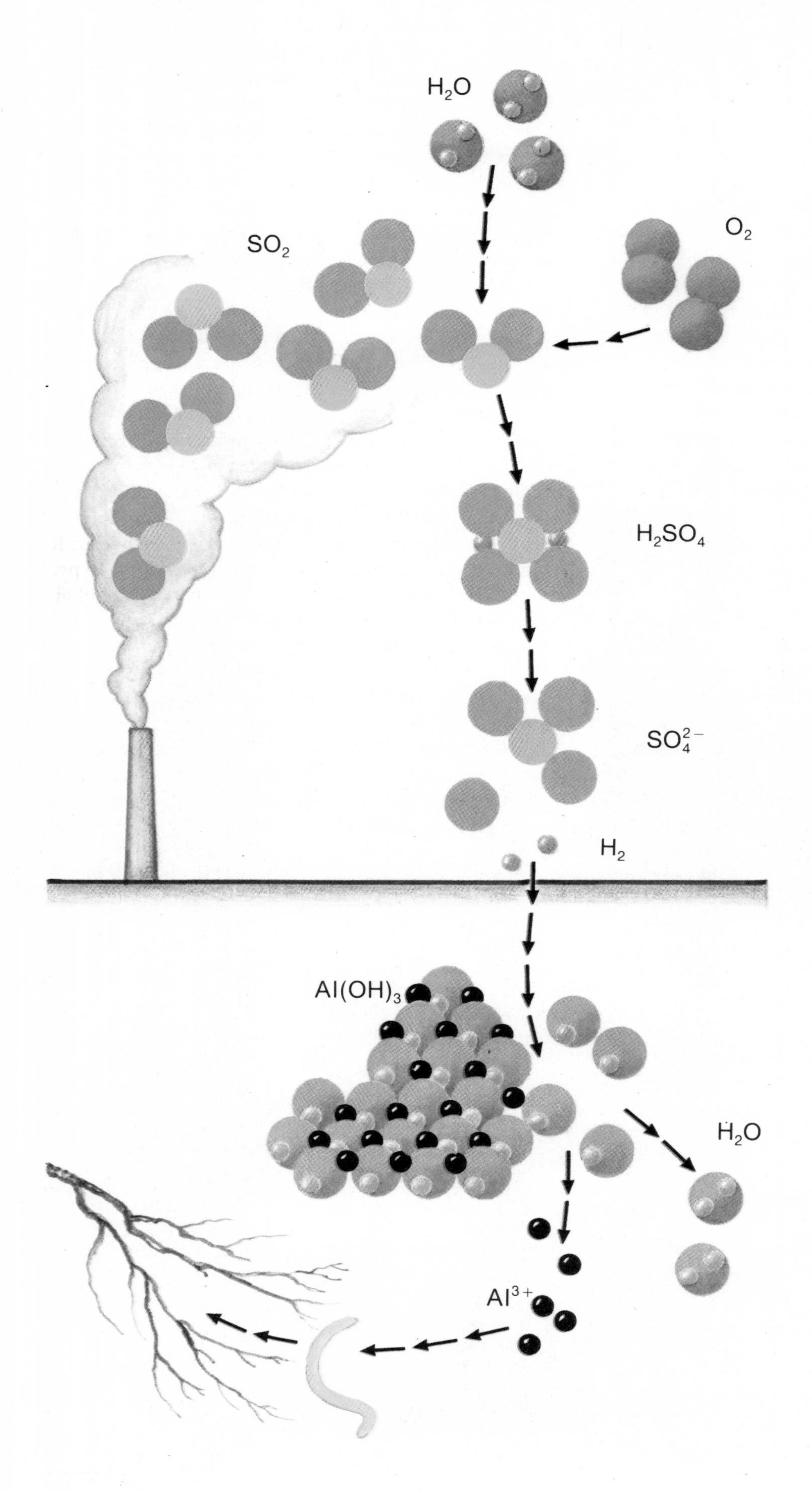

183 The problem of acidification is well known; its consequences are felt by the population of most advanced countries. Causes and effects of acid rain are illustrated by this picture. Sulphur dioxide, originating from the combustion of coal or oil containing sulphur, escapes from the place of its origin. Its reaction with water in the atmosphere and ensuing oxidation result in the formation of sulphuricacid. Contact with the soil releases free hydrogen ions, causing the slow disintegration of the structures of aluminosilicate minerals. The free aluminium ions thus produced are toxic. They penetrate organisms and micro-organisms which die as a result.

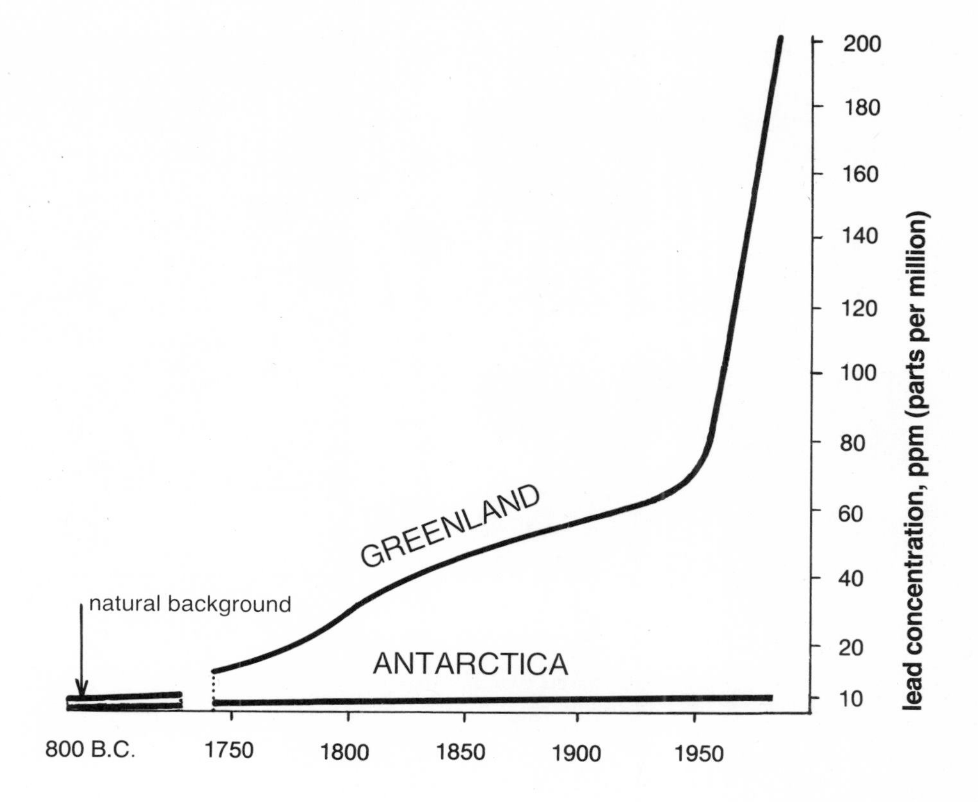

184 Pollution, measured in millionths of 1 per cent or even smaller units, is barely perceptible without perfect analytic technology. Illustrated here is the increased lead pollution in Greenland, particularly its rapid increase in the last 40 years. This period coincides with the huge increase in the numbers of motor cars in the advanced countries of the northern hemisphere. Also, the increasing lead content in the Antarctic ice, however slight, is still alarming.

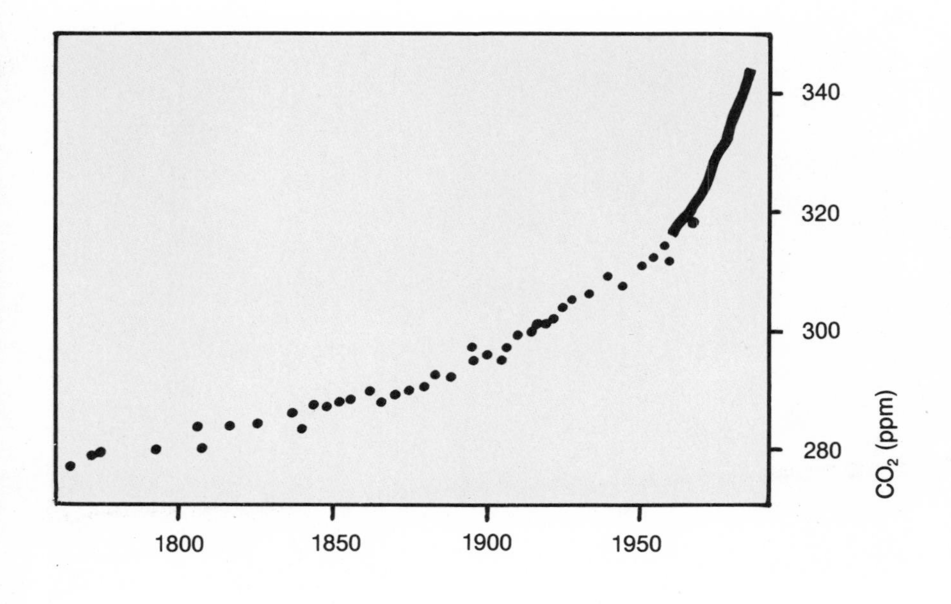

185 Carbon dioxide content in Antarctic ice compared with its content in the Earth's atmosphere is shown in dots. The analyses of CO_2 content in the air, obtained by direct measurements, are shown by the solid line. The undisputed increase of this gas in the Earth's atmosphere, with its greenhouse effect, is a warning. Even in the interglacial periods, when the planet warmed, the CO_2 content did not rise so quickly and did not attain such high levels as today. In the glacial periods its content varied between 190 and 220 parts per million. Its present content, however, is about 350 parts per million. In the interglacial periods its content was about 280 ppm.

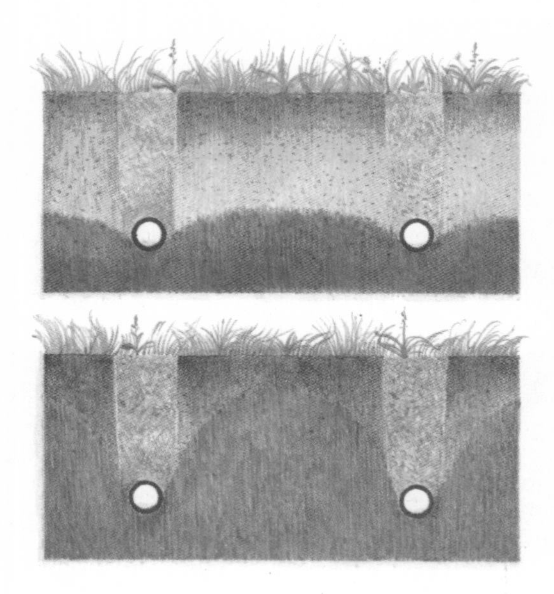

186 Irrigation and drainage are popular methods of agricultural land improvement. However, these methods are not without drawbacks. They change the ground water balance significantly. In highly permeable rocks the ground water table may drop to an unacceptable level (first picture). In impermeable rocks, such as clayey sediments (second picture), the drainage has a very small effect.

187 Catastrophes can be prevented if people realize that landscape management is not merely a matter of politics. It requires knowledge of the structure and composition of the Earth's crust. Storage or accidental release of toxic waste in areas with a hydrologically simple structure is a clear example.

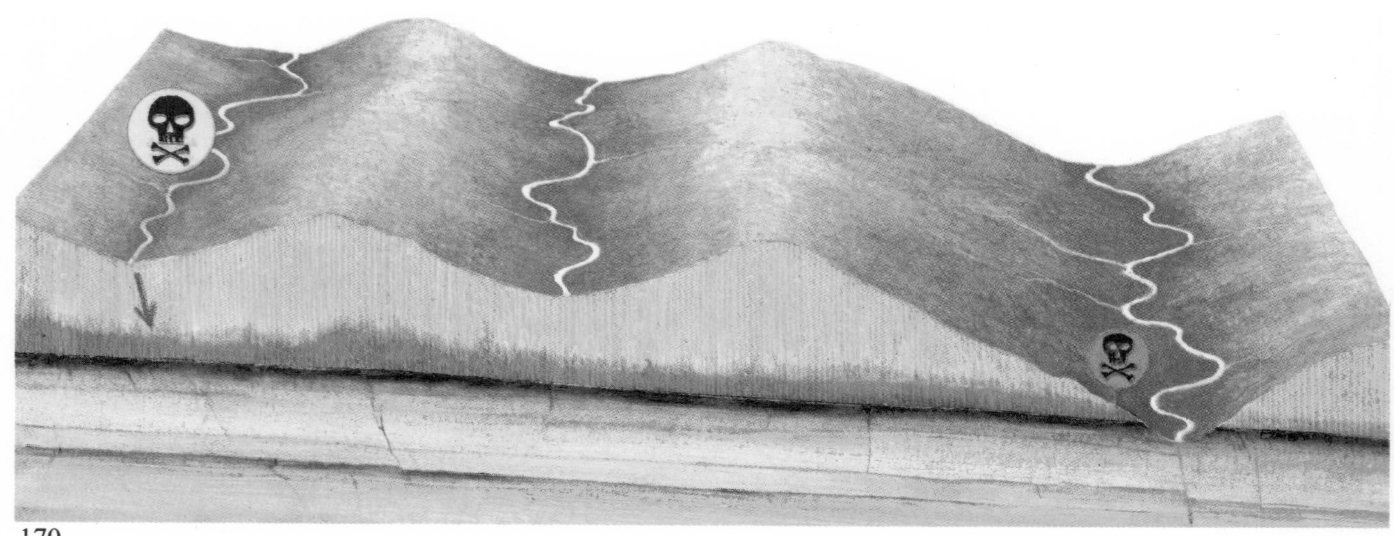

188 The destruction of conifers by acid rain is a great problem in Central Europe. This example is from Germany in 1984. There are, however, countries where the damage is even greater. For instance, the forest systems of the frontier area between the Czech Republic and Germany, the Ore Mountains (Erzgebirge), were destroyed completely by sulphur dioxide emissions over the last 40 years. A similar situation prevails in Poland. An ailing conifer forest is one in which 11—12 per cent of needles have been destroyed.

ous elements into the ocean in the geological past and present. It likewise shows that the amount of soil currently reaching the oceans is appreciably higher than it was when Man first began to practise agriculture on the planet. This involves not only the washing away of soil from cultivated fields in the pre-vegetation period; a huge amount of soil is simply blown into the ocean by the wind. Soil from North Africa has been recorded on islands in the Atlantic, and Asian soil has been found in Hawaii in the Pacific. The present situation, and the increasing population of the planet, are compelling farmers not only to practise intensive cultivation of the soil, but also to cultivate land high up in the mountains, where the soil is more sensitive and prone to erosion, places where natural systems would otherwise have been preserved.

In many places, energy in the form of artificial fertilizers is put into the soil, or intensive irrigation is practised. Elsewhere, huge tracts of land are worked using heavy machinery, which alters the soil and changes both its character (the structure and arrangement of soil components) and quantity at an extremely rapid pace. This rate of change is far too fast for natural regeneration processes or the formation of a new soil horizon to keep pace. It is possible, therefore, that the price of food will rise: the energy investment into food production, in the form of fertilizers, would suggest this. Both the price of food and food shortage in the developing world should give rise to serious thought about the way soil is being treated worldwide.

Salinization is another problem. Water, in particular that which occurs below the surface, often contains dissolved salts, which concentrate in the soil where there is excessive irrigation and inadequate drainage. In the United States, for example, over 6,000 m^3/7,848 yd^3 of water are used per hectare in a season. Most of this water evaporates, leaving an even higher salt concentration in the soil. This is of no use to plants for their tissue construction. It could happen that Man will be deprived of the substrate soil on which he lives.

There are only two possible future scenarios for the Earth. One is that it should return to a state of equilibrium and life. The other is for it to die.

Man is so far the only creature in the history of the Blue Planet to study it and try to understand it. He has managed to observe, describe and make known the causes of natural disasters. If he is capable of studying the Earth, he must also be capable of seeing himself in a sufficiently critical light in order to see his own part in the slow disintegration of the ecology of his planet.

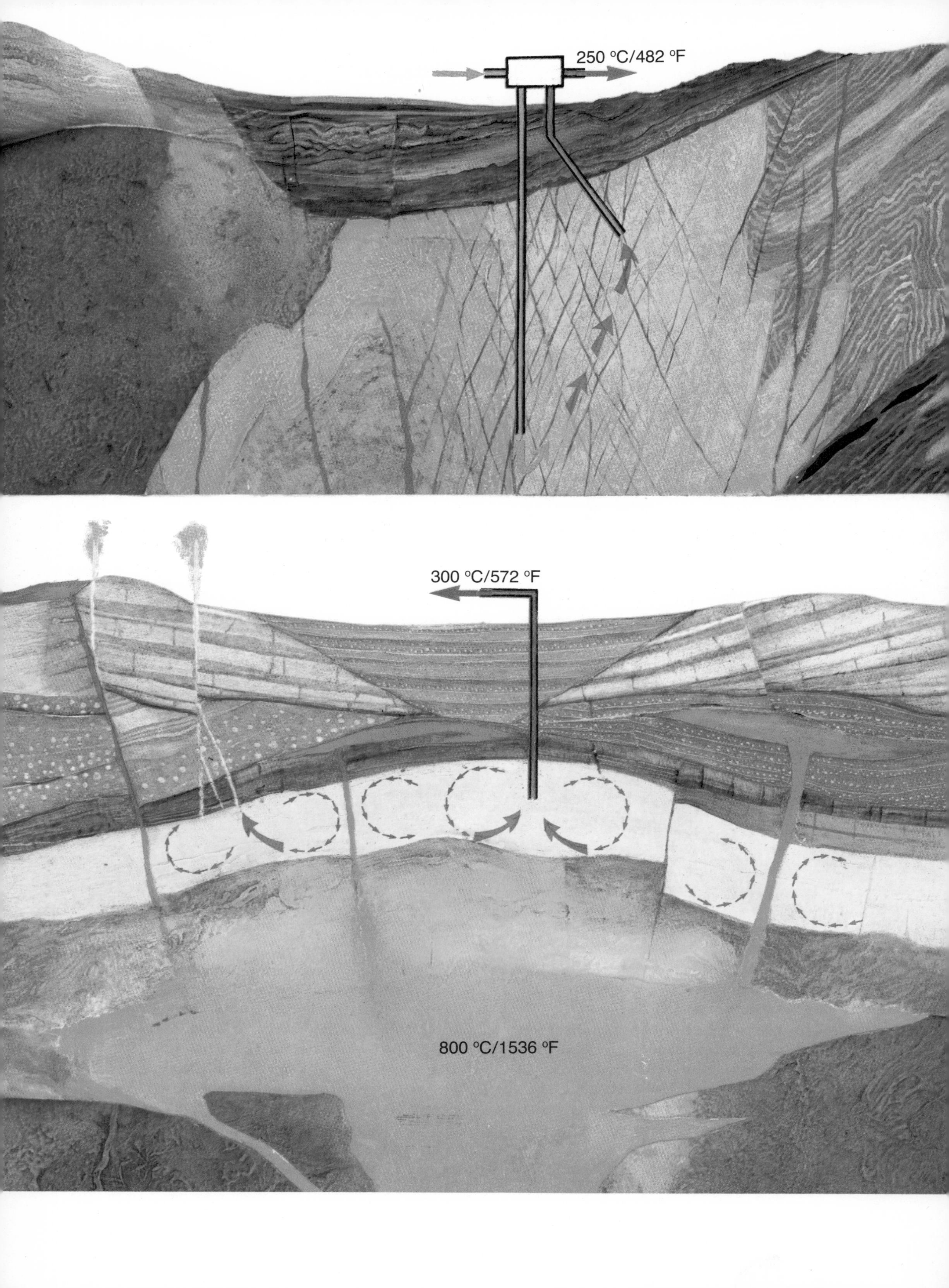

250 °C/482 °F
300 °C/572 °F
800 °C/1536 °F

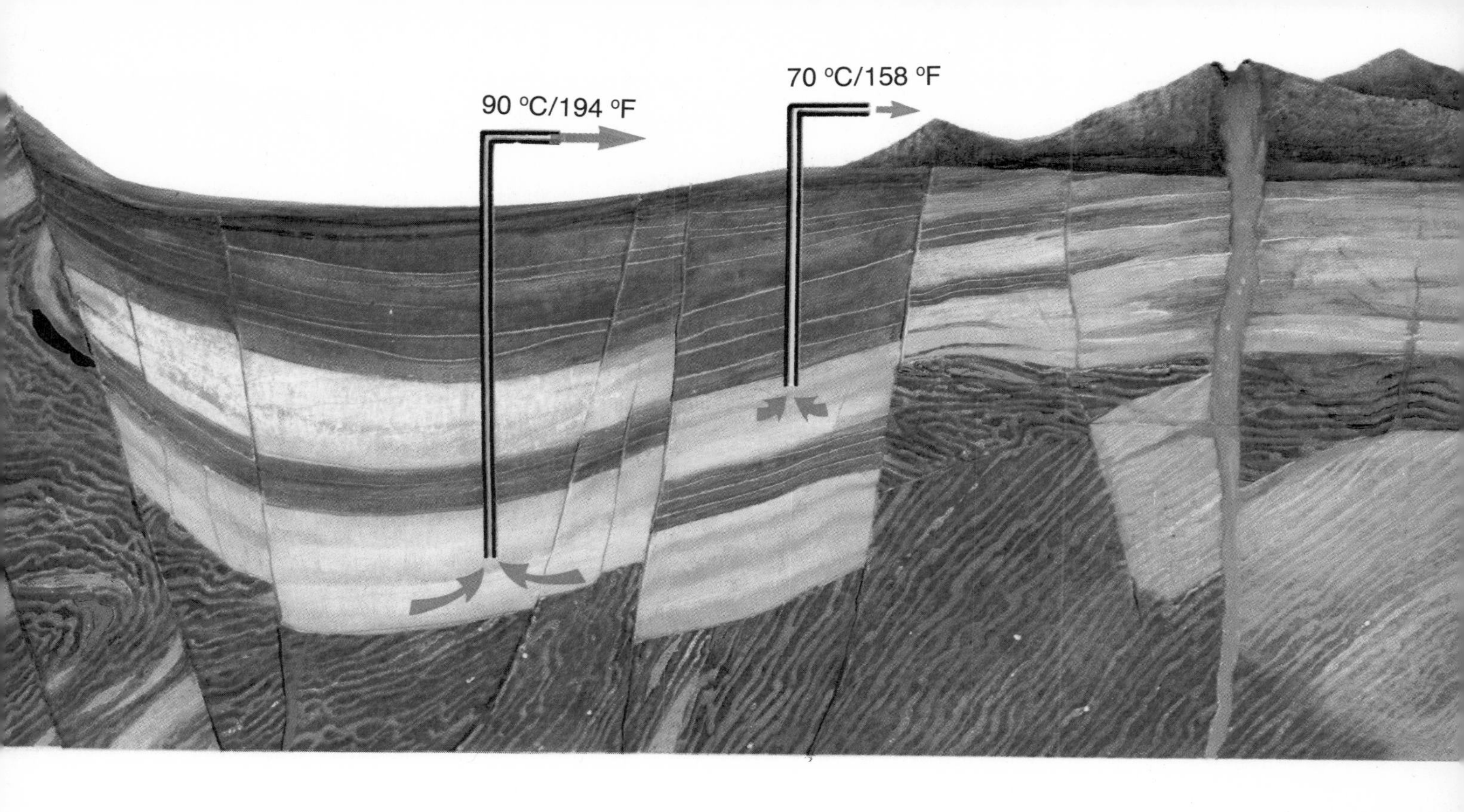

THE FUTURE PLANET

189 The need for 'clean' energy that will not pollute the environment is becoming ever more urgent. The increase in gases which cause the greenhouse effect, due to the burning of fossil fuels, threatens to lead to a global catastrophe. Nuclear energy is not acceptable to many people as they do not consider it safe. However, a completely 'clean' energy source is not in sight. Most alternative energy sources require large amounts of collecting equipment in order to produce small amounts of energy. This type of energy is known as low density and can be wind energy, tidal energy, solar energy as well as geothermal energy. The installation of underground collectors allows the exploitation of geothermal heat produced by slow radioactive decay. At present, geothermal energy accounts for only a fraction of 1 per cent of all energy produced. The possible exploitation of geothermal energy has been tested by a number of projects worldwide. The three methods of exploitation of geothermal energy shown in the picture have a common denominator: heat is transmitted through water. On sites which are hydrogeologically favourably situated, hot water is pumped from deep boreholes, and used directly, as a rule (upper right). The number of such regions is relatively high; nevertheless, their energy potential is low. Hot water is used for heating or for balneological purposes; however, it is difficult to use for electric power generation. Another system, the 'hot dry rock' technique, is used in areas abundant in high thermal production rocks (e.g. granites). The rock is penetrated by two boreholes, usually formed by underground explosions. Water is pumped into the cracks, which function as heat exchangers. Hot water is pumped from another borehole (upper left). An ideal environment for the exploitation of geothermal energy is a volcanic region, a site where recently solidified or still liquid rock is present not far below the surface, and where there are natural hydrothermal systems with boiling water. Where natural conditions are not favourable, nature can be assisted by a deep borehole (below). Such systems bear very hot water which can easily be used for electric power generation. Disadvantages include pipes clogging and their easy corrosion caused by the quality of substances dissolved in the water, along with a number of other technical problems.

As an individual, Man can easily adopt a frame of mind in which the future holds no concern. He can adopt the attitude of 'make hay while the sun shines'. A short time later he may have an attack of conscience; Man can be a fickle creature whose concerns change from day to day. Most people, however, do take an interest in the future; parents would not like to think of a bleak future ahead for their children or grandchildren. In the same vein, people have always been interested in predicting the future, whether accurately or not.

Chance plays a significant role in the life of an individual, but the life of society should not be built on chance. There is always an element of uncertainty in life, but in many ways Man can plan his future. It is up to him to find

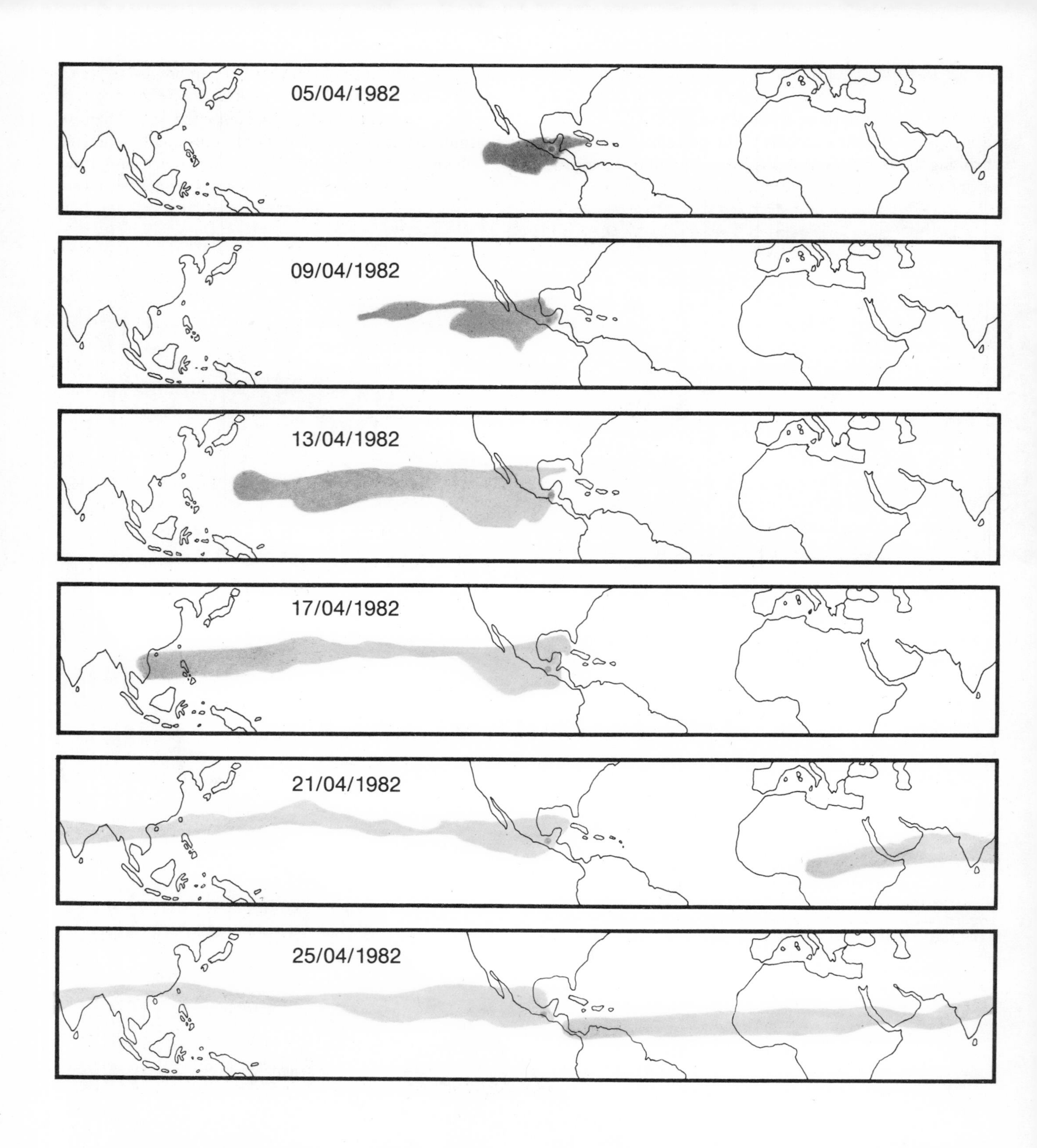

environmentally friendly ways of producing energy, materials for industry, and chemicals, and also to find more acceptable methods of disposing of his various types of waste. As Man strides ahead in his search for knowledge about other planets, he is confronted with a vision of the Earth's future. True, we do not know the causes of the drying out of the Moon and Mars, but these examples give us an accurate picture of what a dead planet Earth would look like. It should be enough for us to look and learn — to take steps immediately to prevent the decline and eventual death of our planet.

Volcanoes provide a perfect illustration of what could happen in the event of nuclear explosions and of the ensuing situation on Earth. We will not deal here with the effects of radiation, a direct explosion or nuclear fallout. Let us examine only one single geological event. During a major volcanic eruption, a huge amount of material is released into the terrestrial atmosphere. The recent eruption of the El Chicón volcano in Mexico illustrates this. This was a massive eruption and huge amounts of geological material, rich in sulphur, reached the upper layers of the atmosphere (the stratosphere). The presence of satellites orbiting the Earth made it possible to monitor the movement of this material. Within a few days, stratospheric convection had distributed this volcanic matter across a broad belt extending round the entire globe. In this case, El Chicón behaved in the same way as many volcanoes had done in the past. Ash from these volcanoes, as well as the effects of acidification, have been observed by scientists in Arctic and Antarctic ice. In older ice layers there are remnants of earlier explosions known from history, for example the eruption of Krakatoa at the end of the last century, and other eruptions documented in ancient historical records.

Significant in this exercise are ensuing changes in the weather in the years following major volcanic eruptions. Records of the time include accounts of strange sunsets, portents in the sky, poor wine quality for those years. The correlation between dust particles in the stratosphere and a reduction in the amount of sunlight reaching the Earth need leave us in no doubt that the weather cooled down during periods such as these. This in turn set in motion a chain of other changes, such as an extension of glacial regions, a shift in climatic belts, and consequently changes in the biosphere.

Contemporary scientists are not eccentrics who spend all their time locked in dusty offices or laboratories. Many of them are concerned human beings who have access to incredible amounts of data and supercomputers which contain the results of vast amounts of different types of scientific research. With their combined knowledge of volcanic eruptions, the effects of collisions beween the Earth and other bodies, and of the chain reactions known to exist in the biosphere, these scientists are acutely aware of the possible consequences of a nuclear war. They have also devised the scenario of a nuclear winter. If this were to happen it would be a catastrophe of global proportions.

What has been described concerning the effects of the scattering of volcanic dust particles throughout the atmosphere represents only a fraction of the nuclear winter scenario which could result from a worldwide nuclear war. In such a case, the nuclear war effect would far outweigh that of one or even a small number of terrestrial volcanic eruptions.

A large number of nuclear explosions could have a cooling down effect similar to that known to have happened in the past. Subsequent changes in the biosphere,

◁
190 The future vision of 'nuclear night' has come about through observing natural processes. The eruption of the El Chicón volcano in Mexico in 1982 ejected into the atmosphere not only dust but also a considerable quantity of sulphur compounds. The satellite observation, shown here, confirmed that within 20 days the volcanic dust had encircled the Earth.

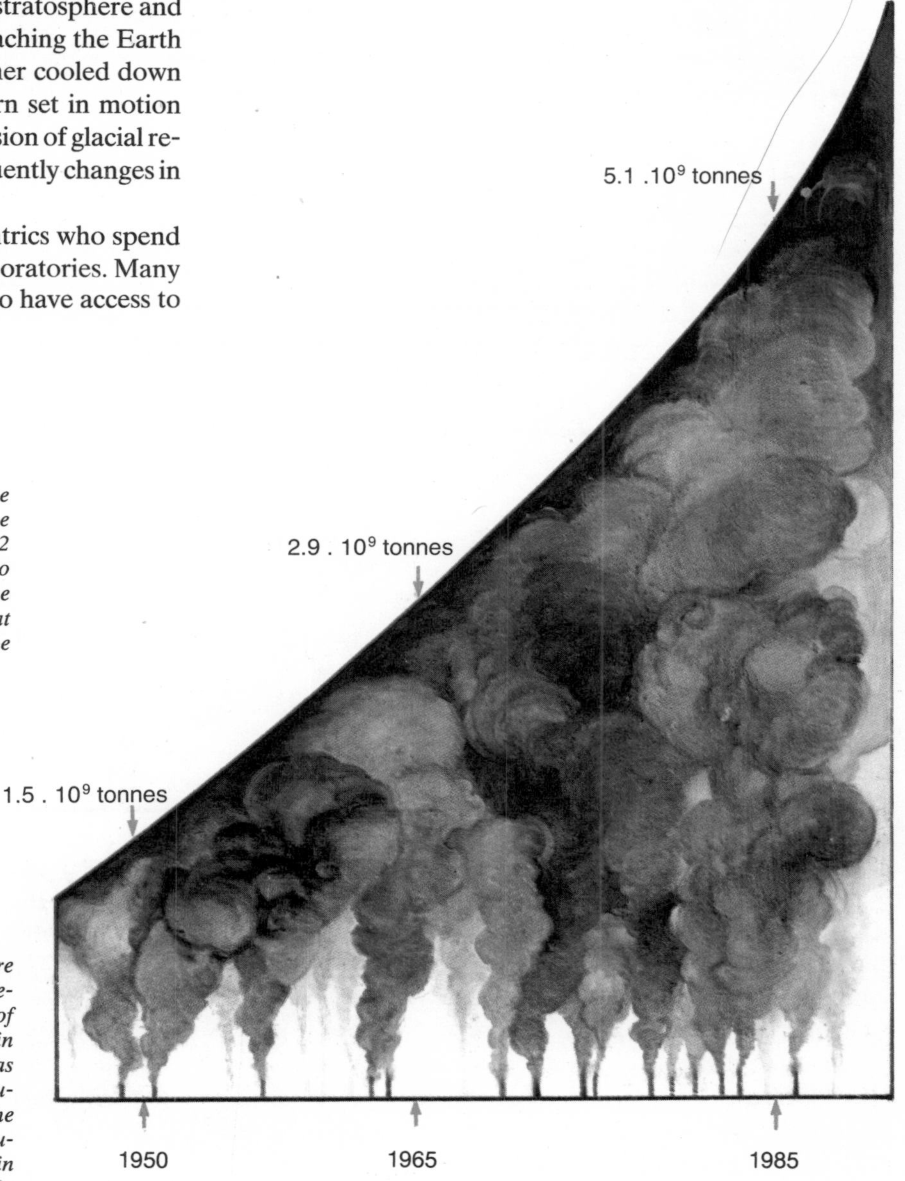

191 Overall pollution of the Earth's atmosphere has been increasing at an extreme rate since the beginning of the Industrial Revolution. Amounts of gases emitted throughout the world vary. While in North America the quantity is falling, Europe has maintained its level (with a reduction in Western Europe and an increase in Eastern Europe), and the proportion emitted by developing Asia, particularly China, has risen significantly. The figures in the picture give the amount of emissions in tonnes in the atmosphere.

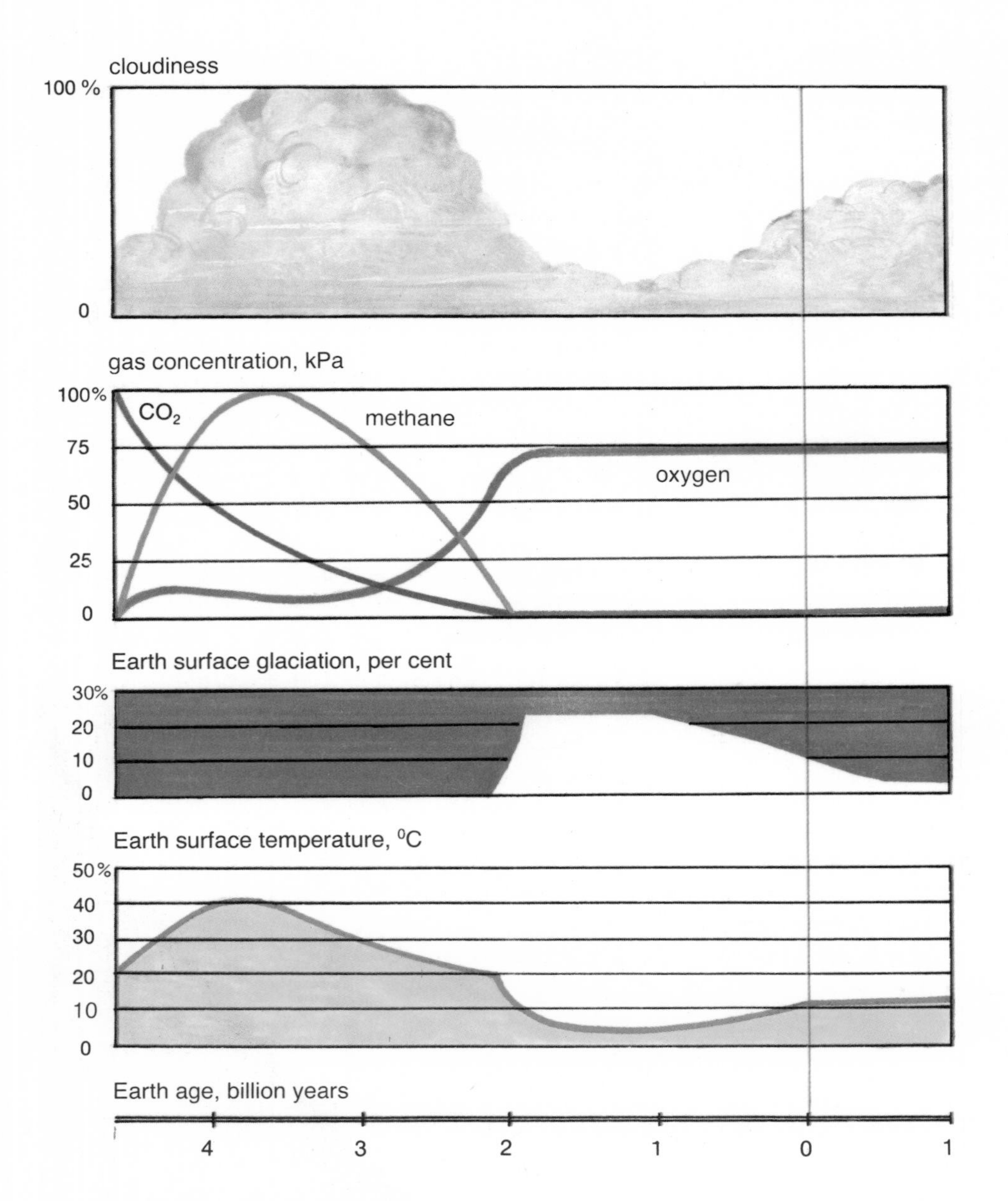

192 Historical knowledge of the Earth, derived from geological records, also enables the forecasting of the future of the planet. On the horizontal axis of the diagram there is the age of the Earth in billions of year; our time is denoted with a zero (O). The period of man's presence on Earth is so short that it cannot be expressed. The individual rectangles (top) represent: cloudiness on the planet, concentration and pressure of carbon dioxide, methane and oxygen. White on blue background represents the glaciation of the planet surface. The mean temperature on Earth is given at the bottom.

water cycle and circulation of the atmosphere and the number of possible directions in which the Earth's development could go would be too many to count. We are still quite a long way from this situation, but equally, the Earth is a long way from being Utopia.

However, let us not end this account of the natural history of the Earth on such a note of pessimism. The world does not have to be ruled by Murphy's law. There is every possibility that the Earth will continue to evolve in a way that is beneficial to us, and maintain its steady state.

The term 'total symbiosis' was coined in 1954 by two Dutch scientists, the Odum brothers, who were studying the co-existence of seaweed and polyps on the small Eniwetok coral reef in the Pacific Ocean. They discovered the degree of reciprocity, or mutualism, there was total and self-supporting. Over twenty years later, one of the brothers raised the question of whether this discovery on a coral atoll might not have some significance for modern urban Man. The answer that emerged was that both on a coral reef and in a desert oasis there is mutualism between producers and consumers which, together with the effective use of energy and a recycling of substances, is the key to maintaining prosperity. This discovery is valid for every society on Earth in which resources are limited. Since there are no unlimited resources in the lithosphere or biosphere, it is valid for the whole world.

Planet Earth is like a small coral atoll in the ocean of space. We might add that mutualism, whether among individual people, or between humanity and living or inanimate Nature, is the only possible way of ensuring a future for our world.

The only acceptable solution for the future evolution of our planet, therefore, is total symbiosis — but what does this mean in practice? The simplest way of looking into the future is to draw from the past, even though this does have its drawbacks. Let us look, for example, at the 'species explosion' of the last 500 million years on Earth. Then let us look at the growth curve of the global population during the last century. This is, in fact, an explosion of one species at the expense of the others. This particular explosion is bringing about changes which are unparalleled in the Earth's history. This is apparent from the amount of en-

193 The correlation between actions on the Sun and the Earth assist in forecasts for the near future. Eruptions on the Sun are followed by more intense cosmic radiation in the proximity of the Earth; only slightly later, disturbances in the magnetic field and the nature of polar auroras follow. The picture suggests that causes of change and their consequences can be discovered within natural processes and that it is possible to foresee the future of the Earth on the basis of its history.

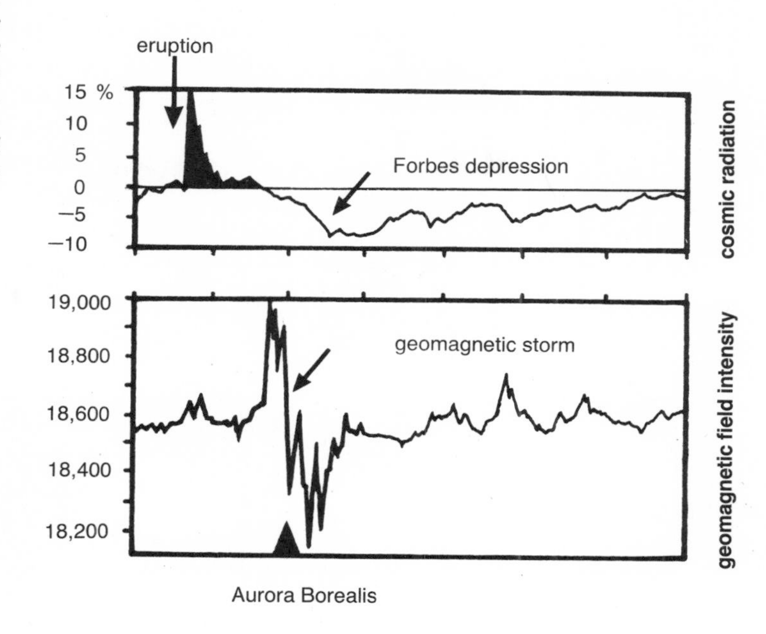

194 Energy balances of planets nearest the Earth and of the Earth itself have shown what a balanced energetic system the Earth is. The high temperature of the surface strata of Venus is due not only to twice the input of solar energy experienced by the Earth, because of its proximity to the Sun, but primarily to the effect of its atmosphere which, because of its high carbon dioxide content, prevents the heat escaping from the planet. Most of the heat is absorbed by the atmosphere and only a small part is reflected back into space. The energy balance of Mars is entirely different. Not only is the amount of energy that is received from the Sun substantially lower (about half as low as that of the Earth), but the thin atmosphere is incapable of retaining heat in the surface layer of the planet. Most of the heat is reflected back into space. The message is simple: a balanced energy input must be maintained, conditioned by the optimum composition of the Earth's atmosphere. Any change such as an increase in carbon dioxide content similar to that of Venus, or loss of atmosphere similar to that of Mars, would be catastrophic.

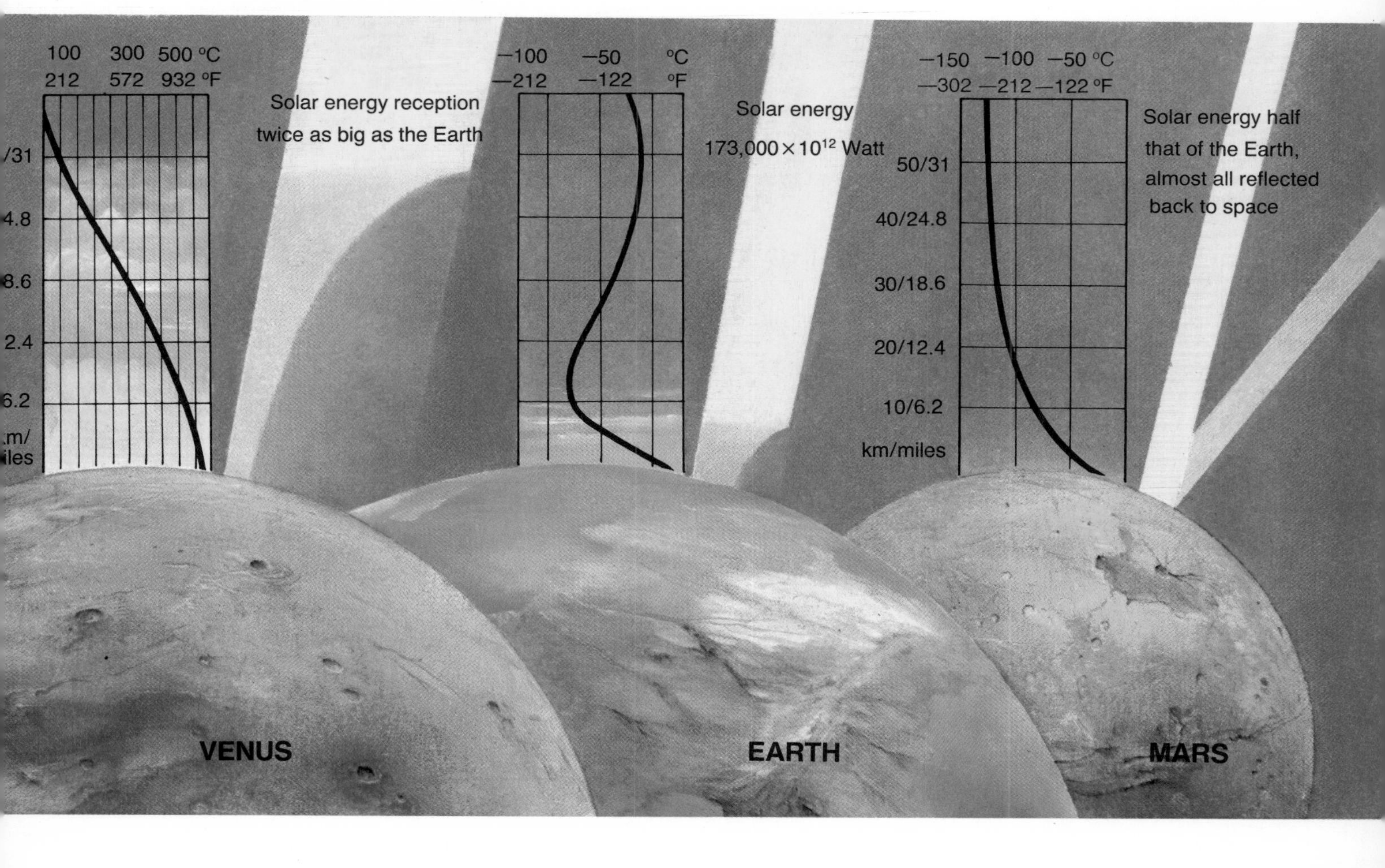

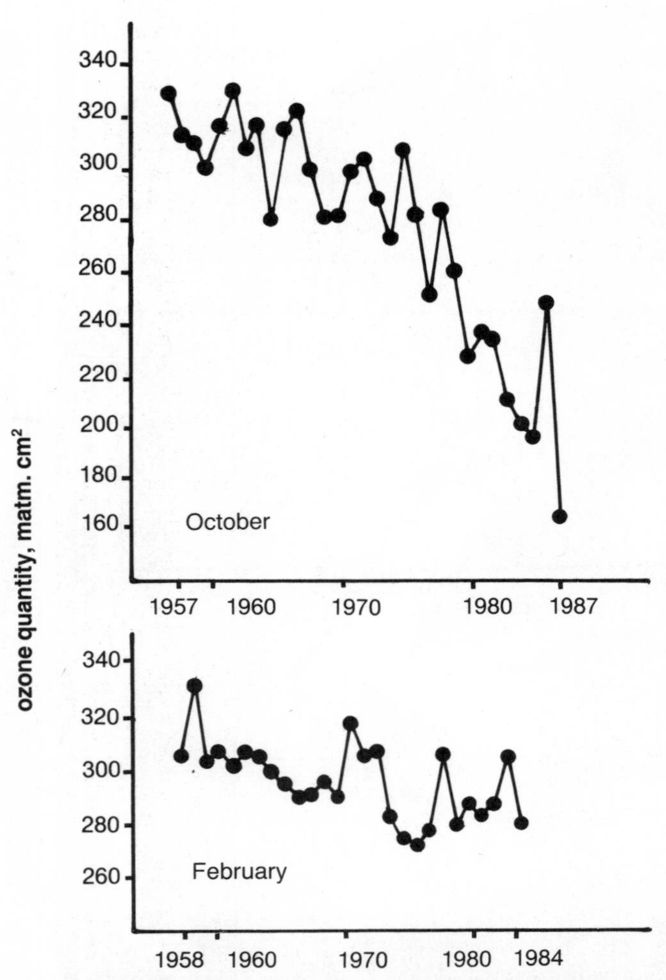

195 The diagram shows the depleted ozone content of the atmosphere. As this content changes according to the seasons, the ozone content is given in two month intervals, in milliatmospheres per 1 sq cm. The significant decrease in ozone content, which began in the 1970s, i.e. since a conspicuous rise in the consumption of freons (chlorofluorocarbons), is alarming.

ergy resources extracted by Man in the last twenty years, or from the amount of chemical elements exploited in the course of human history. In many cases these amount to exponential curves. In the case of chemical elements, the ceiling has already been reached: the number of elements we know to be exploitable so far is 90, and Man is exploiting 90. There is already a natural limit determined by the amounts of cultivable soil, energy resources and raw materials on Earth.

Whenever an attempt has been made by individuals or groups to carry out such an analysis and to predict the future on this basis, a wave of opposition has always arisen from one quarter or another, depending on philosophical or political views. People do not like pessimistic predictions. Here too we can draw on history, quoting not only economists of the 19th century (e.g. Malthus), but also the group of scientists who started the Roman Club in the 1960s as well as modern forecasters, such as Alvin Toffler, who speak of the information society.

Since it began, science has been slowly uncovering the history of the Earth, the evolution of life, and of the formation of the atmosphere, crust and hydrosphere. Scientists investigate the past temperature of the terrestrial surface, the movement of the poles and of lithospheric plates, the state of deserts and high mountain ranges, and the changing sea levels. They are increasing their knowledge of the interrelationship between the weather and volcanic explosions, the movement of magnetic poles and the process whereby plant communities become extinct. A link has also been discovered between iron ores and the oxygen content in the atmosphere. Fascinating connections have also been found to exist between living organisms and inanimate Nature. The connection between organisms such as seaweed and bacteria and the formation of an oxygen atmosphere is a superb example of just how far mutual

196 This is an alarming diagram with a pessimistic forecast: the horizontal axis on the left records geological occurrences during the past 12 million years. The scale on the right represents only the past 100 years and the next 100 years. The red curve represents temperature, the blue carbon dioxide content in the atmosphere. The relation between the increase of the carbon dioxide and that of temperature can be seen immediately. The temperature rise of 3°C/37°F may mean the thawing of glaciers and a rise in sea level with all its accompanying phenomena, e.g. loss of agricultural land and the migration of billions of people, etc. What nature has been creating for 12 milion years, people are capable of changing totally within a mere 200 years.

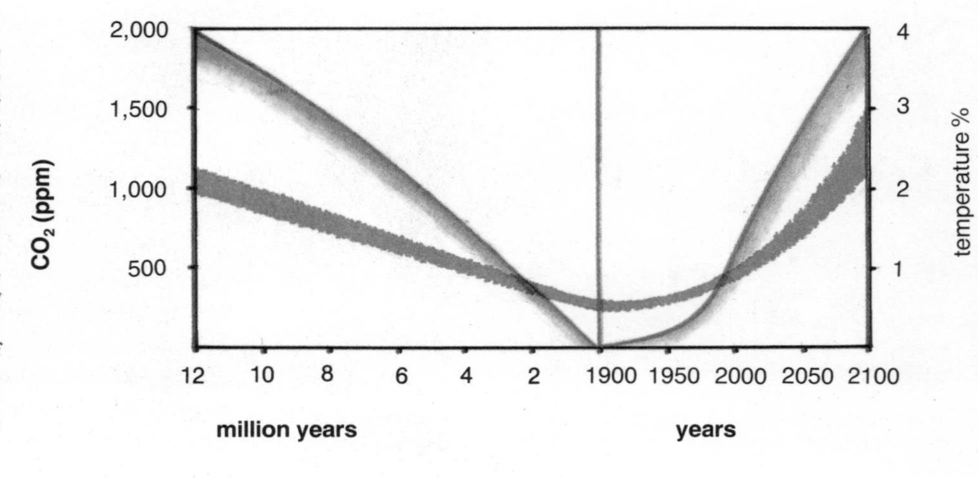

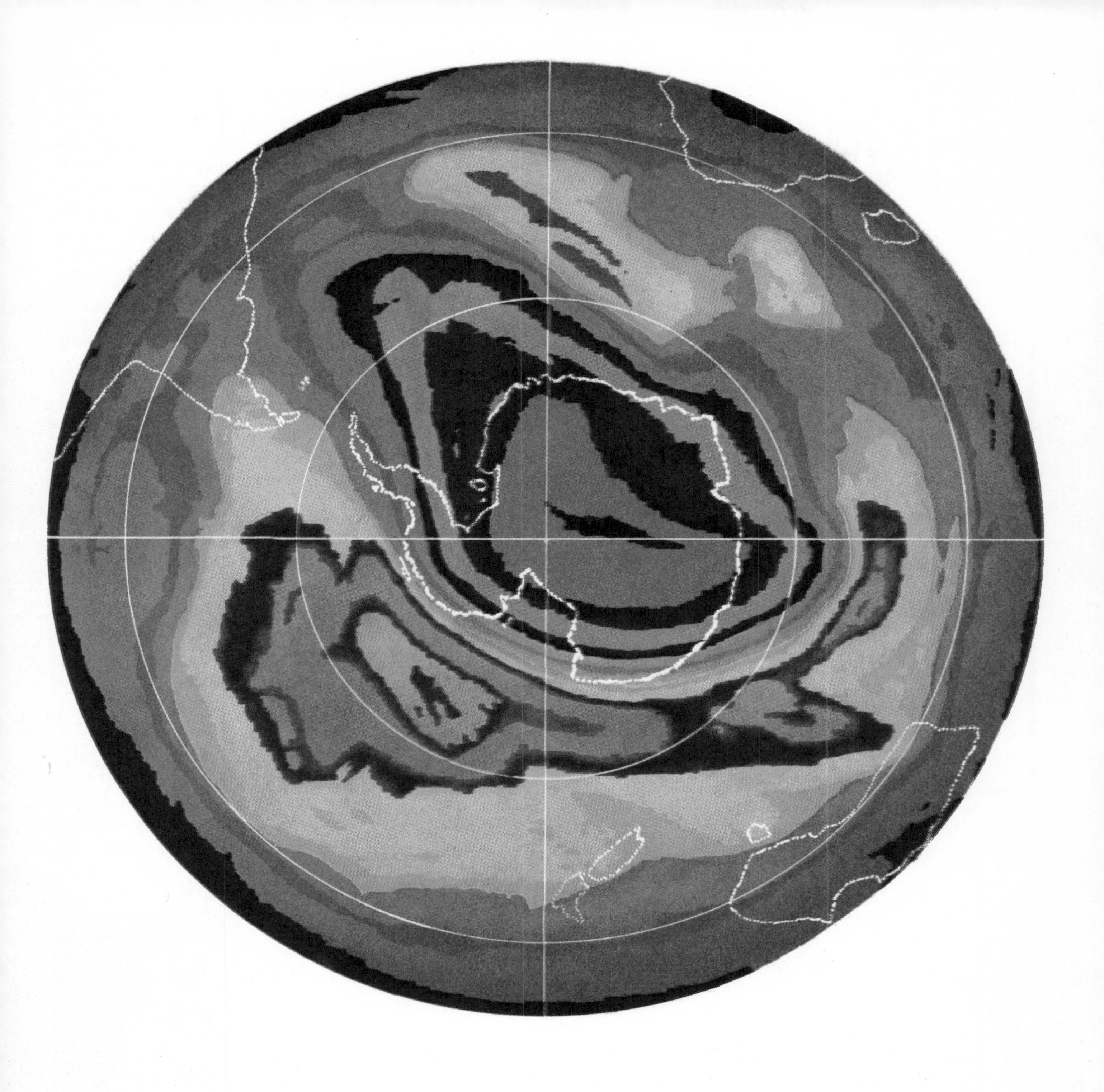

197 Polar view of the southern hemisphere shows the depletion of the ozone layer causing a large increase in ultraviolet and cosmic radiation. This in turn causes disturbances in animate nature. In the centre of the picture is the South Pole, with the continental outlines drawn in white. Coloured lines represent ozone concentrations. The lowest concentration is shown in dark blue (in the centre); slightly higher, but still far below average concentrations, appear black and grey. Green and orange lines show relatively higher ozone levels.

dependence can go. Whichever way we look at it, however, it all comes back to the mutual bonds existing between living and inanimate Nature, and to our introductory image of a flexible but complex spider's web. In geological history, the formation of an oxygen atmosphere was clearly brought about by living organisms, probably minute bacteria of some kind. The formation of this oxygen atmosphere, and the accompanying drop in its carbon dioxide content, as well as the presence of water, are crucial factors in regulating the heat balance in the layer of air which surrounds the Earth's surface. They are to a certain extent also weather regulators. We may therefore continue our line of thought, adding that water is

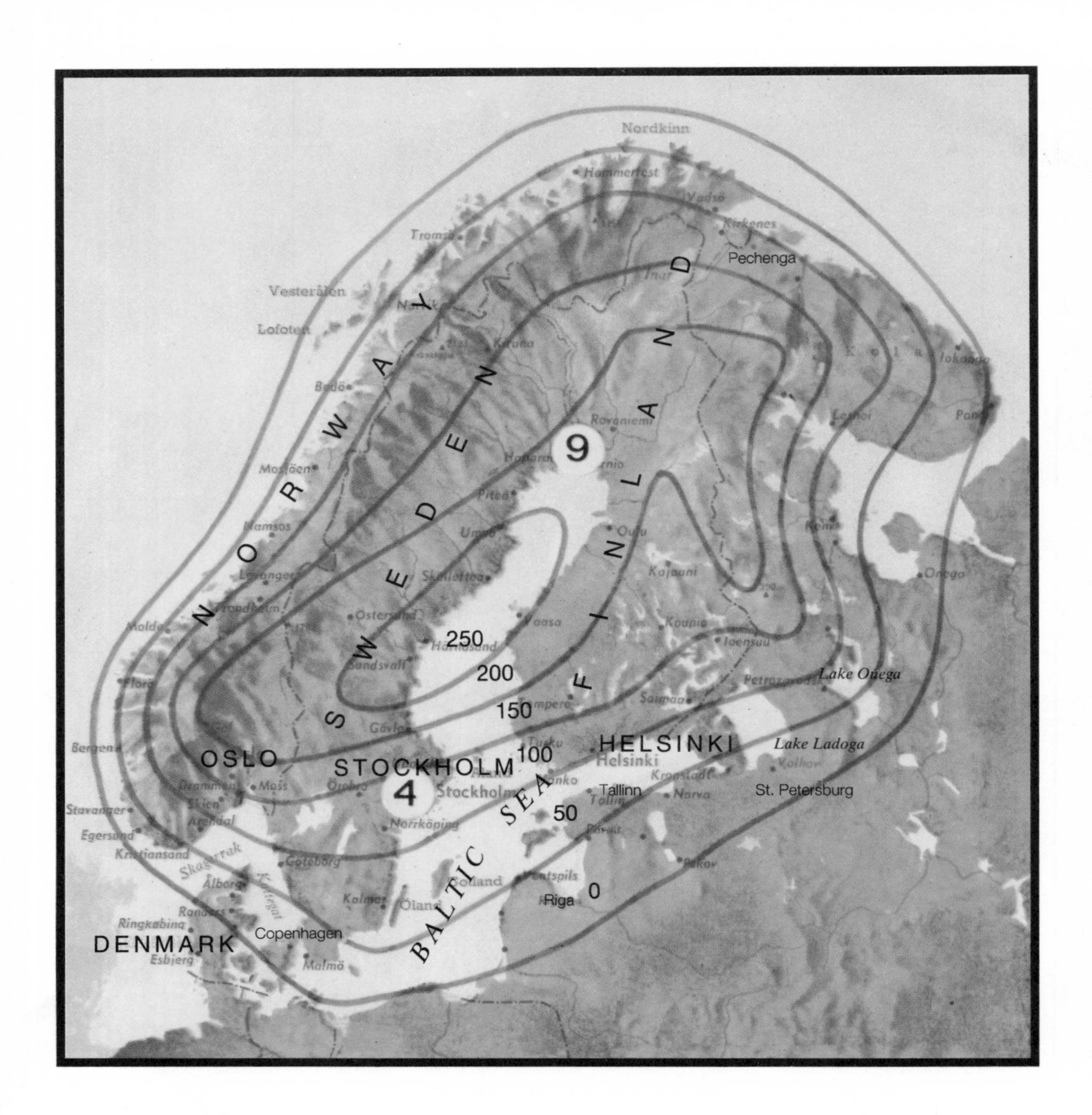

198 The reactions of the Earth and of its parts to sudden changes are slow. Contemporary Scandinavia is still being uplifted as a result of the disappearance of the continental glacier, the weight of which 'pressed' this part of the Earth's crust into the mantle during the Ice Age. Isostatic compensation is reminiscent of the slow rise of a cork stopper in a heavily viscous liquid, such as oil. The figures in the picture give the rise of Scandinavia (in metres) since the retreat of the glacier. The figures in circles give the annual rise in centimetres.

responsible for geological evolution, the formation of ridges, subduction, volcanic action in the island archipelagoes, volcano chains and the formation of the continental crust. All these processes and forces may seem so mighty that geological changes are unstoppable and irreversible. Absurd though the idea may seem, however, it should be conceded that something of this kind may be possible, and that our knowledge of the relationship between living and inanimate Nature is not sophisticated enough for us to dismiss the idea out of hand.

We might try at this point to outline a possible picture of the future Earth, based on knowledge of plate movements, the energy stored within the planet, solar activity and geological forces. As we have seen, the carbon dioxide content of the Earth's atmosphere is rising, so let us try to estimate, on the basis of accessible data, what the Earth will look like in only 50 or 60 year's time. The lithospheric plates will continue to move; North America will be further from Europe, and South America a good 1.5 metres/5 feet further away from Africa, and accordingly that much closer to Asia in the east. The Himalayas may be a few millimetres higher as a result of the continued colli-

199 The biggest carbon dioxide emissions into the atmosphere are yet to come. The diagram is plotted from assumed population growth against assumed increase of energy requirements (the present requirements equal 1), the most substantial part of which will still be generated by the combustion of fossil fuels in years to come.

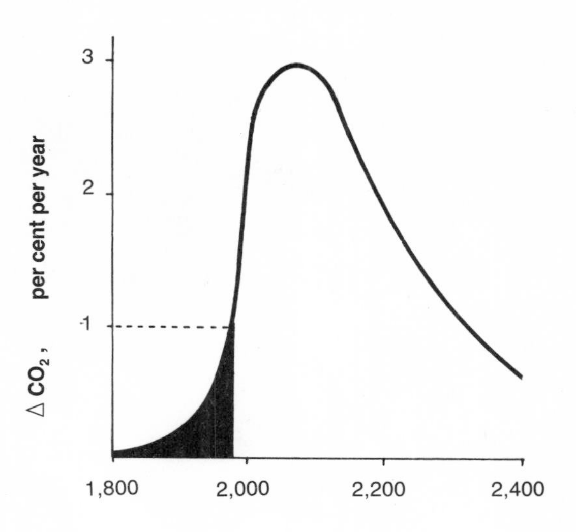

sion between the Indian and Asian plates. Scandinavia will also be higher: not because of collision, however, but as a result of the ice caps melting (illustrated in the picture). The Red Sea will have widened, part of it flooding the Eritrean peninsula. However, all these will merely be imperceptible natural changes arising out of the Earth's essential nature and the functioning of its metabolic system. There will be earthquakes or volcanic explosions, but the Earth will be 3–5 °C/4.8–8 °F warmer as a result of human activity, therefore also having a somewhat wetter climate, with rather more rainfall. This may seem to be of benefit to agriculture, but in fact it will alter the worldwide distribution of precipitation. Erosion will be more marked, and meteorologists are predicting the possibility of part of Africa being wetter and cooler, the central western part of the United States, on the other hand, becoming hotter and dryer. Similarly, geologists studying the history of the last ice age are drawing attention to changes in the composition of plant cover in connection with the ice melting. The conifer boundary in the northern hemisphere, for example, is advancing northwards, and it has been calculated that a temperature of only 1–2 °C/1.6–3.2 °F higher over the course of a thousand years can

200 However much he tries to husband the land he cultivates, man contributes to the degradation of the soil horizon. Irrigation, fertilizing with artificial products and intensive cultivation with heavy machinery cause changes in soil structure and composition. These examples are taken from Central Europe. They show places with almost identical initial parameters: climatic conditions, bedrock, etc. The upper group of diagrams shows a more natural soil horizon — a site used as a meadow. The lower diagrams show an intensively cultivated arable soil. The diagrams record the following soil characteristics: pore volume, soil density, organic carbon content and soil acidity.

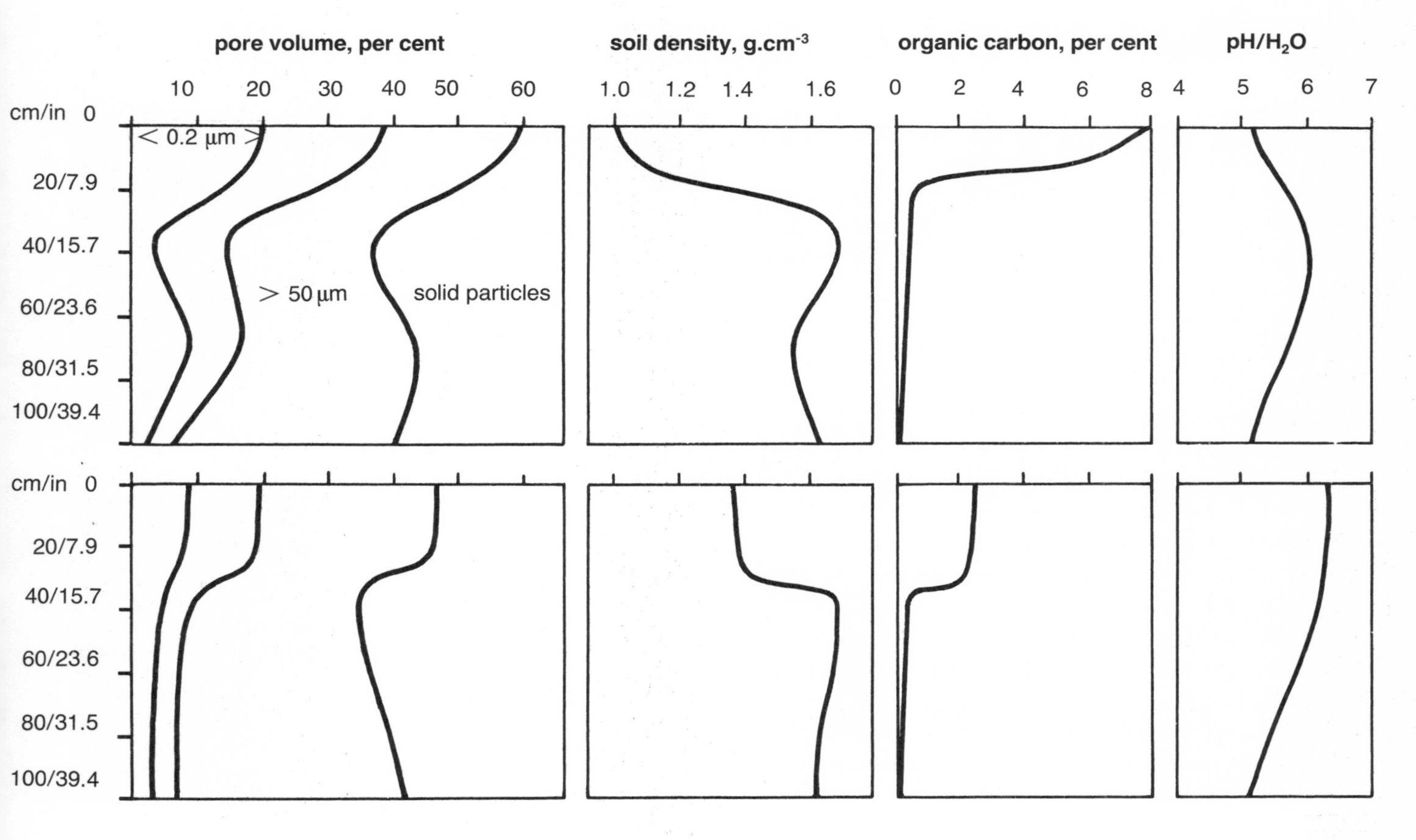

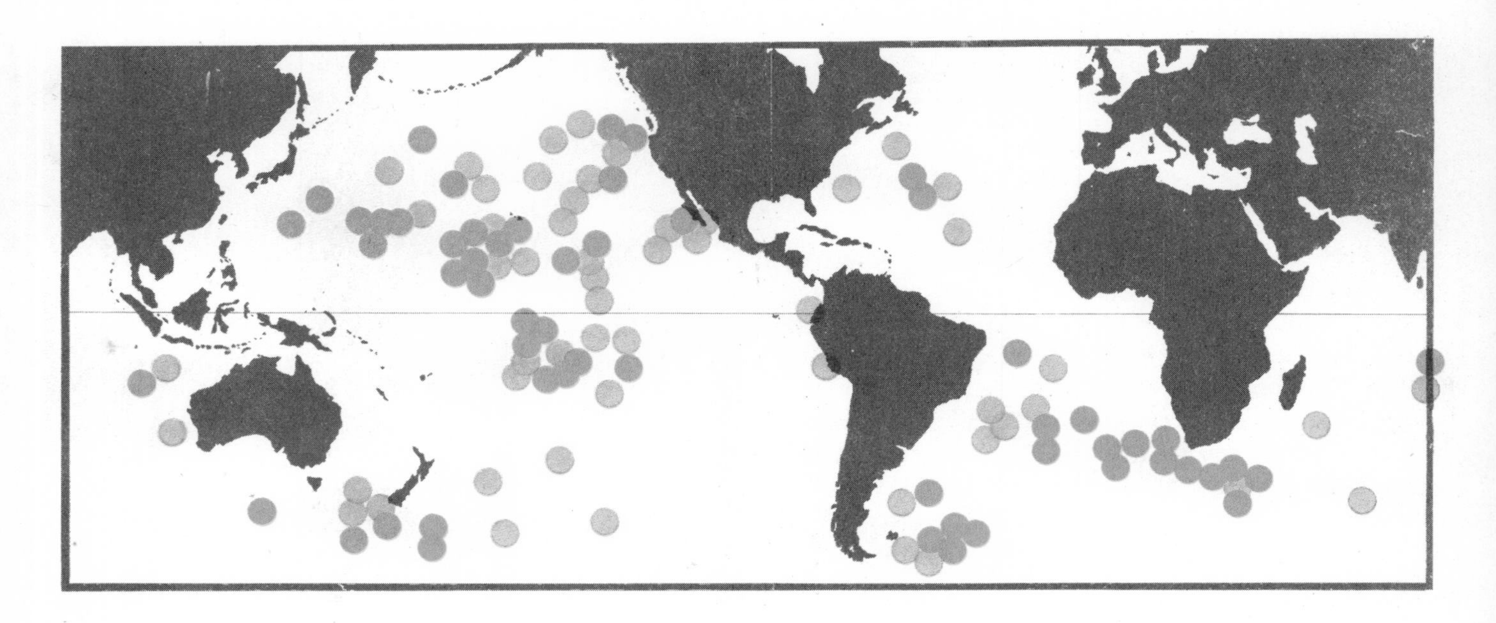

201 The raw material balance of the Earth, with its growing population and its ever increasing consumption, is not encouraging. Great hopes are pinned on the extraction of raw mineral deposits, particularly non-ferrous metals, from the ocean floor. So far this is neither economically nor ecologically sound. The future, however, does rely on ocean floor deposits. The map shows principal sites of manganese nodule deposits which contain (apart from manganese) iron, nickel, copper, zinc and lead. High deposits are shown in orange, lower in yellow.

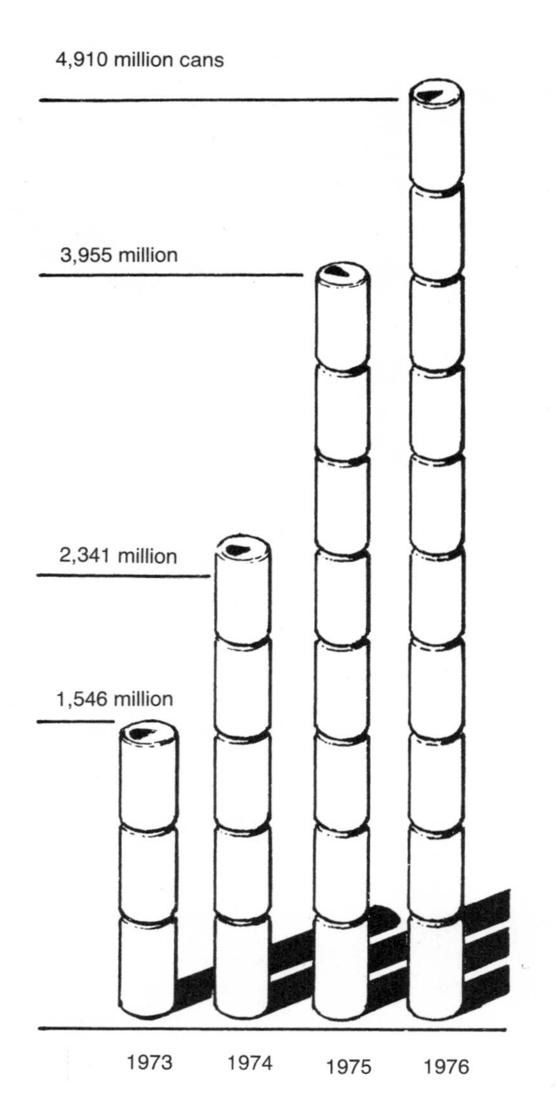

▷
203 A number of studies in many parts of the world has revealed that the energy future of mankind will have to be solved, at least for a certain period, partly by nuclear energy. The safety of operation of nuclear plants, particularly the storage of radioactive wastes is, therefore, one of the key problems of the future, and underground storage of such wastes seems to be one option for its future solution. The storage space proper is marked in blue, the access roads and ventilation ducts in orange.

202 One solution to the shortage of raw materials is recycling of raw minerals, particularly metals. In developed countries a large proportion of raw materials comes from secondary sources. One important aspect of the exploitation of secondary raw materials is the relatively low energy requirements of the manufacture of metal from already existing material compared with its manufacture from ore. In the case of aluminium, for instance, the energy required in the primary manufacture of metal from the ore is more than five times as high as for its manufacture from aluminium waste. The recycling of other raw materials such as paper is widely known. The picture illustrates how the United States has increased its use of aluminium drink cans in past decades. Efficient use of secondary raw materials solves not only problems of diminishing raw materials but also energy and waste disposal problems.

shift the forest boundary by as much as 1 km/0.62 miles annually. In fact, we have no way of knowing whether this estimate of 3–5 °C/4.8–8 °F is correct. We should, nevertheless, be aware of the serious and disturbing nature of the situation. A glance at a demographic map of the world reveals that several thousand million people are currently living 5 m/16 feet above sea level. In 50–60 years this number will be somewhat greater, but they will be homeless if the sea level rises.

Let us take a look at the causes of these predicted changes. The rising carbon dioxide content in the atmosphere, caused by excessive combustion of fossil fuels in the production of energy, does not result solely from the increasing population on the planet. The exponential curve expressing population growth indicates nothing about the quality of the population's demand, either in the past or the present. Everyone aspires to a better quality of life than those before him (an aspiration which alas often remains unfulfilled), so that the consumption of foodstuffs, raw materials and energy resources is increasing at a faster rate than the population. This growth cannot go on indefinitely.

However, there are signs of a possible change for the better. The advanced industrial nations have managed to achieve continued growth in the gross national product while maintaining a constant level of energy and raw material consumption – something which twenty or thirty years ago would have been regarded, and in some countries still is, as an ideal state. This may indeed mark a turn for the better.

The present global warming process is about a thousand times more rapid than a naturally occurring warming process discovered by geologists to have occurred in the periods between the ice ages. If, then, we are to avoid a global catastrophe, there will have to be a change in the way energy is produced. If we had to compile an order of preference for energy production in the coming 50–60 years, we would have to put nuclear energy in first place (despite the objections that many countries have to its use), with solar energy in second place, followed by biomass and then geothermal energy. We shall undoubtedly be obliged to restrict drastically the use of fossil fuels, even though crude oil and gas are somewhat cleaner fuels than coal.

Altering the methods of energy production will, of course, create a demand for different raw materials. As long as energy was produced by burning wood, and no other form of energy than heat energy for keeping warm and roasting meat was used, nothing more than stones for the fireplace, and perhaps some brick-making clay was needed. The more complex the method of energy production used, the greater was the number of other materials consumed.

Every method of energy production creates a chain of raw materials and technologies which are needed as a consequence. Let us imagine future energy being produced directly from solar radiation, volcanic heat, or perhaps even in the same way that the Sun itself produces it — by means of combining simple elements into more complex ones, a reaction which always releases heat. These methods of energy production will likewise create a demand for new mineral resources.

These include gallium, germanium, indium, superclean silicon, metals from the platinum group, osmium, palladium and rhodium.

In view of the pollution given off when fossil fuels are

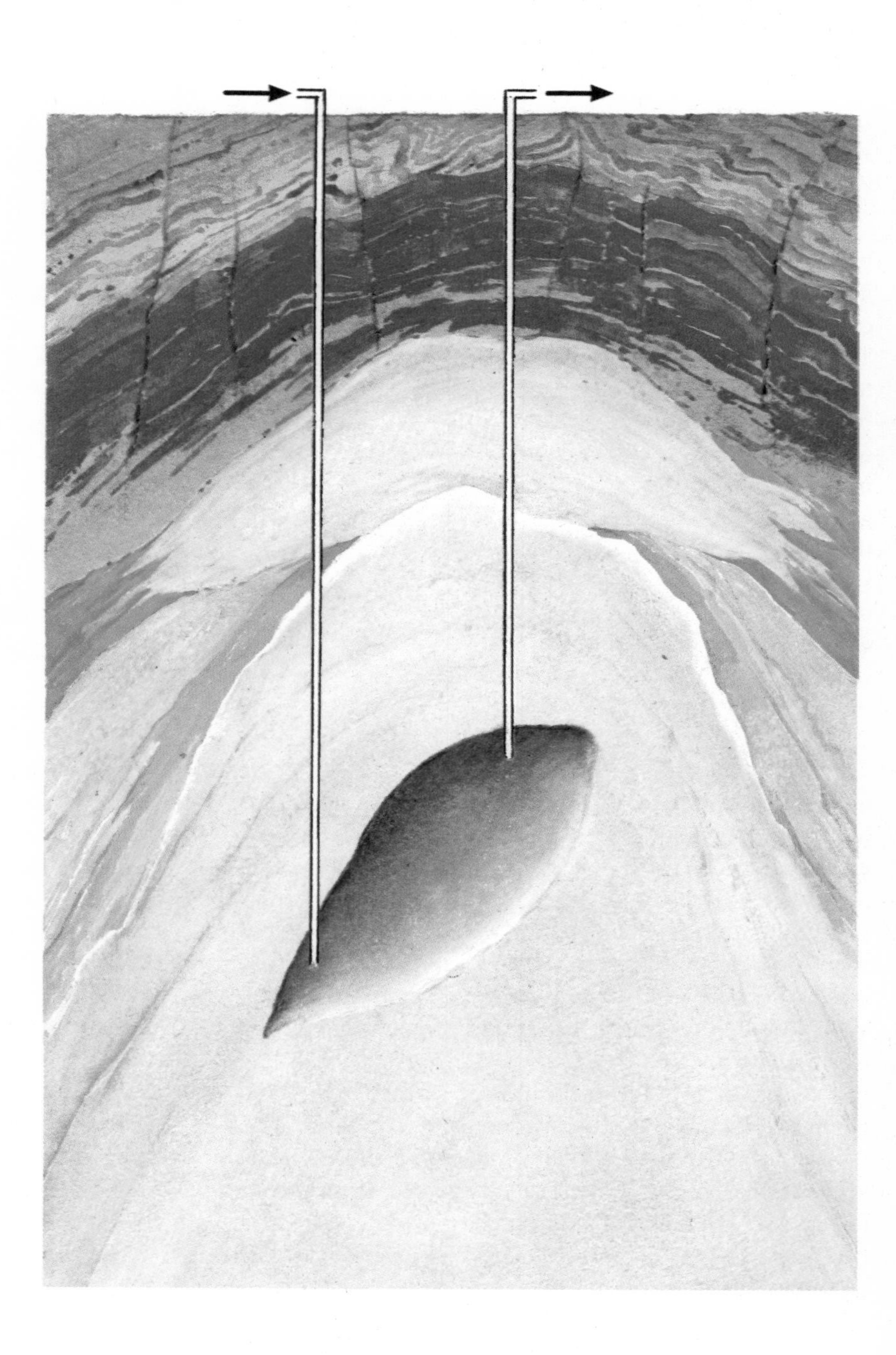

204 The storage of great quantities of mineral raw materials, particularly energy resources — the requirements for which drop markedly in summer and rise in winter — is a long term problem solved also by geologists. Giant gas holders or oil reservoirs are not only ugly but are costly and take up a lot of space which could be used for other purposes. An elegant solution of the storage problem are enormous underground caverns in natural saline domes. Soil is both impermeable and inert to crude oil and is a good insulator. The cavity is generated by making a borehole above the saline dome and by 'controlled' dissolution of the required quantity of salt.

PARTICIPATION IN EMISSIONS, PER CENT	TRANSPORT	SMALL CONSUMERS	INDUSTRY	POWER INDUSTRY	CHEMICAL INDUSTRY
SO_2	3.4	9.3	20.9	62.1	4.3
NO_x (NO_2)	54.6	3.7	11.4	27.7	2.6
CO	65.0	21.0	12.7	0.4	0.9
carbohydrates	39.0	32.4	24.9	0.6	3.1
powder	9.4	9.2	56.8	21.7	2.9

205 Nobody is without guilt. Every man who drives a car or warms himself even by the purest energy — electric power — contributes to the pollution of our environment. The example is taken from Central Europe — Germany.

burned, and its damaging effects on the Earth and its atmosphere, it is becoming more and more important that combustion of crude oil, gas and coal be strictly limited. The amount of coal burned annually, worldwide, is equal to the amount formed geologically in a million years. It is becoming vital that we give more time and attention to researching ways of producing energy in a more environmentally friendly way. The main task to be undertaken by geoscientists in this regard is the collection of basic data on the atmosphere and hydrosphere, and on the state of the soil and vegetation cover. This means, in other words, recording the current state of most factors affecting our existence on the planet. Without this information, the future cannot be predicted. Only a thorough analysis can show the tolerance level of the landscape in a given area and its ability to support development or which regions are more suitable as conservation areas. First of all, it is necessary to assemble a land profile. This would involve collecting data in respect of its physical characteristics, its location in respect of surrounding areas, information about its climate, etc. When all the data has been collected it may be found that there is some aspect which renders the land unsuitable for the purpose for which it was intended. It should also be taken into account that the amount of cultivable soil will not increase, and that it will be necessary in future to increase agricultural production without further damage to the natural environment, as we have been doing up to now, for example, in tropical rainforest regions. Soil quality will need to be preserved at present levels at least. This will call for new agricultural technologies which will reduce soil degeneration, salinization, erosion and desertification to a minimum. All this will demand both a scientific and holistic approach.

One important international project involving scientific co-operation is the International Geosphere-Biosphere Program, whose aim is to acquire a more accurate, detailed, and, therefore, reliable picture of current changes, in order to make future prediction easier.

One possible solution which would leave more of the landscape untarnished would be to create room for human activity underground. Deeper parts of the Earth are under preparation, and are in some cases already in use. Being well aware of overcrowded cities and the noise of traffic, in an attempt to provide a safe, fast, unobtrusive form of public transport, Man began at the turn of the century to build underground railway systems. Similarly, underground sewage systems were known even in the Middle Ages.

The surface of our planet must be saved for its future inhabitants. People need to be in direct contact with the Sun's rays to remain healthy. They cannot go underground. In the future there will be too many people and not enough space; therefore space will have to be found to store things which are at present kept on the surface. Similarly, other places will have to be found for the processing and disposal of waste. Space underground, which is today unused, could be employed for these purposes. Noisy industrial production, which uses automated processes, could also be moved underground, as could sewage works or nuclear power stations. Heat input from the Earth's interior could be used for cooling.

All these things are so far mere speculation. We may, however, proceed on the assumption that people will not abandon the surface of the Earth in future, either by moving underground, or by travelling to other planets. It depends on us, therefore, what kind of habitat we create for ourselves on Earth.

There is no single solution or global remedy for the environmental imbalances currently found on Earth. The most sensible attitude people can adopt is the ecologists' philosophy, 'Think globally and act locally.'

BIBLIOGRAPHY

Ager, D., *The New Catastrophism.* Cambridge University Press, 1992.

Brown, G. C., Mussett, A., *Inaccessible Earth.* Chapman and Hall, 2nd edition, 1993.

Brown, G. C., Hawkesworth, J. C., and Wilson, R. C. L., *Understanding the Earth. A new synthesis.* Cambridge University Press, 1992.

Bryant, E., *Natural Hazards. Threat, disaster, effect, response.* Cambridge University Press, 1991.

Buckley, R., *Perspectives in Environmental Management.* Springer Verlag, 1991.

Duvigneaud, P., *La synthèse écologique.* Doin éditeurs, Paris, 1980.

Emiliani, C., *Planet Earth.* Cambridge University Press, 1992.

Francis, P., *Volcanoes. A planetary perspective.* Clarendon Press, London, 1993.

Huggett, R. J., *Climate, Earth Processes, Earth History.* Springer Verlag, 1991.

Hutchinson, R., Graham, A., *Meteorites. The key to our existence.* Natural History Museum, London, 1992.

Kula, E., *Economics of Natural Resources and the Environment.* Chapman and Hall, 1992.

Meadows, D. H., Meadows, D. L., and Randers, J., *Beyond the Limits.* Earthscan Publications Ltd., London, 1992.

Schipper, L., Meyers, S., *Energy Efficiency and Human Activity.* Cambridge University Press, 1992.

APPENDIX

MAN'S ACTIVITIES AND THEIR INFLUENCE ON THE GEOLOGICAL ENVIRONMENT

Man's activities	influence on geological environment
Mining:	change of landscape character
	landslides
	subsidence
	water pollution
	lowering of ground water table
	damage due to explosions
Civil engineering construction:	landslides
	mud flows
	rock falls
	ground water table
Industrial production:	water pollution
	fallout
	air pollution (sulphur, nitrogen oxides)
Agriculture and forestry:	erosion
	landslides
	soil salting
	water pollution
	torrents, floods
Tourism:	water and soil pollution

GEOSYNCLINE – GEOSYNCLINAL CONCEPT

The classical geological concept of a geosyncline is a depression in the Earth's crust (usually near a continental margin or between two continents), in which a great quantity of sediment collects. The geosyncline is a markedly mobile formation: according to the geosynclinal concept of geological history, first the floor of the geosyncline subsides; later, after the accumulation of sediments, a compression takes place and a mountain range is created by folding (orogenesis). Current theories regarding geological history described in this book are based on the concept of plate tectonics, differing significantly from the classical geosynclinal concept. While in the geosynclinal concept mountain ranges result from the folding of a geosynclinal complex, the plate tectonics theory is based on mountain ranges forming as a result of collisions of lithospheric plates.

GLOBAL CHANGE

The Earth is a living, changing body, both geologically and geographically. These changes are best perceived on its surface. Natural changes such as shifts in the permanent ice boundaries and consequently in the sea level, through which the Earth has passed in the course of geological periods, have been influenced by man's industrial and agricultural activities over the past century. The changes of area and composition of forests in the temperate zone, the expansion of deserts on many continents, changes in ground water table, shrinking glaciers, earthquakes and volcanic activity, changes in the composition of the atmosphere connected with an increasing concentration of gases causing the greenhouse effect, acid rain and subsequent acidification of soils, lakes and rivers as well as a reduction in the number of biological species. All these factors, and many others, contribute to **global change**.

ENVIRONMENT

The initial definition of the term 'environment' was somewhat narrower than it is today. Environment meant merely Man's ecosystem. Gradually the concept of 'environment' was extended to include all animate and inanimate mutually interconnected components, so that at present we speak of a complex of natural, built and social components of human life. However, even this definition is not wide enough and has to be extended to include also the technical, economic, political, legislative and cultural aspects. Nevertheless, Man has remained in the centre of all these concerns.

The chemical composition of the Earth, meteorites or planets can be expressed by figures, percentages of weight or atoms. The following table illustrates, without figures, the most substantial differences between the Sun, the meteorites, the Earth and its crust. At the same time it illustrates the different processes which separate the chemical elements in the solar system. Taking into consideration all these differences, scientists believe that all these celestial bodies have a common predecessor or source. The elements are ranked in order of their frequency of occurrence:

The Sun:	H, He, O, C, N, Si, Mg, S, Fe, Ca, Ni, Na, Al, Cu, Cr
Meteorites:	O, Fe, Si, Mg, S, Ni, Ca, Al, Na, Cr, Mn, P, Co, K, Ti
The Earth:	Fe, C, Si, Mg, Ni, S, Ca, Al, Na, Cr, Mn, Co, P, K, Ti
Earth crust:	O, Si, Al, Fe, Ca, Na, K, Mg, Ti, H, P, Mn, F, Ba, Sr

SPHERES AND THEIR DEFINITIONS

We can often get the impression that scientists make a smoke screen around their disciplines by using highly technical terminology when dealing, for example, with the individual parts, spheres or layers of the Earth. Such terminology can best be clarified by referring to an etymological dictionary. The terms, although coined in the 20th century, were derived mostly from classical Greek or Latin words.

Lithosphere (*lithos* means stone in Greek and is, consequently, a symbol of strength) in the past meant the Earth's crust. In the new definition, which corresponds with the tectonics of lithospheric plates, lithosphere means the solid, rigid part of the Earth consisting of both the entire Earth's crust and the solid (and, consequently, cold and rigid) part of the upper mantle.

Asthenosphere (*asthenes* means without strength, weak) means the 'weak' zone of the mantle which behaves as if it were plastic, perhaps because it is warm and 'soft', and probably also contains partly molten areas.

Atmosphere (*atmos* means vapour or breath) denotes that part of the Earth which we breathe (although in some parts of the Earth the atmosphere is not very 'breathable'). It is the gaseous envelope which surrounds the Earth and adheres to it by gravity.

Hydrosphere (*hydor* means water in Greek) is a term used collectively for all waters on the Earth, including those which are contained underground.

Biosphere (the Greek word *bios* means life, living organism) comprises those parts of the planet (atmosphere, lithosphere and hydrosphere) in which metabolizing organisms regularly occur.

Cryosphere (*kryos* is the Greek word for cold, frozen, frost) is the part of the Earth which is covered with ice or in which the soil is permanently frozen (also called permafrost).

Pedosphere (*pedos* is Greek for soil) is that part of the Earth which is covered with soil — the soil horizon.

PRINCIPAL PARAMETERS ON THE EARTH

Mean equatorial radius of the Earth is 6,378.165 km/3,963.21 miles.
Mean polar radius of the Earth is 6,356.752 km/3,949.903 miles.
Polar flattening is 1/298.257.
Weight of the Earth is 5.97×10^{24} kg (which represents 1/330 000 of the weight of the Sun).
Volume of the Earth is 1.0832×10^{21} cu.m.
Gravity acceleration on the surface of the Earth is 9.81 $m.s^{-2}$.
Distance of the Earth from the Moon is, on the average, 384,402 km/238,856 miles.

COMPOSITION OF THE CRUST, MANTLE AND THE EARTH AS A WHOLE (PER CENT BY WEIGHT)

Component	Continental crust	Oceanic crust	Mantle	Core
SiO_2	60.1	49.9	38.3	
TiO_2	1.1	1.5	0.1	
Al_2O_3	15.6	17.3	2.5	
Fe_2O_3	3.1	2.0		
FeO	3.9	6.9	12.5	
FeS			5.8	
Fe			11.9	90.8
Ni			1.4	8.6
Co			0.1	0.6
MgO	3.6	7.3	24.0	
CaO	5.2	11.9	2.0	
Na_2O	3.9	2.8	1.0	
K_2O	3.2	0.2	0.2	
P_2O_5	0.3	0.2	0.2	

A.U. — ASTRONOMIC UNIT

One astronomic unit is the mean distance of the planet Earth from the Sun, which is 149,597,870 km/92,955,629 miles. This unit is used for the measurements of distance between planets and between the planets and the Sun. For example, the distance of the planet Pluto from the Sun is 40 A.U.

RADIOACTIVE ELEMENTS USED FOR GEOLOGICAL TIME MEASUREMENTS (SELECTION)

mother isotope, radioactive	daughter isotope, radiogenous	half-life period, years
14_{C}	14_{N}	5.73×10^3
40_{K}	40_{Ar}, 40_{Ca}	1.3×10^9
87_{Rb}	87_{Sr}	5.0×10^{10}
147_{Sm}	143_{Nd}	1.1×10^{11}
187_{Re}	187_{Os}	4.0×10^{10}
232_{Th}	4_{He}, 208_{Pb}	1.41×10^{10}
238_{U}	4_{He}, 206_{Pb}	4.51×10^9
235_{U}	4_{He}, 207_{Pb}	7.13×10^8

HEAT PRODUCING CHEMICAL ELEMENTS

Element	Heat output, Wkg^{-1}
Uranium (mixture of natural isotopes)	$9.35 . 10^{-5}$
Thorium (232 isotope)	$2.64 . 10^{-5}$
Potassium, natural (0.012 per cent of ^{40}K isotope)	$3.55 . 10^{-9}$

AIR COMPOSITION

Component		Concentration, ppm*	Average time of presence in the atmosphere
H_2	(hydrogen)	0.5	4–7 years
H_2O	(water vapour)	$4.4 . 10^3$	10 days
He	(helium)	5.2	
CO	(carbon monoxide)	0.1	0.3 year
CO^2	(carbon dioxide)	325	10 years
CH_4	(methane)	1.5	5 years
N_2	(nitrogen)	$7.808 . 10^5$	2.10^7 years
N_2O	(nitrogen monoxide)	0.25	4 years
NO	(nitrogen oxide)	0.001	9 days
NO_2	(nitrogen dioxide)	0.002	11 days
NH_3	(ammonia)	0.006	6 days
O_2	(Oxygen)	$2.0946 . 10^5$	10^4 years
O_3	(ozone)	0.025	0.3 year
Ne	(neon)	18	
SO_2	(sulphur dioxide)	0.0002	4 days
H_2S	(hydrogen sulphide)	0.0002	4 days
$C1_2$	(chlorine)	0.0006	
Ar	(argon)	$1.34 . 10^3$	
Cr	(crypton)	1.1	
Xe	(xenon)	0.086	

*) ppm — parts per million means that in one million of volume parts of air (or any other substance, for that matter) there is x parts (x ppm) of the given substance.
1 ppm = 10^{-4} per cent.

PLATFORM

This is a part of the Earth's crust in which only very slight movements and only very slight or no volcanic activity take place. It is the opposite of the platform that is a two level structure: the lower level consists of a folded (e.g. geosynclinal) set of rocks, the upper level of sediments in a still, homogeneous structure. The shield is also a geologically peaceful region; however, it is a one-level formation and is not covered with horizontally deposited sedimentary rocks like the platform.

HEAT FLOW

The Earth radiates a certain amount of thermal energy from its surface. The heat flow indicates the amount of heat passing through a unit area of the Earth's surface per unit time. The heat flow is given in $mW.m^{-2}$. The mean heat flow of the Earth is 60 $mW.m^{-2}$.

AEONS

Geologists measure time in years. However, for such a long history one year is a relatively short and awkward unit. For this reason they often use mathematical abbreviations, writing, for instance, three million years as 3.0×10^6 years. Because even one million years is not a sufficiently large unit to express the age of the Earth or the duration of long periods of its history, an even larger unit is used, i.e. the aeon. Formerly this term was used to indicate a very long, usually not specified, period. Today it is used to indicate one billion years, i.e. 1×10^9 years.

GEOBIOCENOSIS

A landscape consists of plant and animal communities. Such communities are called biocenoses. However, every biocenosis is markedly dependent on abiotic factors of the environment in which it lives. Together they form a perfect ecological unit or ecosystem. Such a unit represents the complex of all biological and chemical components circulating in it. The abiotic components and the organisms are in mutual interaction and each of them is indispensable for the maintenance of the harmony of life.

SOLAR CONSTANT

The overall quantity of solar energy of all wave lengths passing through a unit area in the mean distance between the Earth and the Sun (i.e. at a distance of one astronomic unit – A.U.) is called the solar constant. In the past the value of the solar constant was given in calories per sq.cm per minute. At present it is given in watts per sq.m (1 watt is one joule per second).
The value of the solar constant is $S = 1400\ W.m^{-2}$

ACID RAIN

This term has not been in use for long; it means rain contaminated with sulphur oxides and, consequently, with sulphuric and sulphurous acids, and nitrogen oxides (nitric acid). These pollutants are generated by industrial activity, in the case of sulphur compounds particularly through the combustion of fossil fuels such as coal and oil; in the case of nitrogen oxides through the operation of internal combustion engines.

EARTHQUAKE INTENSITY – EMPIRIC SCALE AND MAGNITUDE

Degree	Indication	Magnitude according to the Richter scale	Manifestation
I	Imperceptible	–	Recorded by sensitive seismographs only
II	Very weak	2.5	Sensed by individuals, in higher parts of buildings
III	Weak	–	Perceptible in buildings, slight swinging of suspended objects
IV	Mild	3.5	Noticed by many people in buildings and stationary cars, wakes people up, cracking walls can be heard
V	Fairly strong	–	Noticed by all people in buildings, animals are restless; cracking of windows, swinging of ceiling lights, slight damage to buildings
VI	Strong	–	Noticeable even outside buildings, many people are scared; furniture moves, chimney pots fall, brick buildings are damaged, landslides, changes of ground water table
VII	Very strong	5.5	People run out of houses; perceivable even in a running car; single examples of damage to reinforced concrete buildings, waves on water surfaces
VIII	Destructive	6.0	General alarm, branches of trees break, furniture is overturned. Light buildings are destroyed, reinforced concrete buildings damaged, cracks in the ground
IX	Devastating	6.5	General panic, reinforced concrete structures seriously damaged, pipes burst, cracks in ground, large waves on water surfaces
X	Ruinous	7.0	Considerable damage to buildings, dams, bridges, corrugation of roads cracks in the ground metres wide
XI	Catastrophic	8.0	Buildings, bridges, underground pipelines destroyed, changes of Earth surface, wide cracks and displacement of the ground
XII	Great catastrophes	8.5	All human works destroyed, ground waves originated on the Earth's surface, changes of Earth's surface, rock falls

DATA ON THE PLANETS OF THE SOLAR SYSTEM

Planet	Distance from the Sun, A.U.	Weight, M	Density, $g.cm^{-3}$	Radius, km
Mercury	0.3872	0.055	5.53	2,439
Venus	0.723	0.815	5.25	6,052
Earth	1.000	1.000	5.517	6,378
Mars	1.524	0.107	3.94	3,387
Jupiter	5.203	319.9	1.31	71,398
Saturn	9.539	95.2	0.71	60,000
Uranus	19.182	14.6	1.71	25,400
Neptune	30.058	17.2	1.77	24,750
Pluto	39.293	0.003	1.00	1,400

The mathematical expression of the quantity of simultaneously originating impact craters on the Earth is $0.36 \times 10^{-14}\ km^2$ per year. This means that a crater in excess of 20 km/12.4 miles in diameter originates in contemporary conditions once in 30 million years and will remain on the Earth for 600 million years.

CONSUMERS' PARTICIPATION IN GLOBAL CATASTROPHFE

Operation of one car generates about 5 tonnes/4.9 tons of carbon dioxide per year. Approximately the same amount of carbon dioxide per year is generated by the production of electric power from fossil fuels for one household, and only a slightly higher quantity of carbon dioxide is released by the heating from one household with fossil fuels (oil).

The earthquake which, according to preserved documents, claimed the greatest number of victims took place on January 24, 1556, in China. Some 830,000 people died. However, 20th century statistics are not very encouraging either. The following table shows 20th century earthquakes in which the number of victims exceeded 20,000.

Date	Place
4.4.1905	India (Jammu and Kashmir)
6.8.1906	Chile (Valparaiso)
28.12.1908	Italy (Messina)
13.1.1915	Italy (Abruzzi)
16.12.1920	China (Kansu Province)
1.9.1923	Japan (Tokyo)
7.3.1927	Japan (Tadjima)
22.5.1927	China (Nan Shan)
26.12.1932	China (Kansu Province)
31.5.1935	Pakistan (Quetta)
24.1.1939	Chile (Chillan)
26.12.1939	Turkey (Erzincan)
27.–28.12.1940	Turkey (Anatolia)
October, 1948	Turkmenistan (Ashkhabad)
31.5.1970	Peru (Huascaran)
11.–12.5.1974	China (Southwest)
4.2.1976	Guatemala
28.7.1976	China (Tangshan)
17.9.1978	Iran (Tabbas)
19.–20.9.1985	Mexico (Mexico City)
7.12.1988	Armenia
21.6.1990	Iran (Northwest)
30.9.1993	India (Southwest)
17.1.1994	California (Los Angeles)

To those who care seriously about the future of the Earth, ozone has become the major symbol of possible catastrophe. The atmosphere, particularly in the higher strata and in some parts of the world, is deficient in ozone, as a result of which more cosmic rays and a greater amount of ultraviolet radiation reaches the Earth's surface, which has an unfavourable influence on living organisms. Few people, however, have asked how ozone, this three-atom molecule of oxygen (O), originates and becomes extinct.

Oxygen in ordinary molecules O_2 forms part of the air. Ultraviolet radiation breaks down the double molecule into individual atoms of oxygen (O) which combine with the ordinary oxygen molecules (O_2) and form ozone (O_3). In the language of chemical equations it appears as follows:

$$O_2 \rightleftarrows O + O$$
$$O + O_2 \rightleftarrows O_3$$

However, if the highly sensitive ozone layer comes into contact with chlorine atoms (which are present in the atmosphere not only in natural quantities and from natural sources but also in the form of chlorofluorocarbon compounds used by people as propellent gases in sprays and as coolants in refrigerators) the reaction of ozone and chlorine is almost instantaneous. The result is chlorine monoxide and the initial oxygen molecule. The reaction can be recorded once again simply as follows:

$$Cl + O_3 = ClO + O_2$$

The chlorine monoxide reacts with ordinary oxygen and forms another oxygen molecule and a free atom of chlorine. The oxygen molecule seems to be in order (so much is obvious, oxygen forms part of the atmosphere), but the free atom of chlorine remains and reacts with another ozone molecule. Thus the whole cycle of ozone liquidation begins again.

The presence of ozone in the upper or uppermost strata of the atmosphere, where 90 per cent of all ozone is concentrated, is beneficial for the Earth, while higher concentrations of ozone in the lowest atmospheric strata are undesirable. In the lowermost stratum ozone creates breathing difficulties and its molecules cause smog.

GREENHOUSE EFFECT

Should an observer measure the Earth's temperature from outer space, he would ascertain 18 °C/64.4 °F. That is the temperature corresponding with the wave length on which the Earth 'radiates' and the intensity of its radiation. The heat to which we are accustomed is trapped between the uppermost layers of the Earth's surface and the upper layers of the atmosphere. We could say that we are living in a greenhouse. We are surrounded by the 'glass' of the atmosphere preventing the escape of heat. The present day atmosphere has the 'correct' composition and thickness, which do not permit the occurrence of too high or too low temperatures in 'Earth's greenhouse'. However, every change in the chemical composition of the atmosphere may mean a change in its ability to retain or release heat. Gases capable of trapping heat are those responsible for the greenhouse effect. They include carbon dioxide, methane and chlorinated and fluorinated carbohydrates (CFC).

NATURAL AND MAN-MADE FLOW OF METALS INTO THE OCEANS (IN THOUSANDS OF TONNES PER YEAR)

Element	Natural flow (computed for geological periods)	Man-made flow
Iron	25,000	319,000
Manganese	440	1,600
Copper	375	4,460
Zinc	370	3,930
Nickel	300	358
Lead	180	2,330
Molybdenum	13	57
Silver	5	7
Mercury	3	7
Tin	1.5	166
Antimony	1.5	40

ENERGY RESOURCES

1 **Non-renewable resources**	
(a) fossil fuels	peat
	lignite and brown coal
	hard coal (pit coal)
	crude oil
	gas
	bituminous shales and tar sands
(b) nuclear fuel	uranium, thorium
2 **Renewable resources**	solar energy
	wind energy
	hydraulic energy (incl. tidal energy and ocean streams)
	geothermal energy
	biomass energy

EARTH'S SURFACE AND ITS DIVISION

Area of world oceans	361×10^6 km²
Area of continents	149×10^6 km²
Area of ice carapace – oceans	20×10^6 km²
Area of ice carapace – continents	16×10^6 km²
Total area of the Earth's surface	510×10^6 km²

Mean elevation of continents	850 m/2,788 feet
The highest mountain on continents	8,882 m/29,140 feet
Mean depth of ocean	3,800 m/12,467 feet
The greatest ocean depth	11,034 m/32,920 feet

HEAT OUTPUT SOME ROCKS

Rock	Density, g. cm³	Heat output, W.kg⁻¹
Granite	2.6	106.64×10^{11}
Earth crust (average	2.85	45.34×10^{11}
Basalt	3.3	22.19×10^{11}
Dunite	3.5	0.5×10^{11}
Stone meteorites	3.2	1.25×10^{11}
Iron meteorites	7.8	0.17×10^{11}

AVERAGE CHEMICAL COMPOSITION OF SEA WATER

Component	Concentration, g/kg of water of 35 per cent salinity
Cl^-	19.353
Na^+	10.760
SO_4^{2-}	2.712
Mg^{2+}	1.294
Ca^{2+}	0.413
K^+	0.387
HCO_3^-	0.142
Br^-	0.067

ENERGY CHARACTERISTICS OF THE EARTH

Kinetic energy of rotation	2.2×10^{29}J
Quantity of energy incident on the Earth (in the form of radiation) from the Sun	5.4×10^{24} J/year
Quantity of heat released by the Earth (internal heat sources)	0.7×10^{21} J/year
Quantity of energy released in the form of earthquakes	$10^{18} - 10^{19}$ J/year
Quantity of energy released in volcanic eruptions	$5.10^{17} - 5.10^{18}$ J/year